THE FOUR-COLOR PROBLEM

Pure and Applied Mathematics

A Series of Monographs and Textbooks

Edited by

Paul A. Smith and Samuel Eilenberg

Columbia University, New York

Pure and Applied Mathematics

A Series of Monographs and Textbooks

In preparation:

THE
FOUR-COLOR
PROBLEM

OYSTEIN ORE

Department of Mathematics
Yale University
New Haven,
Connecticut

ACADEMIC PRESS
New York · London

 1967

ACADEMIC PRESS INC.
111 Fifth Avenue, New York, New York 10003

United Kingdom Edition published by
ACADEMIC PRESS INC. (LONDON) LTD.
Berkeley Square House, London W.1

LIBRARY OF CONGRESS CATALOG CARD NUMBER: 66-30095

PRINTED IN THE UNITED STATES OF AMERICA

PREFACE

Puzzling problems permeate mathematics, and this is probably the strongest reason for the burgeoning growth of this queen of the sciences. A few of these problems have stood out as unscalable peaks for a century or more; each of them has given the incentive for new and fertile mathematical studies. Let us mention the three most famous studies: Fermat's conjecture in number theory, Riemann's hypothesis in function theory, and the four-color problem in graph theory. They have all been tantalizing to mathematicians by permitting closer and closer approaches, yet always denying the final step. Nevertheless, they have all given great rewards by inspiring progress in the development of mathematical methods that are applicable in fields often quite remote from the original scope.

The object of this book is to discuss the methods in graph theory that have been developed in the last century for attacking the four-color problem. It may be said without exaggeration concerning the writers on graph theory in this period, that however practical were the problems they examined, or however abstract their papers may appear to be, the author nearly always seems to have had some thoughts in mind regarding their application to the four-color problem.

The literature on the subject is voluminous and widely scattered. This book gives the first comprehensive analysis of this material and a discussion of the results that exist. All proofs and presentations have been examined and in many cases extensively revised. It has been the author's intention to take into account all important related studies in graph theory. No proof of the four-color problem is included, of course. But, as one often sees in the history of mathematics, a fresh and comprehensive review of a subject has been the starting point for strong progress by the younger generation of mathematicians. If this book should exert some influence of this kind, I shall feel that the labor involved has been amply rewarded.

A book on the four-color problem must lean heavily on general graph theory, and various aspects of graphs had to be developed as an adjunct to our discussions. The introductory chapters of the book contain a discussion of planar graphs, various results on the representations of such graphs, the Kuratowski characterization, the dual theory including Whitney's formulation, consequences of Euler's relation, and self-dual planar graphs. One chapter is devoted to Hamilton circuits in planar graphs with the Whitney–Tutte theorem and its immediate application to the four-color problem.

Then follows a discussion of the various colorations for graphs, vertices, edges, and faces with the simplest reductions. Here one finds Heawood's five-color theorem as well as the general coloration theorem of Brooks. There is a discussion of general color functions and their relation to the possible ways of directing a graph, including the theorem of Minty.

Chapter 8 deals with various formulations of the four-color problem in planar graphs while the subsequent chapter contains the formulations in the reduced case of cubic graphs, and various of the properties of cubic graphs—their construction, special configurations, and relation to interchange graphs.

Chapter 10 is devoted to Hadwiger's conjecture, one of the most promising recent approaches to the four-color problem. It includes a proof of Wagner's equivalence theorem bringing the four-color problem in close connection with general graph problems. The basis theorems of Wagner and Halin are also developed, as well as results by Dirac on the existence of subgraphs that are conformal to simplexes.

Chapter 11 contains a discussion of critical graphs, critical with respect to vertices, edges, or contraction; all concepts introduced by Dirac. The edge critical graphs have been studied particularly by Dirac, Hajós, and Gallai. In addition, various new results by the author are included; new formulations of Hadwiger's conjecture and of the four-color conjecture, as well as explicit construction of such graphs for every possible number of vertices.

Chapter 12 is devoted to the much-discussed subject of the properties of irreducible five-chromatic planar graphs. Here one finds an account of the results of Birkhoff, Franklin, Errera, Bernhard, Reynolds, and the numerous contributions by Winn. The last section contains a derivation of Winn's result—that a planar graph which is not four colorable must have at least thirty-six faces, the best result known so far.

In Chapter 13 one finds a discussion of three-colorations of graphs. One of the main results is the theorem of Grötzsch that a planar graph without triangles is vertex colorable in three colors; the extension of this theorem by Grünbaum is also given.

Chapter 14 deals with the edge coloration of graphs. The theorems of Shannon and Vizing are derived in a new manner, and sharper forms are obtained as well as a new criterion by the author.

Many of these chapters have been the subject of seminars on graph theory given at Yale University during the last few years; others have been the topic of invited lectures before meetings of the Mathematical Association of America.

I am greatly indebted to Professor Joel Stemple for a careful scrutiny of the manuscript and for assistance in the proofreading.

New Haven, Connecticut   Oystein Ore

INTRODUCTION

The Origin of the Four-Color Problem

The four-color problem is a little more than a century old. Several articles on the history of the conjecture have been published through the years, yet a number of erroneous facts have persisted until the present. It has been mentioned that the problem was known to the prolific Euler, the first writer on graph theory, also to Möbius, the German pioneer in topology. It has also been indicated that the problem originated with medieval or renaissance map makers. None of these statements seems to have any foundation in fact according to a recent and well-reasoned article by May.

Our first known source indicating the problem is a letter from Augustus de Morgan, Professor of Mathematics at University College, London, to his friend and colleague Sir William Rowan Hamilton at Trinity College, Dublin. The letter is dated October 23, 1852, and runs in part as follows:

"A student of mine asked me today to give him a reason for a fact which I did not know was a fact and do not yet. He says that if a figure be anyhow divided, and the compartments differently coloured, so that figures with any portion of common boundary *line* are differently coloured —four colours may be wanted but no more. Query: cannot a necessity for five or more be invented? As far as I see at this moment, if four ultimate compartments have each boundary line in common with one of the others, three of them inclose the fourth, and prevent any fifth from connexion with it. If this be true, four colours will colour any possible map, without any necessity for colour meeting colour except at a point."

At the time the problem created no stir. Not until nearly thirty years later did it appear in print in the mention of a question posed by Cayley, June 13, 1878, in a meeting of the London Mathematical Society. In the first volume of the Proceedings of the Royal Geographical Society (1879)

Cayley again stated the problem. Shortly afterwards unsatisfactory proofs were published by Kempe and Tait, arousing the sporting instincts of the mathematicians, and so the hunt was on.

The identity of de Morgan's student who had originally stated the problem was revealed by the physicist Frederick Guthrie in a note in the Proceedings of the Royal Society of Edinburgh, 1880:

"Some thirty years ago, when I was attending Professor de Morgan's class, my brother, Francis Guthrie, who had recently ceased to attend them (and who is now professor of Mathematics at the South African University, Cape Town) showed me the fact that the greatest necessary number of colors to be used in coloring a map so as to avoid identity of color in lineally contiguous districts is four. I should not be justified, after this lapse of time, in trying to give his proof, but the critical diagram was as in the margin.

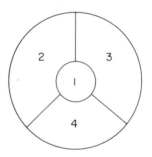

"With my brother's permission I submitted the theorem to Professor de Morgan, who expressed himself very pleased with it; accepted it as new; and as I am informed by those who subsequently attended his classes, was in the habit of acknowledging whence he had got his information."

Francis Guthrie lived until 1899 but never published anything on his problem, but occasionally the four-color conjecture has been referred to as Guthrie's problem.

CONTENTS

Chapter 5 / Large Circuits

Chapter 6 / Colorations

Chapter 7 / Color Functions

Chapter 8 / Formulations of the Four-Color Problem

Chapter 9 / Cubic Graphs

Chapter 10 / Hadwiger's Conjecture

Chapter 11 / Critical Graphs

Chapter 12 / Planar 5-Chromatic Graphs

Chapter 13 / Three Colors

Chapter 14 / Edge Coloration

CHAPTER 1

PLANAR GRAPHS

1.1. Planar Representations

A graph G is called *planar* when it is isomorphic to a graph $G(\pi)$ whose vertex set V is a point set in a plane π while the edges are *Jordan curves* in π such that two different edges have, at most, end points in common. It is possible to represent the graph in π in many isomorphic ways; each of them is called a planar *representation*. Evidently, every subgraph of a planar graph is planar.

The definition of a planar graph implies that the vertex set has a cardinal number not exceeding that of the continuum. Actually, we shall assume throughout in the following that the planar graph G is finite, that is, it has a finite number of edges and vertices.

Some of the standard properties of Jordan curves shall be used without proofs: A closed Jordan curve J divides the rest of the plane into two connected open domains, the *interior domain* (int J) and the *exterior domain* (ext J). Correspondingly there is a disjoint decomposition of the whole plane

$$\pi = J + \text{int } J + \text{ext } J.$$

The closed domains for J are the sets

$$\overline{\text{int }} J = J + \text{int } J, \quad \overline{\text{ext }} J = J + \text{ext } J.$$

A *Jordan curve* is a section of a closed Jordan curve. For any pair of vertices $j_1 \neq j_2$ on a closed Jordan curve J and any point $u \in \text{int } J$ there exist Jordan curves $T(j_1, u, j_2)$, having only their endpoints on J. Such a curve we call an *inner transversal* for J. An *outer transversal* is defined analogously.

1

We observe further: Let J_1 and J_2 be closed Jordan curves such that one includes no section which is a transversal for the other. Then either J_1 lies inside of J_2 or J_2 lies inside of J_1 or the two curves have disjoint interior domains.

A planar graph may also be represented isomorphically on a sphere. Such a representation is obtained, for instance, by projecting the plane stereographically upon a sphere S tangent to π. Conversely, when a graph is represented on a sphere it can be projected stereographically upon any one of its tangent planes. By selecting the projection center on S such that it does not lie on G one obtains a planar representation lying within a bounded part of the plane.

For most investigations on planar graphs it is immaterial whether they are represented in the plane or on a sphere. However, as we shall see, the representation on the spheres produces a certain formal unity in concepts and results which, in part, make the statements of the theory more elegant.

The form of the representation of a planar graph can be varied greatly by means of the *Jordan–Schönflies theorem*: When C_1 and C_2 are closed Jordan curves in the plane and η is a homeomorphism between them, then η can be extended to a homeomorphism of the whole plane. This implies, for instance, that any planar graph enclosed by some Jordan curve C_1 can be represented as a planar graph lying inside (or outside) any other such curve C_2. Furthermore, the vertices of G on C_1 can be made to correspond to the vertices on C_2 in the second representation in the same (or reverse) cyclic order. This fact is useful, for instance, when there is a question of fitting together planar graphs.

We have supposed that the edges of the graph in the plane are Jordan curves. Since such curves can be approximated arbitrarily closely by polygonal arcs, one can assume that the edges consist of straight-line pieces. We shall show shortly that for most questions one can suppose that the edges actually are straight lines.

1.2. The Faces

We shall study a planar graph G with a given representation in a plane π. Any edge (a, b) is a Jordan curve which is closed only when the edge is a loop. Therefore, a graph arc is represented by a Jordan curve, while a graph circuit is represented by a closed Jordan curve.

A circuit in G is *minimal* when it has no inner transversals; it is *maximal* when there are no outer transversals lying in G. The interior of a minimal circuit is a *minimal inner domain*; its exterior is a *maximal outer domain*. The exterior of a maximal circuit is a *minimal outer domain* and its interior a *maximal inner domain*.

At this point, the advantage of using a representation of the graph on a sphere becomes manifest. The distinction between minimal and maximal circuits then disappears. On the sphere, a circuit is minimal when one of its two domains has no transversals consisting of graph edges. Its minimal domain is the domain without transversals.

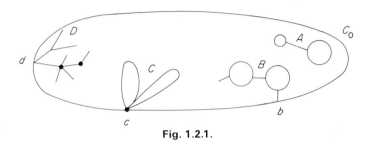

Fig. 1.2.1.

In general, a minimal circuit C_0 may have edges of G lying in its minimal domain; however, these edges cannot form any transversals. This means that the components of the graph of interior edges must have either no vertices of attachment on C_0 or only a single such attachment. The situation is illustrated in Fig. 1.2.1. The components inside C_0 without vertices of attachments (such as A) are connected components of G; they may possibly reduce to a single isolated vertex. Those with one vertex of attachment are indicated at B, C, D; their attachments are b, c, d, respectively. For the minimal outer domain in the case of a representation in the plane, the situation is similar.

One sees that when G is a connected graph without separating vertices there are no edges of G within any minimal domain.

The edges of a graph fall into two categories; (a) the circuit edges lying on some circuit, and (b) the separating edges or acyclic edges lying on no circuit. We shall prove the following theorem.

Theorem 1.2.1. Every circuit edge lies on the boundary of exactly two minimal domains.

Proof: Let C be a circuit including E. If C is not minimal, it will have inner transversals and one finds a circuit inside C including E. By repetition this leads to a minimal circuit C_1 inside C including E. The same construction applies when C has outer transversals. One obtains a minimal (maximal) circuit C_2 including E such that

$$\text{int } C_1 \cap \text{int } C_2 = \emptyset,$$

or possibly

$$\text{int } C_1 \cap \text{ext } C_2 = \emptyset,$$

when C is maximal (Fig. 1.2.2). One may have $C_1 = C_2$.

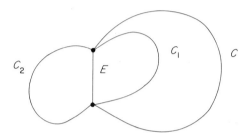

Fig. 1.2.2.

Let p be a point in the plane π which does not lie on G. The points in π connected to p by Jordan curves disjoint from G, we call the *face* $F(p)$ defined by p. A face $F(p)$ is *finite* when p lies inside some circuit of G. Points p not within circuits can be connected to each other by a Jordan curve without points on G so that they all define the same face F_∞, the *infinite face*. When G is considered to lie on a sphere, no face is distinguished in this way.

All points in a finite face $F(p)$ must lie within the minimal circuit C_0 enclosing p. To obtain $F(p)$, one must eliminate from int C_0 all points of G as well as all those points of π which lie on or inside circuits lying within C_0 (see Fig. 1.2.1).

One could also have defined the face $F(p)$ as follows: The point p divides all circuits in G into two categories

$$\{C_i\} \quad \text{and} \quad \{C_j'\},$$

characterized, respectively, by

$$p \in \text{int } C_i, \qquad p \notin \text{int } C_j'.$$

One then has

$$F(p) = \bigcap_i \text{int } C_i - \bigcup_j \overline{\text{int } C_j'} - G.$$

This formula applies also to the infinite face F_∞; here there are no circuits C_i so that

$$F_\infty = \pi - \bigcup_j \overline{\text{int } C_j'} - G.$$

The complement $\bar{F}_\infty$ of F_∞ we may call the G-*domain*. It consists of G and all points in the finite faces.

The boundary of a face $F(p)$ is a part of G. It consists of:

1. The edges of the minimal circuit C_0 within which p is located.

2. The edges of those maximal circuits within C_0 which are not enclosed by larger circuits within C_0.

3. The acyclic edges and isolated vertices within C_0, but not within any of the maximal circuits in 2 (see Fig. 1.2.1.).

The boundary of F_∞ consists of the edges of the maximal circuits lying within no other circuits, as well as the acyclic edges and isolated vertices lying within no circuits. This boundary of F_∞ is also the boundary of the G-domain and we may call it the G-*boundary*. It is only defined with respect to a particular planar representation of G.

Theorem 1.2.2. A circuit edge E_0 lies on the boundary of just two faces, an acyclic edge E_1 is on the boundary of a single face.

Proof: Theorem 1.2.1 shows that the circuit edge E_0 lies on the boundary of the two faces defined by its adjoining minimal domains. For an acyclic edge E_1, one can find from any point p on E_1 a closed Jordan curve J_1 returning to p having no other points in common with G. The face F_1 to which J_1-p belongs is the only face adjoining E_1.

In the case of connected graphs without separating vertices the preceding observations simplify considerably. The boundaries of the faces are the minimal circuits. There is a single maximal circuit which is at the same time the boundary of G and the boundary of the infinite face.

We may define in the general case: A corner of a face F is a common end point c_0 of two boundary edges.

$$E_1 = (c_1, c_0), \qquad E_2 = (c_0, c_2)$$

and two such boundary edges define an *angle* of F at c_0.

1.3. Maximal Planar Graphs. Straight Line Representations

We consider graphs with no loops or faces bounded by two edges. It may be possible to add a new edge to the given representation of G such that these properties are preserved. When no such adjunction can be made, we call G *maximal planar*. Clearly, every representation of a graph is contained in a maximal planar graph with the same vertex set. A planar graph is called *triangulated* when all faces have three corners.

Theorem 1.3.1. A planar graph is maximal if, and only if, it is triangulated.

Proof: If some face has more than three corners, one can add diagonal edges. If each face has three corners, no edges can be added without giving a nonplanar graph or loops or a face with two boundary edges. The same result holds if one restricts the definition of a maximal planar graph slightly by requiring that it shall have no multiple edges.

Theorem 1.3.2. A maximal planar graph is two-vertex connected. It is three-vertex connected when there are no multiple edges.

Proof: Any connected component can be joined by an edge to one of the other components. A lobe graph in G can be joined by a new edge to another lobe graph such that G remains planar and has no face with two boundary edges. If G has no multiple edges, it cannot be separated by two vertices a and b into two components $G = A + B$ (see Fig. 1.3.1). It would imply that the inner and outer faces I and O bounded by A and B would have to be triangular and this is only possible when a and b are connected by two edges. In Fig. 1.3.2 one finds an example of a maximal graph which is two-vertex separable.

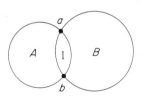

Fig. 1.3.1.

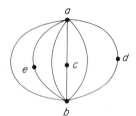

Fig. 1.3.2.

The next result is due to Fáry.

Theorem 1.3.3. A finite planar graph G without loops or multiple edges has a planar representation G_0 in which all edges are straight-line segments.

The proof includes a little more; by any representation of G the straight-line graph G_0 can be chosen such that the infinite faces correspond and an edge within a face in G (as in Fig. 1.2.1) has an image lying within the corresponding face in G_0.

The theorem is true for planar graphs with $n = 1, 2, 3, 4$ vertices as one can readily verify. Therefore, it may be proved, in general, by induction with respect to the number of vertices. It is evidently sufficient to establish it for maximal planar graphs. One can suppose that there are at least three edges at each vertex, because if there were only two edges (a, b) and (b, c) at a vertex b, they could be joined into a single edge (a, c).

Suppose first that G has a *separating triangle*, that is, there are three edges forming a circuit,

$$C = (a, b)(b, c)(c, a),$$

such that there are vertices of G both inside and outside of C. We denote by H_1 the subgraph consisting of C and the edges of G lying in its interior, by H_2 the subgraph consisting of C and the edges in its exterior. By assumption, there is a straight-line representation of $H_1^{(0)}$ of H_1 in which the infinite face will be bounded by the triangle $C_1^{(0)}$ corresponding to C. Similarly, there is a straight-line representation $H_2^{(0)}$ of H_2 in which C corresponds to a triangle $C_2^{(0)}$ without interior edges. Through an affine transformation of the plane, carrying straight lines into straight lines, one can achieve the result that the triangle $C_1^{(0)}$ is congruent to $C_2^{(0)}$. Then the graph $H_1^{(0)}$ can be placed within $C_2^{(0)}$ to give a straight-line representation G_0 of the whole graph with the required properties.

The case remains where G is a maximal planar graph without separating triangles. Let v be some vertex at which one has the edges

$$E_i = (v, a_i), \qquad i = 1, 2, \ldots, \rho \qquad (1.3.1)$$

in cyclic order. Since the case of three vertices in G is trivial we may suppose that v lies inside the maximal triangle. Because G is triangulated, there exist edges

$$F_i = (a_i, a_{i+1}), \qquad i = 1, 2, \ldots, \rho, \qquad a_1 = a_{\rho+1}, \qquad (1.3.2)$$

where each of the triangles E_i, F_i, E_{i+1} defines a face. The circuit

$$C = F_1, F_2, \ldots, F_\rho \qquad (1.3.3)$$

is the smallest containing v in its interior.

In (1.3.1) one must have $\rho \geqq 3$ since G has no multiple edges. Also $\rho = 3$ is excluded because then C would form a separating triangle when there are at least five vertices. We now eliminate v and all edges

(1.3.1) from G and replace them by the $\rho - 3$ new edges (see Figs. 1.3.3 and 1.3.4).

$$E_i' = (a_1, a_i), \qquad i = 3, \ldots, \rho - 1. \qquad (1.3.4)$$

The graph G_1 constructed in this manner is triangulated. It cannot have any multiple edges, for an edge (a_1, a_i) on the outside of C would imply the existence of a separating triangle, $(v, a_1)(a_1, a_i)(a_i, v)$, in the original graph G.

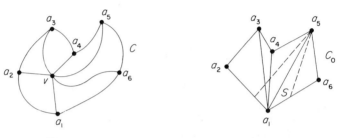

Fig. 1.3.3.   Fig. 1.3.4.

At each vertex a_i in (1.3.4) there exists a certain angular section S_i within the polygon C_0 including the straight line (a_1, a_i), but no other corners of C_0. The intersection of all these sections is a nonvoid set D including a_1 and certain interior points v of C_0. Any such point v can be connected by straight lines (v, a_i) to all corners of C_0 to give the desired representation of G.

When the edges of the graph are straight lines, the face boundaries are polygons. It is natural to ask when the planar representations can be constructed such that all these face polygons are convex. Problems of this kind have been examined by Tutte.

We shall add a further observation on maximal planar graphs due to

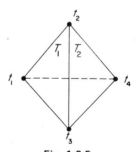

Fig. 1.3.5.

Wagner. In the maximal graph G let $T_1 = (t_1, t_2, t_3)$ and $T_2 = (t_2, t_3, t_4)$ be two adjoining triangular faces (Fig. 1.3.5).

The edges of these faces form a quadrangle (t_1, t_2, t_3, t_4) with the diagonal (t_2, t_3). When this diagonal is replaced by a new diagonal (t_1, t_4), one obtains a new maximal graph G' with the same vertices and the same number of edges and faces. We shall say that G' has been obtained from G by a *diagonal transformation*. Two maximal graphs G_1 and G_2 are equivalent under diagonal transformations when one can be obtained from the other by a series of such changes. We then have the following theorem.

Theorem 1.3.4. Any two maximal graphs with n vertices are equivalent under diagonal transformations.

The proof shall be based upon the fact that a maximal graph can be transformed into normal form in Fig. 1.3.6 depending only upon the number of vertices in G. We select an arbitrary face (a, b, c) as the infinite face. The edge (a, b) defines an adjoining triangle with a corner v_1.

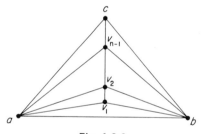

Fig. 1.3.6.

The other triangles with a corner at a and b have the series of corners

$$v_1, v_2, \ldots, v_{n-1}, c, \qquad v_1, u_2, \ldots, u_{m-1}, c,$$

respectively; they are joined by the arcs

$$A = (v_1, v_2, \ldots, c), \qquad B = (v_1, u_2, \ldots, c).$$

When A and B coincide, we have a graph of the desired type. Suppose they coincide until the vertices $u_i = v_i$ while $u_{i+1} \neq v_{i+1}$. We then obtain the adjoining triangles $(a, v_i, v_{i+1}), (v_i, v_{i+1}, u_{i+1})$ and by a diagonal transformation one arrives at a new graph in which the arcs A and B have a further vertex in common.

By counting the number of edges and faces of the graph in the normal form (Fig. 1.8) one obtains the following theorem. (For another proof see Theorem 4.1.7.)

Theorem 1.3.5. When v_v is the number of vertices in a maximal graph, the number of edges and faces in the graph are given by (1.3.5).

$$v_e = 3v_v - 6, \qquad v_f = 2v_v - 4. \tag{1.3.5}$$

Next, let C be a circuit in G of length l. The number of vertices, edges, and faces inside and outside C shall be denoted by v_v', v_v''; v_e', v_e''; v_f', v_f'', respectively, so one has in G,

$$v_v = v_v' + v_v'' + l, \qquad v_e = v_e' + v_e'' + l, \qquad v_f = v_f' + v_f''. \tag{1.3.6}$$

We eliminate all vertices and edges outside C and replace them by a single vertex V with l edges to the vertices on C. The resulting graph is maximal and the number of its vertices, edges, and faces is $v_v' + l + 1$, $v_e' + 2l$, $v_f' + l$. Since these numbers must satisfy (1.3.5) we find Theorem 1.3.6.

Theorem 1.3.6. The number of edges and faces lying inside a circuit C of length l in a maximal graph is

$$v_e' = 3 \cdot v_v' + l - 3, \qquad v_f' = 2 \cdot v_v' + l - 2$$

where v_v' is the number of inside vertices.

For $v_v' = 0$ one obtains the following theorem as a special case.

Theorem 1.3.7. The maximal number of nonintersecting diagonals which can be drawn in a circuit C of length l is $l - 3$ and they divide the interior of C into $l - 2$ triangles.

These observations can be generalized. Let D_i, $i = 1, 2, \ldots, k$ be a family of disjoint domains in the plane, each bounded by edges in the maximal graph G. The boundaries are edge disjoint, but may have vertices in common. The complementary part of the plane

$$\bar{D} = P - \sum D_i$$

shall contain v_v', v_e', v_f' vertices, edges, and faces of G. Next, we omit from the graph all vertices and edges lying within any domain D_i and replace them by a single vertex $d_i \in D_i$, and all edges from d_i to the vertices on the boundary of D_i. The new graph G' is maximal planar. Its number of vertices, edges, faces are, respectively,

$$v_v' + k + l_v, \qquad v_e' + 2l_e, \qquad v_f' + l_e \tag{1.3.7}$$

where l_v is the number of vertices on the boundaries of the D_i and l_e the number of boundary edges. Since the quantities of (1.3.7) have to satisfy (1.3.5) it follows that the number of edges and faces within $\bar{D}$ are given by (1.3.8).

$$v_e' = 3v_v' + 3k + 3l_v - 2l_e - 6, \quad v_f' = 2v_v' + 2k + 2l_v - l_e - 4. \quad (1.3.8)$$

If $v_v' = 0$, one finds for the maximal number of diagonals, nonintersecting edges which can be drawn inside $\bar{D}$ and the number of faces

$$v_e' = 3k + 3l_v - 2l_e - 6, \quad v_f' = 2k + 2l_v - l_e - 4. \quad (1.3.9)$$

When the boundaries of the domains D_i are vertex disjoint, one has $l_v = l_e$ and from (1.3.8),

$$v_e' = 3v_v' + 3k + l_v - 6, \quad v_f' = 2v_v' + 2k + l_v - 4. \quad (1.3.10)$$

The number of diagonal nonintersecting edges is then

$$v_e' = 3k + l_v - 6, \quad v_f' = 2k + l_v - 4. \quad (1.3.11)$$

Let us say that two disjoint circuits C_1 and C_2 are *parallel* when the distance from any vertex on one to the other circuit is always $d = 1$. From (1.3.11) we obtain the following theorem.

Theorem 1.3.8. Let C_1 and C_2 be two parallel circuits of lengths l_1 and l_2 in a maximal graph G. The number of edges in G connecting C_1 with C_2 is then $l_1 + l_2$.

PROBLEMS

1. Construct maximal planar graphs for the Platonic graphs.
2. Diagonal transformations which leave unchanged the number of vertices, edges, and faces, as well as the number of boundary edges of the two faces, also can be defined for general planar graphs. Try to find normal forms under such transformations.

CHAPTER 2 | *BRIDGES AND CIRCUITS*

2.1. Bridges in General Graphs

For the moment, G shall be an arbitrary graph, not necessarily planar. H denotes a subgraph, its vertex set is $V(H)$. In most applications H is a circuit.

An H-avoiding arc or path in G is a path $P(a_0, a_n)$ in which no edges or vertices belong to H except possibly the end points a_0 and a_n. Two edges E_1 and E_2 not belonging to H are said to be connected outside of H when an H-avoiding path $P(E_1, E_2)$ exists beginning in E_1 and ending in E_2. Under these conditions, we shall also say that E_1 and E_2 are *bridge equivalent* with respect to H.

To show the transitivity of the bridge equivalence let the edges E_1 and E_2 be bridge equivalent and likewise E_2 and E_3. The corresponding H-avoiding arcs shall be $P(E_1, E_2)$ and $Q(E_2, E_3)$. If E_2 has no end point on $V(H)$, the two arcs can be combined to produce an H-avoiding arc $R(E_1, E_2)$. When the last vertex in $P(E_1, E_2)$ is in $V(H)$, an H-avoiding path $R(E_1, E_3)$ is obtained by combining the arcs $P(E_1, E_2) - E_2$ and $Q(E_2, E_3) - E_2$.

All edges which are bridge equivalent to an edge E form a bridge $B = B(E)$ for H. A bridge is a connected subgraph. A bridge is *singular* when $B = E$ consists of a single edge with both end points in $V(H)$; otherwise B is *nonsingular*. No two bridges have common edges and each bridge is edge disjoint from H. Two bridges can only have vertices in $V(H)$ in common. A nonsingular bridge B is a section graph in G–H. Suppose that $E = (a, b)$ is an edge not in H. If there are edges of a bridge B, both at a and b, then some H-avoiding path in B can be continued through E provided both a and b are not in $V(H)$. The observation

12

is true also for a singular bridge, provided G has no multiple edges.

When G is connected, every bridge B must have vertices in common with $V(H)$. These vertices are the only vertices of attachment for the graph B, for at no other vertices can there be edges of both B and $G - B$. When G has no separating vertices and is connected, each bridge has at least two attachments. The bridges can also be characterized as the minimal section subgraphs of $G - H$ having all attachments in $V(H)$.

One may take the subgraph $H = \{h_i\}$ simply as a set of vertices h_i in G. G is usually connected and H is a proper subset of its vertex set $V(G)$. If G has more than one nonsingular bridge with respect to H, then H is a separating set for G; that is, there exists a pair of vertices a and b which are connected only by arcs which pass through vertices in H.

We make the following observations.

Theorem 2.1.1. Let B be a bridge and a_1, a_2, a_3, three of its attachments. Then one can find a vertex v_0 not an attachment such that there exist three edge disjoint arcs in B.

$$A_1(v_0, a_1), \qquad A_2(v_0, a_2), \qquad A_3(v_0, a_3). \qquad (2.1.1)$$

Proof: To construct the arcs of Eq. (2.1.1) we observe that there exists an arc $A(a_1, a_2)$ in B. Since B is not a singular bridge A has an interior vertex v. From v there exists an arc $A_3(v, a_3)$ also in B. When v_0 is the last vertex on A_3 lying on A, the three arcs $A(v_0, a_1)$, $A_2(v_0, a_2)$, $A_3(v_0, a_3)$ satisfy the conditions of the theorem.

2.2. Circuit Bridges

We suppose that G is a connected planar graph and take the subgraph $H = C$ to be a circuit in G. As before, we define the domain of a bridge B to be the set of points on B and the points inside circuits in B. The bridges for G fall into two categories; *exterior bridges* with domain in ext C, *interior bridges* with domain in int C.

We assume for the moment that B is an interior bridge for C. Its attachments on C shall be denoted by

$$c_1, c_2, \ldots, c_k \qquad (2.2.1)$$

in cyclic order. A bridge is *essential* when it has at least two attachments, that is, B includes at least one transversal of C. The bridge is *inessential* when there is only one attachment; in this case c_1 is a separating vertex for G. Thus, a minimal circuit is characterized by the property of having no essential inner (or outer bridges). In the following, we are principally interested in the essential bridges so that the term "bridge" shall be used to mean "essential bridge".

Let us consider the subgraph $G(C, B)$ of G consisting of the circuit C and some inner bridge B. The attachments (2.2.1) divide C into its B-sections.

$$C_i = C_B(c_i, c_{i+1}), \qquad i = 1, 2, \ldots, k. \tag{2.2.2}$$

Each pair of vertices (2.2.1) is connected by an inner transversal of G lying in B. There is a unique *boundary transversal*,

$$T_i = T_i(c_i, c_{i+1}), \tag{2.2.3}$$

in B which is minimal in the sense that the circuit

$$K_i = C_i(c_i, c_{i+1}) + T_i(c_{i+1}, c_i) \tag{2.2.4}$$

has no transversals in $G(C, B)$. Thus K_i defines a unique face F_i in $G(C, B)$ which we shall call the ith *boundary face* for B (see Fig. 2.2.1).

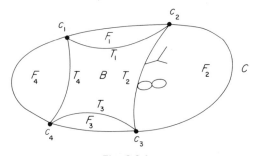

Fig. 2.2.1.

Suppose next that B' is another inner bridge for C. Since B and B' are connected and have no vertices in common in the interior of C it is clear that B' must lie within one of the boundary faces F_i of B in $G(C, B)$. The attachments c_j' of B' must all be located on the corresponding B-section $C(c_i, c_{i-1})$, including possibly one or both of the end points c_i and c_{i+1}. Conversely, B must be located within one of the boundary faces F_j' for B' in C (see Fig. 2.2.2).

B and B' shall be called *neighboring bridges* when a Jordan curve $P(u, u')$ exists inside C, connecting a point b in the domain of B to a point b' in the domain of B' such that b and b' are the only points of P on G (Fig. 2.2.2). The set of all intermediate points x in such connecting curves

$P(b, x, b')$ we denote by $I(B, B')$ and call the *interstice* between B and B'. Such an interstice is a face in G.

It may be, that for some boundary face F_i for B defined by a circuit K_i in (2.2.4), there is no (essential) bridge contained within it. Then K_i is the minimal circuit of a face in G and it is appropriate to include these

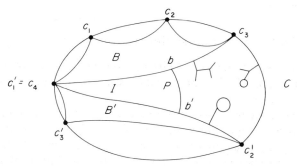

Fig. 2.2.2.

faces among the interstices. They are the faces within C which border only upon a single bridge; they may be called *terminal interstices*. A *terminal bridge* is one for which there is at most one section face which includes other bridges.

According to these definitions, aside from inessential bridges, the interior of C has been divided up into bridge domains and interstices. The relative locations of these sets may be described by means of an auxiliary graph Γ, the *interior bridge graph* for C. Here, Γ is a bipartite graph whose vertex sets correspond to the bridge domains and their interstices respectively. A bridge B and an interstice I are connected by an edge (B, I) in Γ if and only if I has a boundary edge in common with B.

Theorem 2.2.1. The bridge graph is a tree.

Proof: The graph Γ is connected, because one can pass from any bridge domain or interstice to any other along a Jordan curve inside C. For a bridge B, the interstices bordering upon it all lie in separate boundary faces $F_i(B)$. Thus, the bridges following I in any Γ arc must all be located within $F_i(B)$ so the arc cannot return to B. The same argument holds for a Γ-arc beginning in an interstice.

It is readily seen that a tree Γ can be considered to be a bridge graph if, and only if, the distance from any terminal vertex to any other is always even. A further observation shall be made.

Theorem 2.2.2. Within any nonminimal circuit there is at least one terminal bridge and at least two terminal interstices.

Proof: Any nonminimal circuit has bridges, hence a nontrivial bridge tree Γ. In Γ, the two end points of an arc A of maximal length must correspond to terminal interstices and the next-to-the-last vertices in A to terminal bridges.

2.3. Equivalence of Planar Representations

We have observed that for a given graph there are many representations in the plane. We shall now divide these representations into certain equivalence classes.

Suppose that we have two planar representations R and R' of the same graph G. In the isomorphism between R and R' an arc or circuit in R must correspond to an arc or circuit in R' and vice versa. But it does not follow that the edges in the interior of a circuit C in R have images falling within the image circuit C' in R'. Therefore, it is not true in general that a minimal circuit in R corresponds to a minimal circuit in R', nor a maximal circuit to a maximal circuit.

PLANAR EQUIVALENCE. Two representations R and R' of a graph G are plane equivalent when the boundary of a face in one representation always corresponds to the boundary of a face in the other.

We recall that in a planar graph representation one can change the infinite face to any other by projecting the graph stereographically on the sphere and then projecting it back again in the plane from a projection center within the face to be infinite in the new representation. One sees that by such stereographic projections the representations are plane equivalent.

In addition to planar equivalence one can introduce strict planar equivalence.

STRICT PLANAR EQUIVALENCE. Two plane equivalence representations R and R' are strictly plane equivalent when the boundaries of the infinite faces correspond.

In connection with these definitions we observe the following: In a disconnected graph, one can obtain new nonequivalent representations simply by placing the connected components within other faces (as A in Fig. 1.2.1). When G has separating vertices, there will be subgraphs of G such as B, C, and D in Fig. 1.2.1, each attached at a single vertex b, c, d. At each of these, say b, there must be at least two faces. One can change the representation into another nonequivalent one by placing B within one of these faces, still attached at b (see Fig. 2.3.1).

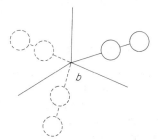

Fig. 2.3.1.

Due to this arbitrariness in placing connected components and one-vertex attached subgraphs, we shall assume that G cannot be separated by less than two vertices.

Theorem 2.3.1. Let R and R' be two planar representations of a connected graph G without separating vertices. Then R and R' are plane equivalent if, and only if, the isomorphism between them has the property: For any circuit C the bridges all retain their character of being outside or inside for the image circuit C' or all inside bridges shall become outside bridges and vice versa.

Proof: Suppose that R and R' have the stated property. Let C be the boundary of a face F, that is, a minimal circuit in R. Since C has no inner bridges, either C' is minimal or it must become the maximal circuit bounding the finite face F_∞'. Similarly, the boundary C_∞ of F_∞ either remains maximal or becomes a minimal circuit.

Suppose, on the other hand, that a circuit C exists for which one of the inner bridges remains inner, while another becomes an outer bridge in C'. Then one can find an interstice I in C such that one of its boundary transversals T_1 belongs to a bridge B_1 remaining inside while another such transversal T_2 belongs to a bridge B_2 transferred into an outer bridge for C'. But this implies that the boundary of I is not transformed into the boundary of a face since the images T_1' and T_2' of T_1 and T_2 are separated by C'.

In the correspondence between plane equivalent representations there is at most one minimal circuit which can change its character into a maximal circuit, leading to the following theorem.

Theorem 2.3.2. When R and R' are plane equivalent representations, they are either strictly plane equivalent or one can be transformed into a strictly plane equivalent representation to the other by a stereographic projection.

2.4. Uniqueness of Representations

We say that the planar representation of a graph is *essentially unique* when the representations are all plane equivalent. To derive a criterion for this to be the case we need some auxiliary observations.

We assume as before that G is connected and without separating vertices. Such a graph is called *properly two-vertex separable* when G has a decomposition,

$$G = H_1 + H_2, \tag{2.4.1}$$

in which the edge disjoint subgraphs H_1 and H_2 are not graph arcs, and they are only connected at the two common vertices a_1 and a_2. Clearly, H_1 and H_2 are connected graphs.

Theorem 2.4.1. A planar connected graph G, without separating vertices, is properly two-vertex separable if, and only if, the boundary of some face has more than one bridge.

Proof: Suppose, for instance, that the maximal circuit C_1 has more than one bridge. We select a terminal bridge B and denote by $C_1(c_1, c_2)$ the B-section (2.2.2) in which the attachments of the other bridges are located. Then the subgraph $H_1 = B + C_1(c_2, c_1)$ is separated from the rest of the graph H_2 by c_1 and c_2. Evidently H_1 and H_2 are connected and are not arcs.

Suppose, on the other hand, that G has a proper two-vertex separation (Fig. 2.4.1). Since H_1 is connected, there exist two boundary arcs $P_1(a_1, a_2)$

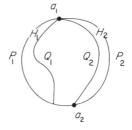

Fig. 2.4.1.

and $Q_1(a_1, a_2)$ for the H_1-domain. The two arcs may have edges in common but they cannot coincide since H_1 is not an arc. Corresponding arcs $P_2(a_1, a_2)$ and $Q_2(a_1, a_2)$ exist in H_2. Then $P_1 + P_2$ is the boundary of the infinite face and it has at least two bridges lying in H_1 and H_2.

Theorem 2.4.2. Let G be a planar connected graph without separating vertices. A necessary and sufficient condition that its planar representation be essentially unique is that it have no proper two-vertex separation.

Proof: Suppose that the representation is not essentially unique. Then, according to the definition, there is a face F with the boundary circuit C such that the image circuit C' is no longer the boundary of a face. This means that C' has both inner and outer bridges, hence also C has at least two bridges. According to Theorem 2.4.1, G has a proper two-vertex separation.

Conversely, let there be such a separation (Fig. 2.4.1). Then a new representation of G is obtained by a reflection or twist of one component, say H_2, making P_2 the inner boundary and Q_2 the outer boundary. In the first representation, $P_1 + P_2$ is the boundary of the infinite face, while in the new representations, the corresponding circuit is no longer a face boundary.

2.5. Transfer of Bridges

A pair of points a, b on a circuit C shall be said to *separate* another pair a_1, b_1 when the four points are distinct and lie in the cyclic order a, a_1, b, b_1 on C. An inner bridge B *separates* an outer bridge B_1 when there exist a pair of attachments, a, b of B, separating a pair of attachments, a_1, b_1 of B_1. When B does not separate B_1, all attachments of B_1 lie on the same B-section and conversely. No inner (outer) bridge can separate any other inner (outer) bridge.

An inner bridge B of C in some planar representation R of G is *transferable* when there exists a representation R' identical with R except that B' has been drawn as an outer bridge.

Theorem 2.5.1. The inner bridge B is transferable only when it is not separated by any outer bridge.

Proof: When there is an outer bridge B_1 separated by B, there are transversals $T(a, b)$ in B and $T_1(a_1, b_1)$ in B_1 where a, b separate a_1, b_1. These transversals cannot both be drawn outside of C without intersecting. On the other hand, when B is not separated by any outer bridge, each

outer bridge has its attachments within a single one of the B-sections
(2.2.2). Therefore, there exists an outer interstice I for C such that all
attachments of B lie on the boundary of I on C. But then B can be drawn
B' in I with the same attachments.

The property of a bridge B to be transferable is not influenced by the
transfer of another bridge B_0 since all vertices of attachment for B_0 lie
within a single B-section. Thus in a suitable representation all transferable
inner bridges may be drawn as outer bridges, or vice versa. The condition
for a transferable bridge can also be expressed.

Theorem 2.5.2. A necessary and sufficient condition that a bridge B be
transferable is that any pair of consecutive attachments c_1 and c_2 separate
G.

Proof: Suppose that B is transferable with the image B' after the transfer.
We denote by G_1 the subgraph consisting of the arc $C(c_1,c_2)$ together with
all outer and inner bridges of C attached in this interval and lying inside
the corresponding boundary faces for B and B'. The remaining part of G
is G_2. Then G_1 and G_2 are separated by the vertices c_1 and c_2 since every
graph arc from G_1 to G_2 must pass through one of them. Conversely, when
such a separation exists for every pair of consecutive attachments, B
cannot be separated by any other bridge.

We notice that the two-vertex separation defined by c_1 and c_2 is a
proper separation if, and only if, there is at least one outer or inner bridge
$B_1 \neq B$ attached only to the closed interval $C(c_1, c_2)$.

Suppose now that we have two nonequivalent representations R and R'
of G. Let F be a face whose boundary circuit does not correspond to a face
boundary C' in R'. A bridge for C corresponds to a bridge for C' but it
may change its character from an inner to an outer bridge, or vice versa.
But Theorem 2.5.2 shows that the property of being transferable is
preserved by the mapping leading to the next theorem.

Theorem 2.5.3. Let C be the boundary of a face in a representation R
while its image C' is not a face boundary in another representation R'.
Then the bridges in C' are all transferable.

After the transfer of the bridges in C' to their original character also
the original interstices in C remain interstices in C'. Since the bridges are
drawn plane equivalent to the original ones, any circuit bounding a face
within a bridge will remain a face boundary. Thus, after the transfer the
two representations have more corresponding face boundaries. A repetition of this process leads to Theorem 2.5.4.

Theorem 2.5.4. Let R and R' be two planar representations of a connected graph without separating vertices. Then R' can be changed into a representation equivalent to R by a series of bridge transfers.

This result extends also to the most general case where G is disconnected or has separating vertices. But in this case it may be necessary to make use in addition of the two operations described in Section 2.3.

1. Transfer of a component to the interior of some suitable face.
2. Relocation of a one-vertex attached subgraph within a suitable face as indicated in Fig. 2.3.1.

These operations may also serve in the construction of plane representations. Suppose that G is a planar graph and that we have a planar representation R_H of a subgraph H of G. One obtains G from H by successive adjunctions of edges $E = (a, b)$. It may happen that the addition of E to R_H is not possible without destroying the plane representation. On the other hand, we know that G has some planar representation R', hence there is a representation R_H' of H in which E connects two vertices on some face boundary. But then, as we observed, R_H' is obtainable by the transfer of connected components, one-attached subgraphs, and bridges.

2.6. Characterization of Planar Graphs

We turn to the problem of finding necessary and sufficient conditions for a graph to be planar. The simplest nonplanar graphs are the two graphs A and B depicted in Fig. 2.6.1.

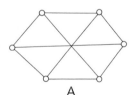
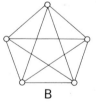

Fig. 2.6.1.

To show that A is nonplanar we observe that in any representation there must exist a hexagonal circuit $(1, 2, 3, 4, 5, 6, 1)$ as in Fig. 2.6.2. Since each pair of opposite vertices is connected by an edge there must be one inner edge, say $(1, 4)$, and an outer edge, say $(2, 5)$. But then there is a circuit $(1, 2, 5, 4, 1)$ having the vertex 3 in its interior and 6 in its exterior so that according to the Jordan curve theorem it is not possible

Bridges and Circuits

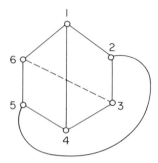

Fig. 2.6.2.

to draw an edge (3, 6) without crossing the circuit. A similar argument, which we shall leave to the reader, yields that the graph B in Fig. 2.6.1 is not planar.

Since the graphs A and B in Fig. 2.5.1 are not planar, any graph *conformal* to these, that is, graphs in which the edges in A and B are replaced by nonintersecting arcs, must also be nonplanar.

The remainder of this section shall be devoted to a proof of the important theorem of *Kuratowski*.

Theorem 2.6.1. A finite graph is planar if and only if it contains no subgraph conformal to the graphs A and B in Fig. 2.6.1.

For the proof we need certain preparatory results. It is fairly obvious that a finite graph is planar if, and only if, its components are planar, and also if each of its lobe graphs is planar.

Theorem 2.6.2. Let G be a two-vertex connected graph having a pair of vertices a and b separating it into two edge disjoint components,

$$G = H_1 + H_2. \tag{2.6.1}$$

An edge (a, b) may or may not occur. Then G is planar if, and only if, each graph,

$$H_1' = H_1 + (a, b), \qquad H_2' = H_2 + (a, b), \tag{2.6.2}$$

is planar.

Proof: When the graphs (2.6.2) are planar, they can be fitted together at a and b to give a planar representation for G. Conversely, assume G to be planar. Each H_i is connected since G is two-vertex connected. Thus, there exist arcs,

$$P_1(a, b), \qquad P_2(a, b),$$

through H_1 and H_2, respectively, so that

$$H_1 + P_2(a, b), \qquad H_2 + P_1(a, b) \qquad (2.6.3)$$

are planar graphs. But then the graphs (2.6.2) can also be drawn in the plane.

We proceed to the proof of Theorem 2.6.1. If it were not true there would exist some nonplanar graph G with a minimal number of edges not containing any subgraph conformal to A or B. The minimal property of G implies that it is connected and has no separating vertices. From Theorem 2.6.2 we draw the still stronger condition that G must be three-vertex connected. If it could be separated by two vertices as in (2.6.1), one of the graphs in (2.6.2) would have to be nonplanar. Since they have fewer edges than G, they would include at least one subgraph conformal to A or B, hence each of the graphs (2.6.3) and so also G would include such a subgraph contrary to assumption.

We now omit an arbitrary edge $E_0 = (a_0, b_0)$ from G. The graph $G_0 = G - E_0$ is planar; if it were not planar, it would include an A, B graph. Since G is three-vertex connected, G_0 has no separating vertex so there are circuits in G which pass through a_0 and b_0. We select such a circuit C that includes a maximal number of edges on its boundary and in its interior. This property entails that each outer bridge has just two attachments; since G is three-vertex connected the outer bridges are single edges. Finally, the maximal property of C yields that any such outer edge $E_1 = (a_1, b_2)$ separates a_0, b_0.

There must exist a nontransferable inner bridge in B* separating a_0, b_0 for otherwise E_0 could be drawn inside C to make G planar. Since B* is not transferable, there is an outer edge $E_1 = (a_1, b_1)$ separating it. We may assume that the four different end points of E_0 and E_1 lie in the order a_1, a_0, b_1, b_0 on C. We introduce the subgraph $H = C + E_0 + E_1$.

Case 1. There is an attachment a_2 of B* different from the four vertices a_0, b_0, a_1, b_1 (Fig. 2.6.3). The notation shall be chosen such that a_2 lies within the section $C(a_1, a_0)$. When B* has an attachment within the section $C(b_1, b_0)$, there is an inner transversal $T(a_2, b_2)$. But then the subgraph $H + T(a_2, b_2)$ is conformal to an A-graph (see Fig. 2.6.3(a)).

When there are no attachments of B* within $C(b_1, b_0)$, let us assume that there is an attachment b_2 within $C(a_0, b_1)$ (see Fig. 2.6.3(b)). This, as before, precludes the existence of an attachment within $C(b_0, a_1)$. On the other hand B* must have an attachment in the section $C(b_1, b_0, a_1)$ since it separates a_1, b_1. This leaves the only possibility $c_2 = b_0$.

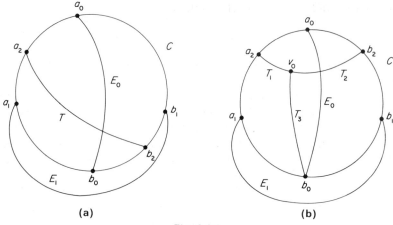

Fig. 2.6.3.

Since B* has at least three attachments, it includes three edge disjoint arcs

$$T_1(v_0, a_2), \qquad T_2(v_0, b_2), \qquad T_3(v_0, c_2)$$

from some vertex v_0 (Theorem 2.1.1). But then the subgraph

$$H - C(b_1, b_0) + T_1 + T_2 + T_3$$

is conformal to a graph A.

Since B* separates a_0, b_0, it must have an attachment on the arc $C(a_0, b_1, b_0)$. There remains only the case $b_2 = b_1$ and again one obtains an A-graph by the preceding argument.

Case 2. B* has no attachments different from a_0, b_0, a_1, b_1.

Due to the separation properties all four vertices must be attachments (Fig. 2.6.4). There exist transversals $T_0(a_0, b_0)$ and $T_1(a_1, b_1)$ in B*. If these have a single intersection a_2, the graph $H + T_0 + T_1$ is of type B (Fig. 2.6.4(a)).

When T_0 and T_1 have several common vertices, let a_2 and b_2, respectively, be the first and the last such vertices on T_1. This yields a subgraph of type A (Fig. 2.6.4(b)) such as

$$H - C(b_1, b_0) - C(a_1, a_0) + T_0 + T_1$$

We have shown in all cases that G contains a subgraph conformal to A- or B-graphs. This contradiction to our original assumption proves the theorem of Kuratowski.

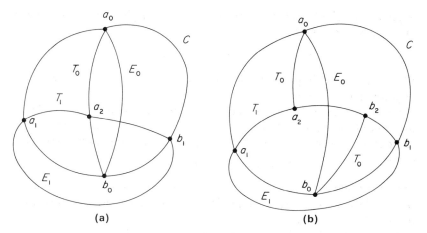

Fig. 2.6.4.

There are a number of proofs of the theorem in the literature. The present one is a simplification of the original proof using ideas from another proof by Dirac and Schuster. Another proof based on similar ideas has been given by Halin.

2.7. Further Observations on Maximal Graphs

It is often convenient to use a special notation for certain classes of graphs. We write

$$G = (t_1, t_2, \ldots, t_k) \qquad (2.7.1)$$

to denote a graph whose vertex set consists of k disjoint sets,

$$V(G) = A_1 + \cdots + A_k, \qquad v(A_i) = t_i.$$

There shall be no edges in G connecting any of the t_i vertices within the same set A_i while there are edges from each $v_i \in A_i$ to all vertices $v_j \in A_j$, $j \neq i$. One sees that the number of vertices and edges in G are, respectively,

$$v_v = \sum t_i, \qquad v_e = \tfrac{1}{2}(v_v^2 - \sum t_i^2).$$

As an example one may take a complete graph or simplex S_n on n vertices. In the notation (2.7.1), one can write

$$S_n = (1, 1, \ldots, 1_n).$$

A general graph (2.7.1) may be called a *simploid*. Both Kuratowski graphs in Fig. 2.6.1 are simploids.

$$A = (3, 3), \qquad B = (1, 1, 1, 1, 1) = S_5$$

We notice that a simploid [Eq. (2.7.1)] can be vertex colored in k number of colors and no fewer.

Let us also elaborate a little upon the concept of conformal graphs as introduced in Section 2.6. From an edge $E = (v_1, v_2)$ in a graph G, one can obtain two edges by inserting a vertex v_0 on E and split E into two parts,

$$E_1 = (v_1, v_0), \qquad E_2 = (v_2, v_0).$$

This operation may be called *vertex insertion*. The reverse operation of *vertex elimination* consists in joining the two edges at a vertex with $\rho(v_0) = 2$ into a single one.

Two graphs, G_1 and G_2, are *conformal*, in symbols

$$\hat{G}_1 = \hat{G}_2 \qquad \text{or} \qquad G_2 \in \hat{G}_1,$$

when one can be obtained from the other by a series of vertex insertions and eliminations. When a graph G has a subgraph H_1 conformal to some graph H, we write $G \supseteq \hat{H}$. Vertex elimination can be performed in any graph in which there exist vertices with valence $\rho = 2$. Thus, any finite graph is conformal to a *primitive graph* H_0, that is, a graph in which there are no 2-vertices. One sees that in each class of conformal finite graphs there is unique primitive graph H_0 to which they are all conformal. Any graph $H \in \hat{H}_0$ consists of arcs $A(a_0, b_0)$ corresponding to edges (a_0, b_0) in H_0. These arcs and end vertices, a_0 and b_0, we may call, for short, H_0-*arcs* and H_0-*vertices* in H.

In maximal planar graphs there are certain classes of conformal graphs which must always occur. In general, let us denote by

$$S_n - E = (2, 1, \ldots, 1_{n-2})$$

the simploid with n vertices which one obtains from a simplex by removing one edge E. This graph can also be considered to be the sum of two simplexes S_{n-1} with a simplex S_{n-2} in common. We prove the following theorem.

Theorem 2.7.1. Any maximal planar graph not an S_3 or an S_4 contains a subgraph conformal to $S_5 - E$.

Proof: We select an arbitrary pair of nonadjacent vertices a and b in G; such vertices exist by the conditions of the theorem. The neighbors of a

lie on a circuit C with a in the interior and b in the exterior (Fig. 2.7.1). Since G cannot be separated by two vertices (Theorem 1.3.2), there exist three disjoint arcs

$$P_1(a, b), \qquad P_2(a, b), \qquad P_3(a, b) \tag{2.7.2}$$

connecting a and b; their intersections with C are c_1, c_2, c_3. Clearly, one can assume that none of the arcs [Eq. (2.7.2)] has any edges in common

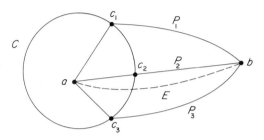

Fig. 2.7.1.

with C. The graph consisting of C and the three arcs P_i is conformal to $S_5 - E$.

By adding a new edge $E = (a, b)$ one obtains a result by Wagner.

Theorem 2.7.2. Let G be a maximal planar graph with at least five vertices. When an arbitrary new edge $E = (a, b)$ is added to G, then $G + E$ has a subgraph conformal to S_5.

When a and b cannot be separated by three vertices in G, there will be at least four arcs $P_i(a, b)$ in [Eq. (2.7.2)] and we may state the following theorem.

Theorem 2.7.3. In a maximal planar graph G with at least six vertices let a and b be nonadjacent vertices not separated by three vertices. Then G has a subgraph conformal to an octahedral graph with a and b as opposite vertices.

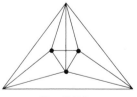

Fig. 2.7.2.

The octahedral graph is the simploid $(2, 2, 2)$. The graph obtained from it by adding a diagonal edge is the simploid $(1, 1, 2, 2)$ in Fig. 2.7.2.

It has been shown by Halin that the result by Wagner in Theorem 2.7.2 can be strengthened as in Theorem 2.7.4.

Theorem 2.7.4. Let G be a maximal planar graph with at least six vertices and a, b is a pair of nonadjacent vertices. Then the nonplanar graph

$$G_1 = G + E, \qquad E = (a, b)$$

has a subgraph including E which is conformal to $(1, 1, 2, 2)$. An exception may occur when a and b are vertices in a subgraph $S_5 - E$ of G; then G_1 has a subgraph conformal to the graph H_1 in Fig. 2.7.3.

$$H_1 = S_5 + S_4, \qquad S_5 \cap S_4 = S_3.$$

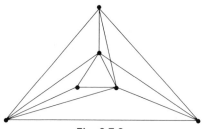

Fig. 2.7.3.

The theorem follows by induction with respect to the number v_v of vertices in G. It is true for $v_v = 6$. Theorem 2.7.3. establishes that it holds when a and b are not separated by three vertices. We may suppose, therefore, that a and b are separated by a triangle T so that

$$G = G_1 + G_2, \qquad G_1 \cap G_2 = T = (x, y, z)$$

$$a \in G_1 - T, \qquad b \in G_2 - T$$

where G_1 and G_2 are also maximal planar. If there exist edges from a and b to each vertex x, y, z, then they belong to a graph $S_5 - E$ defined by these vertices. Since G has at least six vertices, we may assume that there exists a vertex $c \in G_1 - T$ and from c there are three disjoint arcs in G_1 to a, y, z in $S_5 - E$. These arcs together with E produce a graph conformal to H_1.

We may assume that there is no edge $E(a, x)$ in G_1 so that such an edge can be added to G_1. If a and x do not belong to any graph $S_5 - E'$ in G_1, there must be at least six vertices in G_1 as one verifies. By the induction there exists a subgraph in $G_1 + E(a, x)$ conformal to $(1, 1, 2, 2)$ and including $E(a, x)$. But in this subgraph one can replace $E(a, x)$ by an arc

$$A(a, x) = (a, b) + A(b, x), \qquad A(b, x) \subset G_2$$

to obtain a subgraph of G conformal to $(1, 1, 2, 2)$ and including E.

There remains the case where a and x belong to a graph $S_5 - E'$ in G_1. This graph has been drawn in Fig. 2.7.4. Here a and x cannot be on the

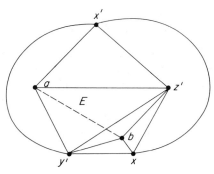

Fig. 2.7.4.

same face boundary since they are not adjacent. This shows that b and G_2 lie within a triangle

$$T' = (x, y', z'), y', \qquad z' \neq a.$$

From b there are disjoint arcs in G_2 to x, y', z'; these arcs together with $S_5 - E'$ and $E = (a, b)$ define a graph conformal to $(1, 1, 2, 2)$.

It is clear that Theorem 2.7.4 represents a sharper form of Theorem 2.7.2 since the graphs in Figs. 2.7.2 and 2.7.3 both include a subgraph conformal to S_5.

CHAPTER 3 | *DUAL GRAPHS*

3.1. Geometric Definition of Duality

We denote by G a planar graph given in some representation R. Within each face F, we select a particular point $m(F)$, the *midpoint* of F. On each edge E, we mark a point $m(E)$ different from the end vertices and call this the *midpoint* of E. Now let F_1 and F_2 be two faces with the common boundary edge E. From the midpoint $m(F_1)$ we draw a Jordan curve within F_1 to $m(E)$ and continue it within F_2 from $m(E)$ to $m(F_2)$ (see Fig. 3.1.1).

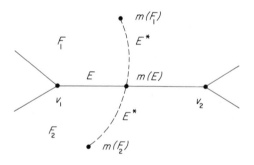

Fig. 3.1.1.

This curve

$$E^*(F_1, F_2) = E^*(m(F_1), m(E)) + E^*(m(E), m^*(F_2)), \qquad (3.1.1)$$

we call the *dual edge* to E. Each of its two pieces is called a *dual half-edge*. The two curves E and E^* have only their midpoint,

$$m(E) = m^*(E), \qquad (3.1.2)$$

30

in common. This point also divides E into two *half-edges*.

$$E(v_1, v_2) = E(v_1, m(E)) + E(m(E), v_2) \qquad (3.1.3)$$

where v_1 and v_2 are the end vertices of E.

The dual half-edges from the midpoint $m(F_1)$ of F_1 form a star graph with one edge to each boundary edge E of F_1. Clearly, they can be drawn such that any two of them have only the midpoint $m(F_1)$ in common. If E is an acyclic boundary edge, we consider it to be a double edge, bounded by F_1 on either side. In this case, we draw two dual half-edges from $m(F_1)$ to $m(E)$, approaching E from either of its two sides (see Fig. 3.1.2).

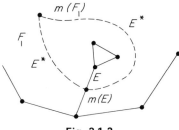

Fig. 3.1.2.

We shall need a further observation on the dual half-edges. Suppose that there are no connected components of G lying within the face F_1. Then the dual half-edges divide F_1 into sectors such that the various corners lie in different sectors. This implies that the corners of F_1 are separated from each other in the sense that no two of them can be connected by a Jordan curve within F_1 which does not cross one of the dual half-edges (see Fig. 3.1.3). This property holds also when there are acyclic boundary edges for F_1, but as one can readily verify, it is no

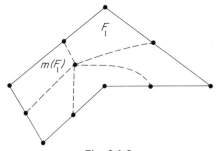

Fig. 3.1.3.

longer true when there are connected components of G located within F_1.

The graph G^*, with the vertices $m(F)$ and the dual edges E^* defined in (3.1.1), we call a *dual graph* to G. One sees that by selecting the midpoints $m(F)$ and $m(E)$ in other ways one obtains graphs isomorphic to G^*. The construction shows that G^* is a planar graph. It is also a connected graph since one can proceed from any face in G to any other by dual edges.

Theorem 3.1.1. Let G be a connected graph. Then the graphs G and G^* are mutually dual. Each vertex $m(F)$ of G^* is the midpoint of a face F of G and each vertex v of G is the midpoint of a face F^* in G^*. There is a one-to-one correspondence between the dual edges E and E^* such that they intersect in a common midpoint (3.1.2) and no other pairs of edges from G and G^* intersect.

Proof: Let F^* be a face of G^*. We shall show that there is just one vertex v of G lying inside F^*. There is at least one such vertex since each boundary edge for F^* is crossed by an edge E in G. The half-edges from such a vertex $v \in F^*$ form a star graph with the other end points lying on the boundary of F^*. These star graphs form a family of bridges for the boundary graph of F^*. The interstices of these bridges are parts of faces of G. If there were more than one bridge, there would be interstices between neighboring bridges and one could pass from a vertex in one to a vertex in the other on a Jordan curve which did not intersect G or G^*. However, when G is connected, this is not possible.

After it has been shown that there is but a single vertex v of G within each face F^* of G^* it is clear that v can be considered to be the midpoint for F^* and that the edges from v in G are dual edges for G^*. This establishes the duality

$$G^{**} = G. \qquad (3.1.4)$$

We notice that in constructing the dual graph each acyclic edge in G corresponds to a loop in G^*. Conversely, each loop E corresponds to an acyclic edge E^*, for there is only one edge E^* through the midpoint $m(E)$ which connects the parts of G^* lying outside and inside E.

The *valence* (or local degree) of a vertex v in the graph G is the number $\rho_G(v)$ of edges with the end point v; in this number any loop at v is counted twice. The *valence* of a face F is the number $\rho_G^*(F)$ of boundary edges for F; in this number each acyclic edge on the boundary is counted twice. On the basis of these definitions one obtains the next theorem.

Theorem 3.1.2. For a connected graph G and its dual G^* one has the valence relations

$$\rho_G{}^*(F) = \rho_{G*}^*(m(F)),$$

$$\rho_G(v) = \rho_{G*}^*(F^*(v)), \tag{3.1.5}$$

where $m(F)$ is the midpoint of the face F in G and v the midpoint of the face $F^*(v)$ in G^*. The number of vertices, faces, and edges of the two graphs are connected by the relations

$$v_v(G) = v_f(G^*), \qquad v_f(G) = v_v(G^*), \qquad v_e(G) = v_e(G^*) \tag{3.1.6}$$

A circuit C^* in G^* corresponds to a circular family of c faces pairwise adjoining each other (Fig. 3.1.4). The edges E^* in G^* connecting these faces correspond to a unique family of crossing edges $\{E\}$ and these edges separate G into two parts. Thus a circuit of length k in G^* corresponds to a family of k separating edges for G so that no smaller part of the family is separating.

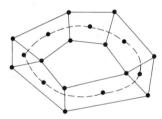

Fig. 3.1.4.

As simple examples of dual graphs, one may take the Platonic graphs. The cube and the octahedron are found to be duals, also the dodecahedron and the icosahedron. The dual of the tetrahedron is a tetrahedron. Such graphs which are isomorphic to their dual one can call *self-dual*.

PROBLEMS

1. Can a graph and its dual have simultaneous straight-line representations?
2. Try to give a general method for constructing all self-dual graphs (see Section 3.5).

3.2. Observations on Graphs and Their Duals

We shall add some further observations on planar graphs and their duals. A G-domain D in G is a connected domain in the plane bounded by edges in G. The boundary of D we denote by $B(D)$. Then D is the set sum of all those faces F_i of G which lie in D, and to these must be added all those edges in the various $B(F_i)$ which lie on the boundary of two different faces F_i and F_j. We can express the boundary of D as a formal sum, as follows:

$$B(D) = B(F_1) \oplus B(F_2) \oplus \cdots. \quad (\text{mod } 2) \qquad (3.2.1)$$

In this *boundary sum* all edges appearing twice are omitted; the acyclic edges occur only in one of the summands and shall be counted singly.

For a given G-domain there will be a certain part of the dual graph G^* lying inside D. This graph $G^* \cap D$ we shall call the D-intersection of G^*. It consists of the vertices $m(F_i)$ of G^* in the various faces F_i and all the dual half-edges from them.

Theorem 3.2.1. The G^*-intersection of a D-domain is connected.

Proof: One can obtain D by successive adjunction of faces F_i such that in each step F_i has a common boundary edge with one of the preceding ones F_j. Then there exists a dual edge in D connecting $m(F_i)$ and $m(F_j)$.

Let us make a remark on the construction of dual graphs. Suppose the connected graph G has a separating vertex v with a corresponding edge disjoint decomposition (see Fig. 3.2.1):

$$G = G_1 + G_2. \qquad (3.2.2)$$

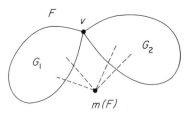

Fig. 3.2.1.

Then there is a face F in G such that when G^* has been constructed one can only pass from faces within G_1 to faces within G_2 by crossing F. This means that $m(F)$ is a separating vertex for the dual graph G^*. Furthermore, one can construct G^* from the duals G_1^* and G_2^* by connecting them at the vertex $m(F)$ which corresponds to the face of G_1 which contains G_2, and vice versa.

Conversely, let G^* have a separating vertex $m(F)$. Then there must exist two families of faces in G such that one can pass from one to the other by dual edges only through the face F. But this implies that G must have a decomposition (3.2.2) in which the two components have at most one vertex in common. Thus, in constructing the dual, the problem can be reduced to the case of connected graphs without separating vertices.

We mentioned that the dual depends on the particular planar representation in which G is given. One may ask when a graph and its dual both have essentially unique representations. We noticed previously that for G to have an essentially unique representation the graph must be connected and without separating vertices. In this case, according to Theorem 2.4.2, each separation of G by two vertices, if it exists, must have

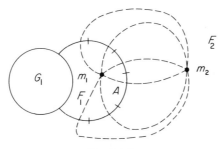

Fig. 3.2.2.

one component which is an arc A (see Fig. 3.2.2). Here A lies on the common boundary of two faces F_1 and F_2. The graph G^* will have as many corresponding edges,

$$(m(F_1), m(F_2)), \tag{3.2.3}$$

connecting these vertices, as there are edges in A. When there are four or more edges in A, this leads to a separation of G^* by $m(F_1)$ such that none of the components is an arc. The same is true for three edges, as one readily verifies, except when G is a triangle. However, then G has no two-vertex separation as presupposed. Finally, let A have only two edges. The separation of G^* by $m(F_1)$ and $m(F_2)$ then has one component G_1^* consisting of the two edges (3.2.3). In order for G^* to have an essentially unique representation it is necessary that the component G_2^* be an arc with at most two edges. Again leaving out the case where G is a triangle it follows that G must be a graph with four edges and three vertices as depicted in Fig. 3.2.3. This graph is self-dual.

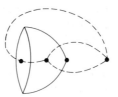

Fig. 3.2.3.

From the construction of the dual one sees that any separation of G by two vertices gives a corresponding separation of the dual. Thus, we can state the following theorem.

Theorem 3.2.2. A necessary and sufficient condition that a graph G and its dual G^* both have essentially unique planar representations is that G have no separation by two vertices. The only exception is the self-dual graph in Fig. 3.2.3.

3.3. Relational Definition of Duality

The existence of a dual is a special property of the planar graphs. It has been shown by Whitney that it may actually serve to characterize the planar graphs. However, by such a characterization one cannot rely upon the preceding geometric definition of duality since it is based upon the fact that the graph is planar. We shall, therefore, introduce a definition of duality based only upon relations between two graphs.

We denote by G a finite graph with a vertex set V with n elements. Each subgraph H of G shall be considered to be a graph with the same vertex set V; the complement of H in G is $\bar{H}$. As before, the number of vertices, edges, and connected components of H are denoted by

$$v_v(H) = n, \qquad v_e(H), \qquad v_c(H).$$

The quantities,

$$\varkappa(H) = n - v_c(H), \qquad \gamma(H) = v_e(H) - n + v_c(H), \qquad (3.3.1)$$

are called the *component rank* and *circuit rank* of H, respectively; clearly

$$\varkappa(H) + \gamma(H) = v_e(H). \qquad (3.3.2)$$

We notice that the numbers (3.3.1) remain unchanged when isolated vertices are added to or eliminated from H.

Denote by G_1 some other finite graph with a vertex set V_1 with n_1 vertices; furthermore, the number of edges in G and G_1 shall be the same:

$$v_e(G) = v_e(G_1). \qquad (3.3.3)$$

Under a one-to-one correspondence between the edges in G and G_1 each subgraph H corresponds to a subgraph H_1 of G_1. This definition yields according to Eq. (3.3.3)

$$v_e(H) + v_e(\overline{H}_1) = v_e(G) = v_e(G_1) \qquad (3.3.4)$$

We now say: The graph G_1 is a *W-dual graph* to G when a one-to-one correspondence exists between the edges of the two graphs such that for each subgraph H of G the corresponding subgraph H_1 satisfies

$$\gamma(H) + \varkappa(\overline{H}_1) = \varkappa(G_1). \qquad (3.3.5)$$

Theorem 3.3.1. When G_1 is a W-dual graph of G one has

$$\gamma(G) = \varkappa(G_1), \qquad \varkappa(G) = \gamma(G_1). \qquad (3.3.6)$$

Proof: The first of these relations follows from the definition (3.3.5) when $H = G$. According to (3.3.2) and (3.3.3) it implies the second. By using the relations (3.3.4) and (3.3.6), the condition (3.3.5) can be re-written,

$$\varkappa(H) + \gamma(\overline{H}_1) = \varkappa(G). \qquad (3.3.7)$$

This may be stated as in Theorem 3.3.2.

Theorem 3.3.2. When G_1 is a W-dual of G, G is also a W-dual of G_1.

Theorem 3.3.3. A dual of a planar graph is a W-dual.

Proof: We shall verify that relation (3.3.5) holds for a planar graph G and its dual G^* in any representation. The duality establishes a one-to-one correspondence between the edges in G and G^*. The relation (3.3.5) is immediate when H is the void subgraph. The general subgraph H of G shall be constructed by adding one edge $E = (a, b)$ at a time and correspondingly eliminating its image E^* in G^* from the complement $\overline{H}_1$.

According to the definition (3.3.1) of $\gamma(H)$ there are two alternatives under this operation.

1. $\gamma(H)$ increases by one unit. This means that by the adjunction of E to H the number $v_c(H)$ of components remains unchanged. Then E connects two vertices in H already connected by an arc $Q(a, b)$, hence there is a circuit

$$C = E + Q(a, b)$$

in H. Since $E^* = (a', b')$ crosses E and no other edge in G the vertices

a' and b' lie on different sides of C. In $\bar{H}_1$, the vertices a' and b' are connected by E^*, but after its removal they are disconnected, since no other edge in $\bar{H}_1$ crosses C. Thus the elimination of E^* decreases the number of components of $\bar{H}_1$, hence increases the number $\varkappa(\bar{H}_1)$ by one unit. We conclude that the relation (3.3.5) still holds.

2. $\gamma(H)$ remains unchanged. $v_c(H)$ is then decreased by one unit so that E connects two components A and B of H. E is an acyclic edge in $H + E$ and the adjunction of E divides no face F_H in H. After the removal of the dual edge $E^* = (a', b')$ crossing E, the two vertices a' and b' in G^* will still lie in the same face F_H as before. According to Theorem 3.2.1 there exists a graph arc $Q(a', b')$ in G^* not including E^* and lying within the G-domain F_H. Here Q belongs to $\bar{H}_1$ since none of its edges cross edges in H. This shows that the removal of E^* does not increase the number of components of $\bar{H}_1$. Therefore $\varkappa(\bar{H}_1)$ is unchanged and (3.3.5) still holds.

The following auxiliary result is evident for a graph G and its dual G^*.

Theorem 3.3.4. Let G and G_1 be W-dual graphs and $E = (a, b)$ and $E_1 = (a_1, b_1)$ corresponding edges under the edge correspondence. Then the graph $G - E$ is W-dual to the graph G_2 obtained from $G_1 - E_1$ by joining a_1 and b_1 into a single vertex a_1'.

Proof: First suppose $a_1 \neq b_1$. Take H as a subgraph of $G - E$ corresponding to H_1 in G_1 and to a subgraph H_2 in G_2. Here $\bar{H}_1$ includes the edge E_1. When it is omitted and the vertices a_1 and b_1 identified, the resulting graph $\bar{H}_2$ in G_2 has the same number of connected components as $\bar{H}_1$ in G_1 while the number of vertices is decreased by 1. This yields

$$\varkappa(\bar{H}_2) = \varkappa(\bar{H}_1) - 1, \qquad \varkappa(G_2) = \varkappa(G_1) - 1$$

and so from Eq. (3.3.5)

$$\gamma(H) + \varkappa(\bar{H}_2) = \varkappa(G_2)$$

as desired. When $a_1 = b_1$ the number of vertices and connected components remain the same in $\bar{H}_1$ and $\bar{H}_2$ after the reduction operation.

Theorem 3.3.5. Two W-dual graphs G and G_1 without isolated vertices are simultaneously connected.

Proof: We use induction with respect to the number of edges. It is trivial for one edge. Suppose that G is connected. We remove an edge E such that $G - E$ remains connected. By assumption the W-dual graph G_2

to G is connected. It remains connected by the reverse process of splitting a vertex into two connected by an edge.

Next, follow a series of auxiliary results preliminary to the proof of Whitney's main theorem. Suppose that

$$G = A_1 + A_2 \tag{3.3.8}$$

is a disjoint decomposition of G. From the definition, it follows directly that

$$\varkappa(G) = \varkappa(A_1) + \varkappa(A_2), \qquad \gamma(G) = \gamma(A_1) + \gamma(A_2). \tag{3.3.9}$$

These same relations (3.3.9) hold when (3.3.8) is an edge disjoint decomposition defined by a separating vertex. To see this form, the graph

$$G' = A_1' + A_2'$$

where the disjoint graphs A_1' and A_2' are isomorphic to A_1 and A_2, respectively. This decomposition does not change the component or circuit ranks since

$$v_c(G') = v_c(G) + 1, \qquad n' = n + 1, \qquad v_e(G') = v_e(G).$$

More generally, when

$$G = \sum_i L_i \tag{3.3.10}$$

is a representation of G as the sum of its lobe graphs, one has

$$\varkappa(G) = \sum \varkappa(L_i), \qquad \gamma(G) = \sum \gamma(L_i). \tag{3.3.11}$$

By the same reasoning, one obtains for any subgraph H of G

$$\varkappa(H) = \sum \varkappa(H_i), \qquad \gamma(H) = \sum \gamma(H_i),$$

where H_i is the subgraph of H lying in L_i, the same relations hold for a subgraph $\tilde{H}_1$ in G_1.

Two graphs shall be called *lobe isomorphic* when their lobe graphs are isomorphic in pairs. Isolated vertices are disregarded. In particular, every graph is lobe isomorphic to a graph whose connected components are its lobes. The preceding discussion shows Theorem 3.3.6 to be true.

Theorem 3.3.6. When G_1 is a W-dual graph to the graph G, then every graph lobe isomorphic to G_1 is a W-dual.

We shall also need the following observation.

Theorem 3.3.7. For an edge disjoint decomposition (3.3.8) of a graph G one has

$$\varkappa(G') = \varkappa(A_1) + \varkappa(A_2) \tag{3.3.12}$$

if, and only if, every attachment of the two components is a separating vertex.

Proof: We have seen that when the attachments are separating vertices for G, the relation (3.3.12) holds. Suppose, conversely, that it is fulfilled. It can be written

$$v_c(A_1) + v_c(A_2) = v_c(G) + s,$$

where s is the number of attachments. By fitting A_1 and A_2 together successively, one of the s vertices at a time, the number of components diminishes by exactly one in each step so that all these vertices must be separating for G.

Theorem 3.3.8. Two graphs G and G_1 are W-duals if, and only if, their lobe graphs are W-duals in pairs.

Proof: The preceding discussion shows that the condition is sufficient. Suppose, on the other hand, that G and G_1 are W-duals. Let there be some decomposition (3.3.8) where the two parts have at most one vertex in common so that

$$\varkappa(G) = \varkappa(A_1) + \varkappa(A_2).$$

Under a duality correspondence to G_1 the graphs A_1 and A_2 have edge disjoint images A_1' and A_2'. When the duality condition (3.3.5) is applied to $H = A_1$ and $H = A_2$, one finds

$$\varkappa(A_1) + \gamma(A_2') = \gamma(G_1),$$

$$\varkappa(A_2) + \gamma(A_1') = \gamma(G_1).$$

When these relations are added and reduced by means of (3.3.6), one obtains

$$\varkappa(A_1') + \varkappa(A_2') = \varkappa(G_1) \qquad (3.3.13)$$

so that A_1' and A_2' consist of a number of lobes of G_1 according to Theorem 3.3.7.

Next we show that A_1' and A_2' are W-duals of A_1 and A_2, respectively. For a subgraph H of A_1 let H_1 be its image in A_1' and $\tilde{H}_1$ its complement in A_1'; the complement in G_1 is

$$\bar{H}_1 = \tilde{H}_1 + A_2'.$$

This also represents a decomposition of $\bar{H}_1$ into a sum of lobe graphs so that

$$\varkappa(\bar{H}_1) = \varkappa(\tilde{H}_1) + \varkappa(A_2').$$

From (3.3.13) and (3.3.5) we conclude

$$\gamma(H) + \varkappa(\tilde{H}_1) = \varkappa(A_1')$$

so that A_1' is a W-dual of A_1.

When our decomposition process is repeated on A_1 and A_2, one eventually reaches the lobe decomposition (3.3.10) with

$$G_1 = \sum L_i'$$

as the corresponding decomposition of G_1. Here each L_i' is dual to L_i and a sum of lobes in G_1. Since the same argument is applicable to G_1, the L_i' must also be lobes.

3.4. Characterization of Planar Graphs

After these preparations we are ready to prove Whitney's main theorem.

Theorem 3.4.1. When G and G_1 are W-dual graphs without separating vertices, then G can be represented in the plane such that $G_1 = G^*$ is a dual of G.

Before proceeding to the proof, let us verify the theorem in the simplest case where $G = C$ is a circuit with n edges. Then

$$\gamma(G) = 1, \qquad \varkappa(G) = n - 1;$$

so for the W-dual graph

$$\varkappa(G_1) = n_1 - 1 = 1, \qquad \gamma(G_1) = n - 1$$

according to (3.3.6). This shows that G_1 has $n_1 = 2$ vertices a_1 and b_1 with n edges connecting them since G_1 can have no separating vertices. But such a pair of graphs are duals in the plane as one sees from Fig. 3.4.1.

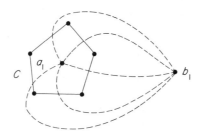

Fig. 3.4.1.

We shall prove Theorem 3.4.1 in general by induction with respect to the number of edges in G. We need the observation shown by Theorem 3.4.2.

Theorem 3.4.2. Suppose G connected without separating vertices and at least two vertices. Then the star graph $S(v)$ at a vertex v corresponds to a circuit in the W-dual graph G_1.

Proof: Under the given conditions there are no loops and $\rho \geq 2$ edges at each vertex. The graph $G - S$ is discovered but for any subgraph S' of S the graph $G - S'$ is connected. This gives

$$\varkappa(G\text{–}S) = n - 2, \qquad \varkappa(G\text{–}S') = n - 1.$$

From the duality condition, (3.3.7), one concludes

$$\gamma(S_1) = 1, \qquad \gamma(S_1') = 0$$

for the corresponding images. This implies that S_1 has a single circuit while no subgraph has a circuit, hence S_1 is a circuit.

The following result is valid also for nonplanar graphs.

Theorem 3.4.3. Let G be a finite connected graph without separating vertices and $\rho(v) \geq 3$ edges at each vertex. Then G has an edge E such that $G - E$ has no separating vertex.

Proof: A graph without separating vertices may be constructed as follows: Select an edge E_1 and a circuit C_1 which includes it. When E_2 is an edge not on C_1, there is a circuit C_2 including E_1 and E_2. We add to C_1 the edge E_2 and the section of C_2 to the two nearest vertices on C_1. The resulting graph we denote by G_2. If there is an edge E_3 not in G_2, we take a circuit C_3 including E_1 and E_3 and proceed as before with respect to G_2. Thus, G may be obtained by successive additions of arcs such that in each step the constructed part has no separating vertices. Since $\rho(v) \geq 3$, the last arc added must be a single edge. We turn to the proof of Theorem 3.4.1.

Case 1. $\rho(b) = 2$ for some vertex b. Denote by

$$E = (a, b), \qquad F = (b, c)$$

the two edges at b. Their image in G_1 is a circuit according to Theorem 3.4.2, so they form a pair of double edges

$$E_1 = (a_1, b_1), \qquad F_1 = (a_1, b_1).$$

Under the W-duality the graph $G - E$ corresponds to $G_1 - E_1$. In $G - E$ we join the vertices a and b into a single one a'. The new graph G' is a W-dual of $G_1 - E_1$ according to Theorem 3.3.4. By the induction assumption there are planar representations of G' and $G_1 - E_1$ such that they are duals. In this correspondence F_1 is the dual intersecting edge to $F' = (a', c)$ (Fig. 3.4.2). When G is reconstructed from G' by replacing F' by $E + F$, the duplicate edge E_1 to F_1 can be added such that E_1 and F_1 cross E and F, respectively, in the planar graph G.

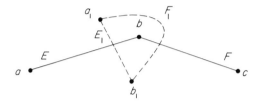

Fig. 3.4.2.

Case 2. $\rho(b) \geq 3$ for every vertex b. According to Theorem 3.4.3 we can select an edge $E = (a, b)$ in G such that $G - E$ has no separating vertices. Under the W-dual correspondence E corresponds to $E_1 = (a_1, b_1)$. We remove E from G and E_1 and G_1. From $G_1 - E_1$ we derive the graph G_1' by coalescing a_1 and b_1 into a single vertex a_1'. By Theorem 3.3.4, $G - E$ and G_1' are W-duals and none of them have separating vertices.

According to Theorem 3.4.2, the $\rho(a_1)$ edges of G_1 at a_1 correspond to a circuit P in G including E. Similarly the edges at b_1 correspond to a circuit Q. Also in G_1' the edges at the coalesced vertex a_1' correspond to a circuit R in $G - E$ and clearly

$$R = (P - E) + (Q - E).$$

By the induction assumption the graphs $G - E$ and G_1' can be mapped as planar duals. Since the edges at a_1' correspond to the edges in R, each of these edges and no other edges in G' cross an edge in R. By the planar duality, R is the boundary of a face in G. Suppose, for instance, that a_1' lies inside R. The missing edge E can be drawn such that it divides F into two faces A_1 and B_1 (Fig. 3.4.3).

We return from G_1' to G_1 by splitting a_1' into the original vertices a_1 and b_1 connected by E_1. We find a planar representation of G_1 by placing a_1 in A_1 and b_1 in B_1 connected by the edge E_1 inside R crossing E. The edges in G_1' originating from edges at a_1 we restore at this vertex and

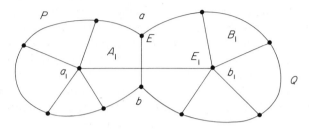

Fig. 3.4.3.

similarly at b_1. This can be done without intersections such that each edge crosses the same edge in R as before, for the edges at a_1 cross edges in P and the edges at b_1 cross edges in Q. This completes the proof of Theorem 3.4.1. It implies Whitney's criterion for planar graphs.

Theorem 3.4.4. A graph is planar if, and only if, it has a W-dual.

The proof of this theorem is, as we have seen, quite involved and it would be desirable to obtain a simpler one. Whitney's criterion is entirely different in form from the Kuratowski criterion, but one can be derived from the other, as shown by Whitney.

There are other ways to characterize planar graphs; we may mention one way due to MacLane. Let G be a planar graph without separating vertices. The minimal circuits form a basis for the set of all circuits in the sense: (1) Each edge lies on just two basis circuits. (2) Any circuit is the sum of basis circuits (mod 2), that is, in the sum the edges appearing twice are omitted. On the other hand, one can show that G is planar when it has a family of basis circuits with these properties.

PROBLEM

1. Show that the Kuratowski graphs have no W-duals.

3.5. Maximal Bipartite Graphs. Self-Dual Graphs

A planar graph G is bipartite when all its faces have an even number of boundary edges. When this condition is fulfilled, let $V = V_1 + V_2$ be the corresponding decomposition of the vertex set such that each edge is of the form

$$E = (v_1, v_2), \qquad v_1 \in V_1, \qquad v_2 \in V_2.$$

A planar bipartite graph without faces bounded by two edges is called *maximal bipartite* when no edge can be added between any two of its vertices without destroying these properties. These graphs have certain properties analogous to those of maximal graphs given in Section 1.3.

Theorem 3.5.1. A graph is maximal bipartite if, and only if, all its faces are quadrilateral.

Proof: If G has a face F bounded by more than four edges, one can draw a diagonal edge across F connecting two opposite vertices. If these vertices should happen to be already connected by an edge, one can select an arbitrary other such pair on the boundary of F. Since G is planar these cannot be connected already. Theorem 3.5.1 shows that the dual of a maximal bipartite graph is regular with valence $\rho = 4$.

Theorem 3.5.2. A maximal bipartite graph G without multiple edges is two-vertex connected. It is three-vertex connected when in addition G has no pair of faces with just two boundary vertices in common, both belonging to V_1 or both to V_2.

Proof: G must be connected and has no separating vertices because otherwise new edges could be added as one readily sees. Suppose that G can be separated by two vertices a and b into two components A and B as in Fig. 3.5.1. One sees from the figure that the corresponding inner and outer faces I and O form a pair of the type defined in the theorem. We notice also that if one reduces G by omitting one of the components A and B the graph remains maximal bipartite.

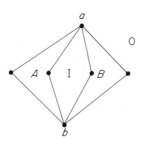

Fig. 3.5.1.

Corresponding to Theorem 2.7.2 one can make the observation also due to Wagner: When an edge E is added to a planar maximal bipartite graph G such that $G + E$ remains bipartite then it includes a subgraph homomorphic to the Kuratowski graph A in Fig. 2.6.1. We leave the proof to the reader.

Let us return to a general planar graph G. In addition to the dual G^* there are several other graphs of interest which can be derived from G. One of these is the *radial graph* $R(G)$. The graph G defines an incidence relation R between the vertex set V and the dual vertex set V^*, the faces of G, when one writes vRF if, and only if, the vertex v is a corner of the face F. The corresponding graph $R(V, V^*)$ is bipartite. One obtains a representation for R by drawing a *radial edge* from the midpoint $m(F)$ of the face to each corner v of F. When v is a multiple corner, one draws one edge for each time v appears in the cyclic order in the sequence of boundary edges. This representation shows that the radial graph is planar.

We suppose that G has no loops. Let F_1 and F_2 be two neighboring faces in b and $E = (v_1, v_2)$ one of their common boundary edges. Then the four edges,

$$(v_1, m(F_1)), \qquad (v_1, m(F_2)), \qquad (v_2, m(F_1)), \qquad (v_2, m(F_2)),$$

form the boundary of a face in R (see Fig. 3.5.2).

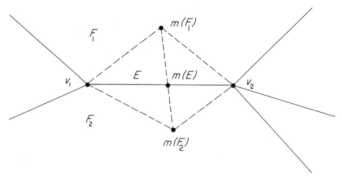

Fig. 3.5.2.

From the figure, one reads off that the constants in R can be expressed by those in G as follows:

$$v_v(R) = v_v(G) + v_f(G),$$
$$v_e(R) = 2v_e(G), \qquad v_f(R) = v_e(G).$$

(3.5.1)

We now have the following result.

Theorem 3.5.3. The radial graph R is maximal bipartite planar and conversely each such graph is a radial graph.

Proof: It remains only to show the second part of the theorem. Let V_1 and V_2 be the two vertex sets for a maximal bipartite graph. Each quadrangle in R has one pair of opposite vertices in V_1 and another in V_2. We define the graph G to consist of all diagonal edges in the faces of R connecting two vertices belonging to the same set V_1. It is then clear that R is the radial graph of G.

Instead of using diagonals between the vertices in V_1 one could have used the diagonals connecting vertices in V_2. One sees that the graph G' obtained in this way is actually the dual of G so that

$$R = R(G) = R(G^*). \tag{3.5.2}$$

This remark may be used to construct all self-dual graphs. Suppose that G is a graph isomorphic to its dual G^*. Then in constructing R one can use either G or G^* according to (3.5.2). The duality isomorphism will then be an automorphism of R which takes the vertex set V_1 into the vertex set V_2 and vice versa. On the other hand let R have such an automorphism. It represents a correspondence between the vertices and faces of G such that two neighboring faces correspond to neighboring vertices and vice versa so that G and G^* are isomorphic.

Theorem 3.5.4. Let R be a maximal bipartite planar graph with the vertex sets V_1 and V_2. Any automorphism of R which interchanges the two vertex sets gives rise to a self-dual graph by the construction just described and all self-dual graphs are obtainable this way.

The *medial graph* $M(G)$ of G is defined as follows: Let $m(E_1)$ and $m(E_2)$ be the midpoints of two consecutive boundary edges of a face F. Then $M(G)$ consists of the edges $m(E_1)$ and $m(E_2)$ connecting all pairs of such midpoints. Since each such edge crosses just one radial edge one sees the following theorem.

Theorem 3.5.5. The medial graph is the dual of the radial graph.

In particular, the valence of each vertex in $M(G)$ is $\rho(m) = 4$. As in Theorem 3.5.3, each graph which is the dual of a maximal bipartite graph is a medial graph, and conversely.

CHAPTER 4

EULER'S FORMULA AND ITS CONSEQUENCES

4.1. Euler's Formula

We shall derive the fundamental relation for planar graphs known as *Euler's formula.*

Theorem 4.1.1. When the number of faces, edges, vertices, and connected components of a graph are denoted by v_f, v_e, v_v, v_c, respectively, then these quantities are connected by the relation

$$v_f - v_e + v_v - v_c = 1. \tag{4.1.1}$$

Proof: We construct our graph from its v_v vertices by the successive adjunction of an edge E. For $v_e = 0$, one has $v_f = 1$ and $v_c = v_v$ and so (4.1.1) holds. When an edge E is added at some stage such that it connects two disjoint components in the previous graph, the number v_e is increased by 1, v_c is decreased by 1, while v_f is unchanged; as a consequence (4.1.1) remains valid. Next, let E connect two vertices, already connected by an arc. Then E divides one of the faces in two, hence v_e and v_f are increased by 1 while v_c is unchanged; so again (4.1.1) is satisfied.

For a connected graph the relation (4.1.1) reduces to the usual *Euler's polyhedron formula,*

$$v_v + v_f = v_e + 2. \tag{4.1.2}$$

In the applications of Euler's formula, one combines it with the expressions for the numbers v_f, v_e, and v_v in terms of the valences and dual valences. We defined the valence $\rho(v)$ at a vertex v to be the number of edges with v as an end point, counting eventual loops twice. Similarly, the dual valence $\rho^*(F)$ of a face F is the number of boundary edges of F, counting the acyclic edges twice. Due to the duality for planar graphs as expressed in Theorem 3.1.2 there must exist a complete duality for these valences also.

Let us denote by r_i the number of vertices at which the valence has the value i and by r_i^* the number of faces with the valence i. By this definition one has

$$v_v = \sum r_i, \qquad v_f = \sum r_i^*, \qquad i = 1, 2, \ldots. \tag{4.1.3}$$

Since each edge has two end points, possibly the same, and since each edge lies on the boundary of two faces, possibly the same, one obtains the formulas

$$2v_e = \sum i r_i = \sum i r_i^*, \qquad i = 1, 2, \ldots. \tag{4.1.4}$$

It is convenient to introduce two new quantities, the average valence ρ_0 and the average dual valence ρ_0^* defined, respectively, by the formulas

$$\rho_0 = \frac{1}{v_v} \sum i r_i = 2\frac{v_e}{v_v}, \qquad \rho_0^* = \frac{1}{v_f} \sum i r_i^* = 2\frac{v_e}{v_f}, \tag{4.1.5}$$

hence also

$$2v_e = \rho_0 \cdot v_v = \rho_0^* \cdot v_f. \tag{4.1.6}$$

We suppose from now on that G is a connected graph. When the expressions (4.1.5) are substituted in Euler's formula (4.1.2), one obtains

$$v_f = \left(1 - \frac{2}{\rho_0}\right) v_e + 2 = \left(\frac{1}{2}\rho_0 - 1\right) v_v + 2,$$

$$v_v = \left(1 - \frac{2}{\rho_0^*}\right) v_e + 2 = \left(\frac{1}{2}\rho_0^* - 1\right) v_f + 2. \tag{4.1.7}$$

According to Eqs. (4.1.3) and (4.1.4) these relations can also be written

$$\sum_i \left(1 - i\left(\frac{1}{2} - \frac{1}{\rho_0}\right)\right) r_i^* = 2,$$

$$\sum_i \left(1 - i\left(\frac{1}{2} - \frac{1}{\rho_0^*}\right)\right) r_i = 2. \tag{4.1.8}$$

By combining the relations (4.1.7), one can express the number of faces, edges, and vertices, using the averages ρ_0 and ρ_0^* as parameters. This leads to the next theorem.

Theorem 4.1.2. In a connected graph one has the expressions

$$k \cdot v_v = 4\rho_0{}^*, \qquad k \cdot v_e = 2\rho_0\rho_0{}^*, \qquad k \cdot v_f = 4\rho_0,$$
$$k = 2\rho_0 + 2\rho_0{}^* - \rho_0\rho_0{}^* \tag{4.1.9}$$

where ρ_0 and $\rho_0{}^*$ satisfy the condition

$$(\rho_0 - 2)(\rho_0{}^* - 2) < 4. \tag{4.1.10}$$

The condition (4.1.10) expresses the fact that k must be positive.

There are other forms of Euler's relation for connected graphs which are of interest. From the expressions (4.1.3) and (4.1.4), one obtains

$$\sum r_i{}^*(2 - i) + 2\sum r_i = 4$$
$$\sum r_i(2 - i) + 2\sum r_i{}^* = 4. \tag{4.1.11}$$

By addition, this gives the self-dual form

$$\sum r_i{}^*(4 - i) + \sum r_i(4 - i) = 8. \tag{4.1.12}$$

Since the left-hand side in (4.1.12) must be positive, Theorem 4.1.3 follows.

Theorem 4.1.3. In any planar graph there is at least one vertex v or one face F satisfying

$$\rho(v) \leq 3, \qquad \rho^*(F) \leq 3. \tag{4.1.13}$$

So far, we have placed no restrictions on the graph G except that it be connected. We shall now introduce some rather mild limitations. Suppose first that for every vertex v one has

$$\rho(v) \geq 3, \tag{4.1.14}$$

that is, G shall have no terminal vertices, nor any vertices with only two edges. According to (4.1.10) this implies

$$\rho_0 \geq 3, \qquad \rho_0{}^* < 6.$$

We conclude, in particular, the statement of Theorem 4.1.4.

Theorem 4.1.4. In a graph satisfying (4.1.14) there must be at least one face with five or fewer boundary edges.

When the condition $\rho_0 \geq 3$ is used in the first two expressions in (4.1.7), one obtains the following theorem.

Theorem 4.1.5. In a connected graph satisfying (4.1.14) one has

$$v_f \geq \tfrac{1}{3}v_e + 2, \qquad v_f \geq \tfrac{1}{2}v_v + 2. \tag{4.1.15}$$

The equality holds only for cubic graphs, that is, graphs with $\rho(v) = 3$ at each vertex.

If instead of (4.1.14), one has the dual condition

$$\rho^*(F) \geq 3, \tag{4.1.16}$$

that is, G has no loops or faces bounded by two edges, then one can draw the following dual conclusions.

Theorem 4.1.6. In a graph satisfying (4.1.16) there is at least one vertex with five or fewer edges.

Theorem 4.1.5 now becomes Theorem 4.1.7.

Theorem 4.1.7. In a connected graph satisfying (4.1.16) one has

$$v_v \geq \tfrac{1}{3}v_e + 2, \qquad v_v \geq \tfrac{1}{2}v_f + 2. \tag{4.1.17}$$

The equality sign holds only for maximal graphs.

We recall that a maximal planar graph was characterized by the property that $\rho^*(F) = 3$ for every face.

In most important applications, one can assume that both conditions (4.1.14) and (4.1.16) are fulfilled, that is, one has the relations (4.1.18)

$$\rho(v) \geq 3, \qquad \rho^*(F) \geq 3, \tag{4.1.18}$$

simultaneously for all vertices v and all faces F. From the inequality (4.1.10) one concludes that in this case

$$3 \leq \rho_0 < 6, \qquad 3 \leq \rho_0^* < 6. \tag{4.1.19}$$

Therefore, the graph must have a vertex v and a face F satisfying

$$\rho(v) \leq 5, \qquad \rho^*(F) \leq 5. \tag{4.1.20}$$

One also concludes Theorem 4.1.8 from Theorem 4.1.5 and Theorem 4.1.7.

Theorem 4.1.8. In a connected graph satisfying (4.1.18) one has

$$v_e \leq 3v_v - 6, \qquad v_e \leq 3v_f - 6 \tag{4.1.21}$$

and both equalities hold only for the tetrahedron graph.

Proof: The equality implies $\rho_0 = \rho_0^* = 3$ and when this is substituted in (4.1.9) one finds

$$v_v = v_f = 4, \qquad v_e = 6,$$

and this is only satisfied for the tetrahedron graph.

PROBLEMS

1. How must the corners be counted for a general face in order to pre-
   serve the circuit property that there shall be the same number of
   corners as boundary edges?
2. Give a stronger form for Theorem 4.1.3.
3. Show that when any pair of integers $v_e \geqq v_f > 0$ is given one can
   construct a connected graph with v_f faces, v_e edges, and $v_v = v_e - v_f + 2$
   vertices.

4.2. Regular Graphs

As usual, we call a planar graph *regular* when $\rho(a) = \rho_0$ has the same
value for each vertex. According to (4.1.10) one must have $\rho_0 \leqq 5$. The
case $\rho_0 = 1$ gives a single edge, $\rho_0 = 2$ gives a circuit when we suppose
that G is connected. Thus, only the regular graphs corresponding to
$\rho_0 = 3, 4, 5$ are of interest. We shall call them, respectively, *cubic*,
quartic, and *quintic* graphs. A graph is *dually regular* when $\rho^*(F) = \rho_0^*$
for every face. Again, only the graphs with $\rho_0^* = 3, 4, 5$ are nontrivial;
we call them *triangular* (maximal), *quadrangular*, and *pentagonal graphs*.

A graph is *completely regular* when it is regular in both ways. The condition 4.1.10 shows that there can only be a small number of completely
regular graphs. The possible values of the integers ρ_0 and ρ_0^* are readily
determined and from these one computes the number of vertices, edges,
and faces by means of the formulas (4.1.9). The results are contained in the
following table.

REGULAR POLYHEDRA

ρ_0	ρ_0^*	v_v	v_e	v_f	Name
3	3	4	6	4	Tetrahedron
3	4	8	12	6	Cube
3	5	20	30	12	Icosahedron
4	3	6	12	8	Octahedron
5	3	12	30	20	Dodecahedron
2	ρ_0^*	ρ_0^*	ρ_0^*	2	Circuit
ρ_0	2	2	ρ_0	ρ_0	Skein

One verifies that for each set of values there is just one planar graph
corresponding to them. It is not necessary to assume that the graph is
connected or without separating vertices.

In cŏnnection with the completely regular graphs let us consider briefly the *mosaic problem*. Here we assume that the plane is gradually being covered by a polygonal net in which each polygon has the same number ρ^* of boundary edges and at each corner there are ρ edges. This is the usual situation in a mosaic floor covering; we suppose also that as the number of pieces laid in position increases, the proportion of the v_v' vertices on the outer boundary tends to zero, in comparison to the total number v_v of vertices.

The total number of edges v_e at each stage has the bounds

$$\rho \cdot v_v \leqq 2v_e \leqq \rho(v_v - v_v')$$

and we conclude that

$$\lim \frac{v_e}{v_v} = \tfrac{1}{2}\rho$$

as v_v increases. Next, we count the edges by means of the boundary edges of the faces. There are $v_f - 1$ faces with ρ^* edges. The infinite face F_∞ has v_v' edges, the same as the number of vertices on the outer boundary of the graph. This gives

$$2 \cdot v_e = (v_f - 1)\rho^* + v_v$$

and as a consequence,

$$2 \cdot \lim \frac{v_e}{v_v} = \rho^* \lim \frac{v_f}{v_v}.$$

We now write Euler's relation (4.1.2) in the form

$$1 + \frac{v_f}{v_v} = \frac{v_e}{v_v} + \frac{2}{v_v}$$

and substitute the preceding limit values. It follows that

$$1 + \frac{\rho}{\rho^*} = \frac{1}{2}\rho$$

or equivalently,

$$(\rho - 2)(\rho^* - 2) = 4.$$

This leads to the conclusion stated by Theorem 4.2.1.

Theorem 4.2.1. The only polygons which can be used in a mosaic covering of the plane are those with

$$\rho = 3, \rho^* = 6; \qquad \rho = 4, \rho^* = 4; \qquad \rho = 6, \rho^* = 3;$$

that is, only hexagons, squares and triangles.

PROBLEMS

1. In the condition for regular polyhedra one uses only the fact that the averages ρ_0 and $\rho_0{}^*$ shall be integers to derive the values for v_v, v_e, v_f in the table (p. 52). Are there nonregular graphs for these values?
2. Find all graphs for which $\rho_0 = \frac{1}{2}m$ and $\rho_0{}^* = \frac{1}{2}n$ with integral m and n.

4.3. The Euler Contributions

We shall derive an elegant form of Euler's relation due to Lebesgue. At each vertex v of G there are $\rho = \rho(v)$ edges, hence the same number ρ of angles α formed by these edges. To such a v-angle α we assign a value $1/\rho$. Each angle is also associated with a face F_α having a corner at v. When F_α has ρ^* boundary edges, we also assign a value $1/\rho^*$ to each of its angles. These definitions show that

$$v_v = \sum \frac{1}{\rho}, \qquad v_e = \sum \frac{1}{2}, \qquad v_f = \sum \frac{1}{\rho^*}$$

where the sums extend over all angles in G; to avoid special definitions we suppose that G has no loops. This leads to *Lebesgue's formula* for a connected graph

$$\sum_\alpha \left(\frac{1}{\rho} + \frac{1}{\rho^*} - \frac{1}{2} \right) = 2, \tag{4.3.1}$$

the sum to be taken over all angles α as before. We shall use it as the starting point for the study of several properties of planar graphs.

The general term

$$\Phi(\alpha) = \frac{1}{\rho} + \frac{1}{\rho^*} - \frac{1}{2} \tag{4.3.2}$$

in the sum (4.3.1) we call the *Euler contribution of the angle* α. When one sums this angle function for all corners of a face F, one obtains the *face Euler contribution*,

$$\Phi(F) = 1 - \frac{1}{2}\rho^* + \sum \frac{1}{\rho} \tag{4.3.3}$$

where the sum extends over the valences at the various corners of F. We recall that there may be multiple corners for F and these must be included according to the several times they occur. Dually, one defines the Euler contribution of a vertex v to be

$$\Phi(v) = 1 - \frac{1}{2}\rho + \sum \frac{1}{\rho^*} \qquad (4.3.4)$$

where the sum is taken over the valences of the various faces at v, keeping account of their possible multiple appearance.

Also, for an edge $E = (v_1, v_2)$, one can introduce an Euler contribution $\Phi(E)$. We denote by ρ_1 and ρ_2 the valences at v_1 and v_2, respectively, and by ρ_1^* and ρ_2^* the valences of the two faces F_1 and F_2 having E as a common boundary edge. There are four angles having E as one leg. When we add their contributions (4.3.2), but take into account that each of them is defined by two edges, we obtain

$$\Phi(E) = \frac{1}{\rho_1} + \frac{1}{\rho_2} + \frac{1}{\rho_1^*} + \frac{1}{\rho_2^*} - 1. \qquad (4.3.5)$$

According to Lebesgue's formula (4.3.1) there is a common type of relationship for each of the four types of Euler contributions, as defined above. This is

$$\sum_\alpha \Phi(\alpha) = \sum_v \Phi(v) = \sum_F \Phi(F) = \sum_E \Phi(E) = 2.$$

Since the sums (4.3.6) are positive and bounded we can make the following general statement.

Theorem 4.3.1. For all graphs G, without loops, and each of the four kinds of Euler contributions there must exist so many positive contributions that their sum is not less than 2. When the sum of the positive terms exceeds 2, there must exist a counter balancing set of negative terms.

Let us make a more detailed study of this condition. One verifies that $\Phi > 0$ whenever $\rho = 1$ or $\rho^* = 1$ for one of the quantities occurring in the expression for Φ. We may suppose, therefore, that $\rho \geq 2$ and $\rho^* \geq 2$.

ANGLE CONTRIBUTIONS. When $\rho = 2$ or $\rho^* = 2$ in the formula (4.3.2), one finds $\Phi = 1/\rho^* > 0$, $\Phi = 1/\rho > 0$, respectively, so that the contributions are positive. The only other possible pairs of values (ρ, ρ^*) with $\Phi > 0$ are

$$(3, 3), (3, 4), (4, 3), (5, 3), (3, 5). \qquad (4.3.7)$$

The corresponding contributions are

$$\Phi(3, 5) = \Phi(5, 3) = \tfrac{1}{30}, \qquad \Phi(3, 4) = \Phi(4, 3) = \tfrac{1}{12}, \qquad \Phi(3, 3) = \tfrac{1}{6}. \qquad (4.3.8)$$

The contribution $\Phi = 0$ can occur only when $\rho = 3$, $\rho^* = 6$, and $\rho = \rho^* = 4$. These observations lead to the following theorem.

Theorem 4.3.2. In a graph satisfying (4.1.18) there exist at least twelve angles belonging to one of the types (4.3.7).

When $\gamma(\rho, \rho^*)$ denotes the number of angles in G having the associated valences ρ and ρ^*, one must have

$$\gamma(3, 3) + \tfrac{1}{2}(\gamma(3, 4) + \gamma(4, 3)) + \tfrac{1}{5}(\gamma(3, 5) + \gamma(5, 3)) \geqq 12. \qquad (4.3.9)$$

When G is a graph in which all angle contributions are positive, the equality sign must hold in (4.3.9). This relation considered as a Diophantine equation shows that there exist only a small number of these graphs. The regular polyhedra all have this property according to the table in Section 4.2.

EDGE CONTRIBUTIONS.   In order that an edge E have a positive contribution it is necessary and sufficient that the quantities in (4.3.5) satisfy the condition

$$\frac{1}{\rho_1} + \frac{1}{\rho_2} + \frac{1}{\rho_1{}^*} + \frac{1}{\rho_2{}^*} > 1.$$

This means that they are solutions of the Diophantine inequality

$$\frac{1}{x_1} + \frac{1}{x_2} + \frac{1}{x_3} + \frac{1}{x_4} > 1$$

in positive integers $x_i \geqq 2$. When (x_1, x_2, x_3, x_4) is a solution set, then any set which it majors,

$$(y_1, y_2, y_3, y_4), \qquad x_i \geqq y_i \qquad i = 1, 2, 3, 4,$$

is also a solution set. Thus, we need only determine the *maximal sets* not majored by any other. Since the condition is symmetric in the four variables it suffices to list the maximal solution sets with

$$2 \leqq x_1 \leqq x_2 \leqq x_3 \leqq x_4.$$

A simple set of computations show that the maximal solutions are the following:

$$\text{I:} \qquad (2, 2, n, m_1), \qquad (2, 3, 6, m_2)$$

where $n \geqq 2$, $m_1 \geqq 2$, $m_2 \geqq 6$ are arbitrary integers.

II : $(2, 3, \ 7, 41)$, $(2, 4, 4, m_3)$, $m_3 \geqq 4$

$(2, 3, \ 8, 23)$, $(2, 4, 5, 19)$

$(2, 3, \ 9, 17)$, $(2, 4, 7, 11)$

$(2, 3, 10, 14)$, $(2, 5, 5, \ 9)$

$(2, 3, 11, 13)$, $(2, 5, 6, \ 7)$

III : $(3, 3, 4, 11)$, $(3, 3, 5, 7)$, $(3, 4, 4, 5)$

The values $\Phi(E) > 0$ can be made arbitrarily small for the types involving numbers n and m. When G satisfies (4.1.18), the maximal value is $H(E) = \frac{1}{3}$ and this occurs when

$$\rho_1 = \rho_2 = \rho_1{}^* = \rho_i{}^* = 3;$$

that is, E is the common boundary edge for two triangles as in Fig. 4.3.1.

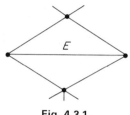

Fig. 4.3.1.

We conclude further, as stated in Theorem 4.3.1.

Theorem 4.3.3. When G is a graph satisfying (4.1.18), then it has at least six edges of the types included in III.

In particular, for these edges at least one of the quantities ρ_1, ρ_2, $\rho_1{}^*$, $\rho_2{}^*$ has the value 3 and a second has the value 3 or 4, etc. Their sum is, at most, 21.

In the case of solutions of type III the minimal value for the Euler contribution is $H(E) = \frac{1}{132}$ and it occurs for the first quadruple. We conclude that for graphs satisfying (4.1.18) there is only a finite number in which all Euler contributions of the edges are positive.

FACE CONTRIBUTIONS. We assume again that the graph satisfies the condition (4.1.18). For a given ρ^* the expression (4.3.3) takes its maximal value when $\rho = 3$ for all terms in the sum and then

$$\Phi(F) = 1 - \tfrac{1}{6}\rho^*. \tag{4.3.10}$$

This shows that the maximal contribution occurs for $\rho^* = 3$ and is equal to

$$\Phi_{\text{max}}(F) = \tfrac{1}{2}.$$

From (4.3.10) one also sees that positive contributions can only occur in the cases

$$\rho^*(F) = 3, 4, 5. \qquad (4.3.11)$$

For each of these values (4.3.11) we must examine the solutions to the inequality

$$\sum \frac{1}{\rho_i} > \frac{\rho^*}{2} - 1.$$

Again, it is only necessary to list the maximal solution sets which are not majored by any others; within each set, the values of the ρ_i can be arranged in increasing order. Through simple calculations one finds the following maximal solution sets:

$$\rho^* = 3: \quad (3, 6, \ n), \qquad (3, \ 7, 41), \qquad (3, \ 8, 23)$$
$$(3, 9, 17), \qquad (3, 10, 14), \qquad (3, 11, 13)$$
$$(4, 5, 19), \qquad (4, \ 6, 11), \qquad (4, \ 7, \ 9)$$
$$\rho^* = 4: \quad (3, 3, 3, n), \qquad (3, 3, 4, 11), \qquad (3, 3, 5, 7), \qquad (3, 4, 4, 5)$$
$$\rho^* = 5: \quad (3, 3, 3, 3, 5).$$

From the relation (4.3.6) and the maximal value $\tfrac{1}{2}$ for $\Phi(F)$ we conclude Theorem 4.3.4.

Theorem 4.3.4. In any graph satisfying (4.1.18) there are at least four faces belonging to the types listed above.

In particular, there are at least four faces with one of the valences $\rho^*(F) = 3, 4, 5$ such that one of the corners has one of the valences $\rho(v) = 3, 4, 5$.

The formulation of the dual results we leave to the reader.

In the preceding discussion we have usually imposed only the conditions (4.1.18) on the valences. Stricter restrictions lead to sharper results. We consider first the angle contributions.

Suppose that

$$\rho(v) \geqq 4, \qquad \rho^*(F) \geqq 3 \qquad (4.3.12)$$

for all vertices and faces. From (4.3.7), one sees that G must then have twelve angles corresponding to the valences $(4, 3)$ and $(5, 3)$. Next, it would be natural to consider the graphs in which

$$\rho(v) \geqq 4, \qquad \rho^*(F) \geqq 4.$$

However, from (4.3.7) one sees that there can be no planar graphs of this kind. This is also a consequence of the inequality (4.1.10).
    When

$$\rho(v) \geqq 5, \qquad \rho^*(F) \geqq 3 \qquad\qquad (4.3.13)$$

are true for all vertices and faces, there is only one possible angle type in (4.3.7), namely $(5, 3)$. Here,

$$\Phi(5, 3) = \tfrac{1}{30}$$

and we may conclude Theorem 4.3.5.

Theorem 4.3.5. In a graph satisfying (4.3.13) there are at least sixty angles belonging to triangle corners with five edges.
    Dually, when the conditions

$$\rho(v) \geqq 3, \qquad \rho^*(F) \geqq 5 \qquad\qquad (4.3.14)$$

hold for all vertices and faces there are at least sixty pentagon angles at vertices with three edges.
    Consider next the Euler contributions of the edges. When (4.3.12) holds, the contribution of an edge $E = (v_1, v_2)$ can only be positive for the three types given in III. For the two combinations $(3, 3, 4, 11)$ and $(3, 3, 5, 7)$ one must have

$$\rho_1^* = \rho_2^* = 3.$$

Hence, E is the common boundary edge of two triangles and

$$\rho(v_1) = 4, \qquad \rho(v_2) \leqq 11$$

or also

$$\rho(v_1) = 5, \qquad \rho(v_2) = 4, 5, 6, 7.$$

The third combination $(3, 4, 4, 5)$ implies that E is the common boundary edge of a triangle with a quadrangle or a pentagon. In the first case one must have

$$\rho(v_1) = 4, \qquad \rho(v_2) = 4, 5$$

and in the second

$$\rho(v_1) = \rho(v_2) = 4.$$

The maximal Euler contribution is $\Phi(3, 3, 4, 4) = \frac{1}{6}$, hence there exist at least twelve edges of the types just described.

When the conditions (4.3.13) are fulfilled, there is only one possible combination in III, namely (3, 3, 5, 7). In this case,

$$\rho_1{}^* = \rho_2{}^* = 3, \qquad \rho(v_1) = 5, \qquad \rho(v_2) = 5, 6, 7.$$

Since the maximal contribution is $(3, 3, 5, 5) = \frac{1}{15}$, we conclude the next theorem.

Theorem 4.3.6. When the conditions (4.3.13) hold, there are at least thirty edges $E = (v_1, v_2)$ which are the common boundary edge of two triangles and satisfy

$$\rho(v_1) = 5, \qquad \rho(v_2) = 5, 6, 7.$$

Dually, when (4.3.14) holds, there are at least thirty edges satisfying

$$\rho(v_1) = \rho(v_2) = 3$$

for the end points while its neighboring faces are a pentagon and a face with 5, 6 or 7 boundary edges.

It remains to examine the Euler contributions of the vertices, or, as we shall prefer here, the faces. We suppose that the condition (4.3.14) is satisfied.

From the preceding list it follows that under these conditions there is only one type of face which can produce a positive contribution, namely (3, 3, 3, 3, 5). The maximal contribution in this case is

$$(3, 3, 3, 3, 3) = \frac{1}{6},$$

and we conclude Theorem 4.3.7.

Theorem 4.3.7. In a graph satisfying (4.3.14) there are at least twelve pentagons with four corners having valence 3 and the remaining one has one of the valences 3, 4, 5.

If one permits vertices with two edges, the preceding results may still hold in weaker form. Suppose that (4.3.14) holds generally, but there is a single vertex with $\rho(v_0) = 2$. Then v_0 is a common corner of two faces F_0 and F_1 and the two edges are boundary edges for both. The Euler contributions of F_0 and F_1 cannot exceed $1 - \frac{5}{2} + (\frac{1}{2} + \frac{4}{3}) = \frac{1}{3}$ so the sum of the contributions of the rest is at least $\frac{4}{3}$ and there are at least eight pentagons of the type described in Theorem 4.3.7. One readily sees that this number can be raised to 9 when one of the corners of F_0 or F_1 has a valence greater than 3.

PROBLEMS

1. Determine the type of edges for which $\Phi(E) = 0$. Repeat the same problem for the face contributions.
2. Determine all graphs in which all angles have a positive Euler contribution.
3. Determine all graphs in which no angle contribution is negative.
4. Repeat Problems 2 and 3 for edge contributions.

CHAPTER 5

LARGE CIRCUITS

5.1. Circuit Arcs

We shall assume that G is a connected planar graph without separating vertices. This is only a restriction of convenience. All concepts used in the following may be defined in general with analogous properties, but in all statements it would be necessary to mention especially inessential bridges with, at most, a single attachment.

An arc L in G is a *circuit arc* when it is a section of some circuit C. We introduce some special notations. The set of vertices on L not including the end points are denoted by $[L]$. When B is a bridge for C, the number of its attachments is $\alpha(B; C)$. When L is an arc of C, the number of attachments of B on $[L]$ and the whole arc L are $\alpha(B;[L])$, $\alpha(B; L)$, respectively. As a consequence,

$$\alpha(B; C) = \alpha(B; [L]) + \alpha(B; C - L). \tag{5.1.1}$$

Let us eliminate from G all edges not belonging to C which have at least one end point in $[L]$. In the remaining graph G_0 there are no edges attached to $[L]$ so that we may consider $L = L_0$ to be a single edge in G_0. In G_0 the edge L_0 is a circuit edge lying on the circuit

$$C = (C - L) + L_0.$$

In G_0 the edge L_0 will lie on the boundary of two faces F_0 and F_1 defined by the minimal circuits $D_0(L)$ and $D_1(L)$. These circuits we call the minimal L-circuits in G_0 and G.

In G_0 the minimal L-circuits D_0 and D_1 are characterized by the property of having no inner transversals. Therefore, a circuit D in G

including L is a minimal L-circuit if, and only if,

$$\alpha(B; D - L) \leq 1 \tag{5.1.2}$$

for every inner bridge. According to (5.1.2) the inner bridges for a minimal L-circuit D_0 in G fall into two types:

δ_0-*bridges* not attached on $D_0 - L$

δ_1-*bridges* with one attachment on $D_0 - L$.

To each of these bridges there is an L-*section* $L(b_1, b_2)$ such that b_1 and b_2 are attachments for B on $[L]$ and all its other attachments on $[L]$ lie between b_1 and b_2. The L-section may be *singular*, that is, consist of a single vertex $b_1 = b$; this occurs only when B is a δ_1-bridge with just two attachments, one on $[L]$ and the other on $D_0 - L$. The L-section of a bridge is *nonsingular* when $b_1 \neq b_2$. For the moment, we shall examine the latter type of bridge.

For two nonsingular bridges B and B' within D_0 we say that B *encloses* B' when there exists an arc $B(b_1, b_2)$ in B such that B' lies within the circuit $L(b_1, b_2) + B(b_2, b_1)$. This implies that B' must be a δ_0-bridge and

$$L(b_1, b_2) \geq L(b_1', b_2')$$

for the corresponding L-sections.

A *maximal bridge* B is a nonsingular bridge not enclosed by any other. An inner *complex* M in D_0 is a subgraph consisting of:

(1) A maximal bridge B

(2) All bridges enclosed by B

(3) The L-section $L(b_1, b_2)$ of B.

These complexes also are of two types:

(1) M_0-*complexes* defined by a δ_0-bridge

(2) M_1-*complexes* defined by a δ_1-bridge.

To the M_1-complexes we also count the singular δ_1-bridges by special definition. In this manner all inner bridges in D_0 have been classified as belonging to a particular complex. One sees that the L-sections of two different complexes have, at most, an end point in common. The various types of complexes are indicated in Fig. 5.1.1.

Let M be a nonsingular complex with the L-section $L(b_1, b_2)$. Within M there are transversals from b_1 to b_2. When T_1 and T_2 are two different transversals such that one does not lie entirely within the other, one can combine them to obtain a third transversal $T_3(b_1, b_2)$ such that a larger part of M' lies within the circuit

$$L(b_1, b_2) + T_3(b_2, b_1).$$

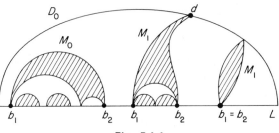

Fig. 5.1.1.

By repeating this process, one obtains a *maximal transversal* $T(M; b_1, b_2)$ such that all other transversals lie within the *M*-circuit,

$$L(b_1, b_2) + T(M; b_2, b_1). \tag{5.1.3}$$

The maximal transversal lies in the maximal bridge B defining M.

There may be a part of the complex M lying outside the M-circuit (5.1.3). In this outside part of M there cannot be any arc connecting vertices lying on $T(M)$ since $T(M)$ is a maximal transversal. Since G has no separating vertices, we conclude in the case of an M_0-complex that it is bounded by the circuit (5.1.3). For an M_1-complex let d be the single attachment of M_1 on $D_0 - L$. The various components of M_1 outside the circuit (5.1.3) can only have attachments t_i on $T(M)$ in addition to d. We conclude, in this case, that the outside components are two-vertex attached, namely, at d and a single vertex t_i. The situation is illustrated in Fig. 5.1.2.

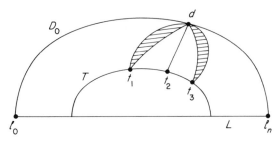

Fig. 5.1.2.

Now let L consist of the edges,

$$L = E_0, E_1, \ldots, E_{n-1}, \qquad E_i = (l_i, l_{i+1}) \tag{5.1.4}$$
$$[L] = \{l_1, l_2, \ldots, l_{n-1}\}.$$

Following this order, one can also order the complexes in D_0 according to the series of their L-sections. For the singular M_1-complexes there may be several with the same attachment b_1; these may then be ordered with respect to their other attachment on $D_0 - [L]$ in the direction from l_0 to l_n.

The arc on D_0,

$$\tilde{L} = \tilde{L}(l_1, l_0, l_n, l_{n-1}) = E_0 + (D_0 - L) + E_{n-1} \qquad (5.1.5)$$

is a circuit arc with the same end edges E_0 and E_{n-1} as L. It completes L in the sense that

$$D_0 = L + \tilde{L}. \qquad (5.1.6)$$

We shall call $\tilde{L}$ the *conjoint arc* to L. Usually there will be two of them, one defined by each of the two minimal L-circuits D_0 and D_1.

The conjoint arc $\tilde{L}$ will itself have a conjoint arc lying on or within D. This, we shall call the *second conjoint* of L and denote by $\tilde{\tilde{L}}$. It has the same end edges as L and $\tilde{L}$. Together with $\tilde{L}$ it forms a minimal circuit for $\tilde{L}$, enclosed by D_0,

$$\tilde{D}_0 = \tilde{L} + \tilde{\tilde{L}}. \qquad (5.1.7)$$

The preceding discussion enables us to give a simple description of the second conjoint. It must consist of all maximal transversals $T(M)$ for the various nonsingular complexes M in D_0, constructing an arc from them by connecting them by those sections of L which lie between the L-sections of these complexes. In Fig. 5.1.3 the second conjoint is drawn in a solid line.

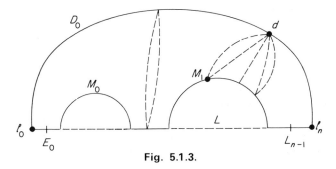

Fig. 5.1.3.

The preceding observations on the complexes and their maximal transversals also show that in $\tilde{D}_0$ all bridges have just two attachments, one on $[\tilde{L}]$ and the other on $[\tilde{\tilde{L}}]$.

Theorem 5.1.1. A circuit arc L is its own second conjoint if, and only if, its minimal circuit D_0 has no nonsingular bridges. Any conjoint is its own second conjoint arc.

Until now, we have principally considered one of the minimal circuits of L, namely, D_0. Evidently, the analogous facts hold for the other minimal circuit D_1. However, in our following applications, we shall select L in such a manner that the conditions in regard to D_1 become particularly simple. We call L a *face arc* when it lies on a minimal circuit D_1 bounding a face F_1 of G. In this case, D_1 has no inner bridges and with respect to it L is its own second conjoint.

We return to the general case where D_0 is a minimal circuit for the arbitrary circuit arc L. Let K be some other circuit in G which also passes through L. The two circuits K and D_0 may have a common initial section from l_0 beyond L,

$$K(l_0, d_1) = D_0(l_0, d_1),$$

before they separate at d_1. The next vertex of K which lies on D_0 shall be d_2. Then the section $K(d_1, d_2)$ lies outside D_0. From d_2 the two circuits may have another common section, possibly only a single vertex,

$$K(d_2, d_3) = D_0(d_2, d_3),$$

and so on. At no stage can K return to any of the vertices on D_0 previously bypassed. Thus, the circuit K consists of L and a sequence of consecutive *common sections* with D_0,

$$K(l_0, d_1), \qquad K(d_2, d_3), \ldots,$$

and a series of *bights* connecting them,

$$K(d_1, d_2), \qquad K(d_3, d_4),$$

including only edges outside of D_0. The same observations apply to the other minimal circuit D_1. In Fig. 5.1.4 the location of K in regard to D_0 and D_1 has been sketched.

We shall classify the inner bridges of K with respect to D_0.

δ-BRIDGES: These are K-bridges whose edges all lie within D_0. They are also bridges for D_0 and therefore identical with the δ_0 and δ_1-bridges previously defined. The single attachment d on $D_0 - L$ for such a δ_1-bridge must also lie on $K - L$.

γ-BRIDGES: K-bridges with no edges inside D_0.

ε-BRIDGES: K-bridges including edges inside D_0 and edges on or outside D_0.

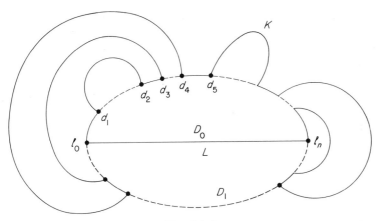

Fig. 5.1.4.

Let us examine first the γ-bridges. Each γ-bridge can have attachments only on a single bight $K(d, d')$. Suppose, namely, that B has an attachment a_1 on $K(d, d')$ and another attachment a_2 not on this bight. Within B there is a transversal $T(a_1, a_2)$. To proceed from a_1 to a_2 this arc would have to cross D_0 (d, d'), hence B could not be a γ-bridge.

The γ-bridges are of two types:

(1) γ_0-*bridges* having no edges in common with D_0.

(2) γ_1-*bridges* having an edge E in common with D_0. Then E lies on the section $D_0(d, d')$ defined by the bight on D_0. As a consequence, the whole section $D_0(d, d')$ must belong to the bridge B and the end points d and d' are among the attachments for B.

ε-BRIDGES. For such a bridge B all attachments not on $[L]$ must lie within the same bight $K(d, d')$. To see this, we observe that B includes an edge lying within the circuit defined by some bight,

$$K(d, d') + D_0(d', d), \tag{5.1.8}$$

or possibly on the arc $D_0(d, d')$. If there were some attachment d_2 for B on $D_0 - L$ but not on $K(d, d')$, there would exist a transversal in B beginning in E and ending at d_2. But this would create a transversal within D_0 connecting two vertices on $D_0 - L$, contradicting the fact that D_0 is a minimal circuit for L.

Since B includes edges within D_0, it must have attachments on $[L]$. From such an attachment there must be a transversal in B to an edge E lying within the circuit (5.1.8) or on its boundary section $D_0(d, d')$. This implies that B has at least one vertex on $D_0(d, d')$ not coinciding with d or d'. But this implies that the whole section $D_0(d, d')$ belongs to B.

The part of B lying inside D_0 must form a family of δ_1-bridges $\{S_i\}$. We may call them the D_0-*supports* for B. There may be several supports having the same attachment d_1 on $D_0(d, d')$. However, there can be no supports attached at the end points d and d' because such a support would by itself be a δ_1-bridge for K. In Fig. 5.1.5 we have indicated the various types of K-bridges.

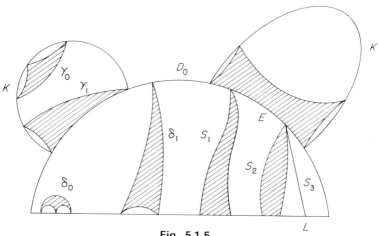

Fig. 5.1.5.

Previously we defined the L-section of a bridge in D_0. For an ε-bridge one can also define its L-section $L(b_1, b_2)$ where b_1 and b_2 are attachments for B such that all other attachments on $[L]$ lie between b_1 and b_2. One can also define the *complex* for B to consist of B, its L-section $L(b_1, b_2)$ and all δ_0-bridges enclosed by a transversal $T(b_1, b_2)$ in B.

5.2. Hamilton Circuits

We turn to the proof of a general theorem on circuits in planar graphs due to Tutte. Under certain conditions it implies that the graph has a Hamilton circuit. Investigations of this kind were begun by Whitney for maximal planar graphs and extended to general planar graphs by Tutte.

Theorem 5.2.1. In a planar graph G let E be an edge lying on the minimal circuits C_0 and C_1 while E' is another edge on C_1. Then there exists a circuit K passing through E and E' such that none of its bridges have more than three attachments while the special bridges having edges in common with C_0 or C_1 have two attachments.

It is sufficient to prove the theorem for connected graphs without separating vertices. It is readily verified for small numbers of edges. Thus, we can base the proof upon induction with respect to the number of edges in the graph. We assume that G is a graph such that the theorem holds for all graphs with a smaller number of edges and prove from this that it holds for G.

The theorem is evident when E and E' form a circuit consisting only of these two edges. Thus, we assume that there exists a face arc,

$$L = C_1(E, E') = C_1(E_0, E_{n-1}), \qquad (5.2.1)$$

where we have put

$$E = E_0 = (l_0, l_1), \qquad E' = E_{n-1} = (l_{n-1} l_n) \qquad (5.2.2)$$

using the notations of (5.1.4). One of the minimal circuits for L is $D_1 = C_1$ while the other enclosing C_0 we denote by D_0 as before.

One may possibly have $C_0 = D_0$ but, in general, the two circuits C_0 and D_0 have only a certain section

$$C_0(l_0, d_0) = D_0(l_0, d_0),$$

in common beyond L. After d_0 they can have no further vertices in common on $D_0 - L$ due to the fact that D_0 is a minimal L-circuit. The remaining arc $C_0(d_0, c_0)$ connecting d_0 with a vertex c_0 on $[L]$ is a transversal of D_0 when $D_0 \neq C_0$ (see Fig. 5.2.1).

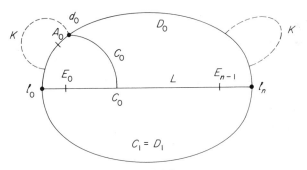

Fig. 5.2.1.

We make the observation, readily verified, that when G is connected and without separating vertices, then these properties are retained when one or more bridges are removed from one of its circuits. From G, we remove all vertices and edges inside the circuit D_0. In the reduced graph G_0 we replace L by a single edge L_0. The minimal circuits for L_0 are

$$D_0{}' = (D_0 - L) + L_0, \qquad D_1{}' = (D_1 - L) + L_0.$$

Since the theorem holds for G_0 there exists a circuit K_0 in G_0 passing through L_0 such that for any bridge B_0

$$\alpha(B_0; K_0) \leq 3, \tag{5.2.3}$$

while

$$\alpha(B_0; K_0) = 2 \tag{5.2.4}$$

when B_0 has an edge in common with $D_0 - L$ or $D_1 - L$.

The induction assumption also shows that one can select K_0 such that it passes an arbitrary edge A_0 on $D_0 - L$. If there exists a last vertex d_0 for C_0 on $D_0 - L$, as just described, we select A_0 such that d_0 is one of its end points. This insures that K_0 passes through d_0.

Next, we reconstruct G by replacing L_0 by L and restoring the interior edges and vertices to D_0. In this process K_0 becomes a circuit K in G and we establish Lemma 5.2.1.

Lemma 5.2.1. The circuit K passes through L and d_0 and its bridges satisfy

$$\alpha(B; K - L) \leq 3 \tag{5.2.5}$$

while

$$\alpha(B; K - L) = 2 \tag{5.2.6}$$

when the bridge B has edges in common with D_0 and D_1.

Proof: It is clear according to (5.2.3) and (5.2.4) that any γ-bridge satisfies the conditions (5.2.5) and (5.2.6). The same is true for the δ-bridges since they have no edges in common with D_0 and D_1 and at most one attachment on $K - L$. It remains to examine the ε-bridges. The part of an ε-bridge B which lies on or outside of D_0 is a bridge B_0 for the circuit K_0 in G_0. Since it has edges in common with D_0, it satisfies (5.2.4). The two attachments of B_0 on K are the two end points d and d' of the section $D_0(d, d')$ which B_0 and B include. Since B has had no other attachments on $K - L$ the relation (5.2.6) follows. The situation for an ε-bridge is illustrated in Fig. 5.2.2.

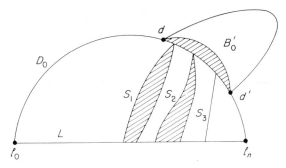

Fig. 5.2.2.

Lemma 5.2.2. The arc $C_0(d_0, c_0)$ lies in a δ_1-bridge for K.

Proof: The arc must lie in a δ_1-bridge for D_0 and this is also a δ_1-bridge for K since K is selected such that it passes through d_0.

The circuit K which we have constructed may have bridges which do not satisfy the conditions of Theorem 5.2.1. We shall call them *exceptional bridges*. For such a bridge B one has

$$\alpha(B; K) \geq 4 \tag{5.2.7}$$

when B has no edges in common with C_0 and C_1 while

$$\alpha(B : K) \geq 3 \tag{5.2.8}$$

when there are such edges.

According to the conditions (5.2.5) and (5.2.6) in Lemma 5.2.1 no γ-bridge can be exceptional. Since there are no edges within $C_1 = D_1$, the exceptional bridges must be δ or ε-bridges for K with respect to D_0. It is also evident that if there are to be exceptional bridges, one must have $C_0 \neq D_0$.

For an ε-bridge B, we saw that there were just two attachments on $K - L$. Since B contains no edges of C_0 and C_1, the relation (5.2.7) must hold, and so according to (5.1.1),

$$\alpha(B; [L]) \geq 2 \tag{5.2.9}$$

when B is exceptional. Any δ_1-bridge B has one attachment on $K - L$; when B is exceptional, (5.2.9) also holds according to (5.2.7) and (5.2.8). For a δ_0-bridge (5.2.9) always holds. Thus we have established Lemma 5.2.3.

Lemma 5.2.3. An exceptional bridge has a nonsingular L-section.

To each exceptional bridge B we form its complex M as described in Section 5.1. The corresponding L-section we denote by $L(b_1, b_2)$ as before.

Our next step is to show that the circuit K can be so modified that it no longer has any exceptional bridges. For this purpose we introduce an auxiliary subgraph of G

$$H(M) = K + M \tag{5.2.10}$$

for each exceptional complex M. In $H(M)$ the circuit K is the boundary of the infinite face. The edges of C_1 which belong to $H(M)$ must lie on K. The same is true for the edges of C_0 except when M is an exceptional complex defined by the δ_1-bridge B which includes $C_0(d_0, c_0)$.

Case 1. M is defined by the maximal δ_0-bridge B. Then there is no attachment of B on the set $[A]$ where A is the arc

$$A = K(b_1, l_0, l_n, b_2). \tag{5.2.11}$$

When we consider A to be a single edge in $H(M)$, this graph has fewer edges than G so Theorem 5.2.1 is valid. As a consequence there exists a circuit through A

$$J = A + J(b_2, b_1) \tag{5.2.12}$$

where J is an arc through M such that all bridges B' for J in $H(M)$ satisfy

$$\alpha(B'; J) \leqq 3 \tag{5.2.13}$$

and also

$$\alpha(B'; J) = 2 \tag{5.2.14}$$

when B' includes an edge of $L(b_1, b_2)$.

Case 2. M is defined by an exceptional δ_1-bridge B. In this case, M has a single attachment d_1 on the arc $[A]$ in (5.2.10). This divides A into two sections

$$A(b_1, b_2) = A(b_1, d_1) + A(d_1, b_2) = A_1 + A_2.$$

At least one of the sections A_1 and A_2 includes more than one edge of the graph G, for otherwise one would have

$$A_1 = E_0, \qquad A_2 = E_{n-1}$$

and L would be a circuit. Since there are no attachments of M on $[A_1]$ and $[A_2]$, we may consider A_1 and A_2 to be single edges in $H(M)$. Theorem

5.2.1 applies to this graph. Since A_1 and A_2 lie on the same face circuit K, there exists a circuit (5.2.12) in $H(M)$ with bridges B' satisfying (5.2.13) and also (5.2.14) when B' includes an edge of $L(b_1, b_2)$.

In the special case where M includes the transversal $C_0(d_0, c_0)$, one must have $d_0 = d_1$. In $H(M)$ the minimal circuits for E_0 and A_1 are the same, namely, K and $C_0' = K(c_0, l_0, d_0) + C_0(d_0, c_0)$. Thus the condition (5.2.14) is fulfilled also for every bridge B' which includes an edge of $C_0(d_0, c_0)$.

Case 3. The complex M is defined by an exceptional ε-bridge B. Then M has just two attachments d_1 and d_2 on the arc $[A]$ defined in (5.2.11). In $H(M)$ one of the minimal circuits for the arc A is K, the other a circuit

$$C_0' = A + S(b_2, b_1),$$

where S is an arc through M. According to the condition (5.1.2) each inner bridge for C_0' can have at most one attachment on $S(b_1, b_2)$.

1. There is some bridge B_0' for C_0' which is attached at d_1 and d_2. It cannot be attached only at d_1 and d_2 because then it would be a γ-bridge for K. Thus B_0' has just one attachment s_0 on S. There can only be one such bridge B_0'. All other inner bridges for C_0' are B_1'-bridges attached at d_1 and some vertex s_1 on S, or B_2'-bridges, attached at d_2 and some vertex s_2 on S. The vertex s_0 must separate the sets $\{s_1\}$ and $\{s_2\}$ (see Fig. 5.2.3).

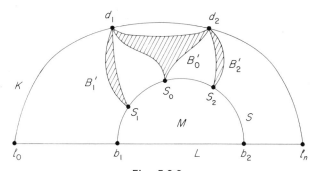

Fig. 5.2.3.

We apply Lemma 5.2.1 and construct a circuit J in (5.2.12) satisfying the conditions (5.2.3) and (5.2.4). Since s_0 lies on a minimal circuit for A, one can select J such that it passes through s_0. But then there can be no exceptional bridges for J with respect to C_0' and A. This is evident for the δ_0- and δ_1-bridges since there are only two possible attachments d_1

and d_2 on $[A]$. An ε-bridge must include a section of $S(b_1, b_2)$. Since s_0 lies on J, this must either be a section of $S(b_1, s_0)$ or a section of $S(s_0, b_2)$. But such an ε-bridge cannot be exceptional since it has only one attachment on $[A]$, namely, d_1 or d_2. The bridges for J having edges in common with $L(b_1, b_2)$ are γ-bridges and have just two attachments according to Lemma 5.2.1.

2. There is no bridge B_0' for C_0' which is attached at d_1 and d_2. There are then only B_1'-bridges and B_2'-bridges as defined above. Still there must exist a vertex s_0 on S such that it separates the two attachment sets $\{s_1\}$ and $\{s_2\}$. Again we use Lemma 1 to construct the circuit J such that it passes through s_0. By the same argument as before one sees that J has no exceptional bridges.

The proof of Theorem 5.2.1 is now completed as follows: For each exceptional complex M we replace its L-section $L(b_1, b_2)$ in K by the corresponding arc $J(b_1, b_2)$ in (5.2.12) with the properties described in the preceding. The resulting new circuit K' has no exceptional bridges.

One may add to the formulation of Theorem 5.2.1 that the circuit K can be constructed such that the two edges E and E' are traversed in the same direction on K as on the minimal circuit C_1.

An immediate consequence of Theorem 5.2.1 is the interesting result of Theorem 5.2.2.

Theorem 5.2.2. A planar graph which cannot be separated by three or fewer vertices has a Hamilton circuit.

CHAPTER 6 | *COLORATIONS*

6.1. Types of Coloration

An arbitrary graph G is said to be *vertex colorable* in k colors when its vertex set V can be decomposed into k disjoint sets

$$V = C_1 + C_2 + \cdots + C_k \tag{6.1.1}$$

such that no edges connect vertices in the same set, that is, the sets C_i are *independent* in G. The decomposition (6.1.1) defines a *color function* $f(v)$ for the vertices v of G when one puts $f(v) = i$, when $v \in C_i$.

Then no vertices with the same *color value* i are connected by an edge. Since the numbering in (6.1.1) may be chosen arbitrarily, any permutation of the values of $f(v)$ also defines a color function. This we shall consider essentially the same coloration.

The smallest number k such that G is k-colorable is the vertex coloration number $\varkappa(G)$. We examined some properties of this number on Ore ([1], Chapter 14). When G is the complete graph on n vertices, one has $\varkappa(G) = n$; when G is the null-graph, that is, has no edges, then $\varkappa(G) = 1$.

There exist analogous concepts for the edges. An *edge coloration* is a decomposition of the edges in G into l classes

$$G = H_1 + H_2 + \cdots + H_l \tag{6.1.2}$$

where no edges in the same class have vertices in common. This may be considered as a coloration of the edges such that no edges with the same color are incident. Equivalently, (6.1.2) represents a decomposition of G into edge disjoint subgraphs H_i such that in H_i

$$\rho_i(v) \leqq 1$$

75

for each vertex v. When ρ_1 is the maximal valence, it is evident that $l \geq \rho_1$. The smallest number l for any edge coloration is the *edge colora-tion number* $\varepsilon(G)$.

For planar graphs, one has the possibility for a third coloration, the *face coloration* of G. This is a decomposition of the set V_F of all faces into disjoint families,

$$V_F = K_1 + K_2 + \cdots + K_m, \qquad (6.1.3)$$

where no family K_i includes adjoining faces, that is, faces with a common boundary edge. The decomposition (6.1.3) may be considered to be a coloring of the faces in G such that adjoining faces always have different colors. As before, a color function for the faces is defined by the decompo-sition. The face coloration number $\varphi(G)$ is the minimal number m in any face coloration (6.1.3).

In considering face colorations, we recall that any acyclic edge lies within a single face surrounding it on both sides. Thus, for face colora-tions, one may assume that all edges are circuit edges. Dually, by vertex colorations, one may assume that there are no loops.

From the duality for planar graphs one obtains the following theorem.

Theorem 6.1.1. A face coloration of a planar graph corresponds under the duality to a vertex coloration for the dual graph G^* and a vertex colora-tion of G corresponds to a face coloration of G^*.

Proof: In each face F of G lies a unique vertex $m(F)$ of G^*. We assign the same color to $m(F)$ and F. This is readily seen to give a vertex colora-tion for G^*. Since each vertex v of G lies in a unique face F^* in G^*, the analogous result follows for a vertex coloring.

When a color is assigned to each edge in G, not necessarily an edge coloration, then a color is assigned to the edges in G^* when one gives E in G the same color as its corresponding edge E^* in G^*. This we may call the *natural color correspondence* between G and G^*.

Theorem 6.1.2. An edge coloration of G under the natural color corres-pondence yields a color assignment to the edges in G^* in which all edges on the boundary of a face have different colors.

Proof: The edges from a vertex v in G under the duality correspond to the boundary edges of the face F^* in G^* which contains v.

6.2. Two Colors

In the simple case of only two colors the coloring problem is readily solvable in all three types of coloring. For a vertex coloring in two colors the vertex set V decomposes into two disjoint sets $V = C_1 + C_2$ where all edges in G connect a vertex in C_1 with a vertex in C_2.

Theorem 6.2.1. A graph has a vertex coloration in two colors if, and only if, it is bipartite.

By an edge coloration in two colors the decomposition (6.1.2) takes the form $G = H_1 + H_2$ where the local degrees in H_1 and H_2 are, at most, one. This means that G is a graph in which the local degrees are, at most, two, so that the connected components are arcs and circuits. In any such arc or circuit the colors of the edges must alternate. Thus we have the next theorem.

Theorem 6.2.2. A graph is edge colorable in two colors if, and only if, its connected components are circuits with an even number of edges, or arcs.

For face coloring we have Theorem 6.2.3.

Theorem 6.2.3. A graph has a face coloration in two colors if, and only if, all its valences are even, that is, the components of G are Euler graphs.

According to Theorem 6.1.1, this theorem is a consequence of Theorem 6.2.4.

Theorem 6.2.4. A planar graph is bipartite if, and only if, its dual has even valences.

Proof: When all circuits in G have even lengths, the face boundaries also have even lengths and so the dual has even valences. Conversely, when G^* has even valences, the face boundaries in G have even lengths so all circuits are even.

Let us mention an example of a class of graphs which can be face colored in two colors. Denote by $\{J_i\}$ a finite family of closed Jordan curves which may intersect, but in which no two curves have a common arc. The graph whose vertices are their intersections and whose edges are the curve sections connecting them is face colorable in two colors (Fig. 6.2.1).

It is evident that in this case the valences are even. As a special case the curves may be taken to be circles. Similarly one sees that any

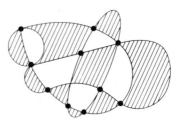

Fig. 6.2.1.

configuration of infinite straight lines divides the plane into faces which may be colored in two colors (Fig. 6.2.2). The problem is reduced to the preceding by projecting the plane stereographically upon a sphere.

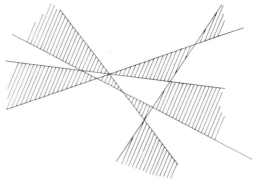

Fig. 6.2.2.

To the preceding results we add the following theorem.

Theorem 6.2.5. Let G be a graph with no faces bounded by two edges and no vertices with valence $\rho(v) = 2$. Then G cannot be both face colored and vertex colored in two colors.

Proof: For G to be both vertex and face colorable in two colors it is necessary and sufficient that all vertices have even degree and all faces be bounded by an even number of edges. However, under the given conditions this is not possible according to Theorem 4.1.3.

6.3. Reductions

Since the coloration problem has been solved for the case of two colors, from now on we are mainly interested in colorations with $k \geqq 3$ colors.

We shall point out a couple of simple reductions which can always be supposed as having been made in the graphs to be colored.

Theorem 6.3.1. A planar graph is face or vertex colorable in k colors if and only if its connected components have this property.

Proof: The statement is immediate for a vertex coloring. In the case of a face coloring let G_1 be one of the connected components in the graph G under consideration. We then have a disjoint decomposition $G = G_1 + G_2$ and G_1 will be located within one of the faces F of G_2. When G_1 and G_2 are colored in k colors, one may select the color for F in G_2 such that it coincides with the color of the infinite face in G_1. By combination of the two colorings a coloring for G is obtained. By repeated applications, one sees that from a coloration of the components one obtains a coloration of G and vice versa.

A similar argument applies to the lobe graphs of G since any two of them have at most a vertex in common.

Theorem 6.3.2. A planar graph is face or vertex colorable in k colors if and only if its lobe graphs are so colorable.

The two preceding theorems show that the coloration problem can be restricted to connected graphs without separating vertices; hence the face boundaries are minimal circuits.

Theorem 6.3.3. By a vertex coloration, one can assume that there are no multiple edges; and by a face coloration that no two faces have more than one boundary edge in common.

Proof: The statement is again evident for the vertex coloration. By the face coloration suppose that the two faces F_1 and F_2 have the two common boundary edges E_1 and E_2. In the case where E_1 and E_2 are incident (see Fig. 6.3.1),

$$E_1 = (a_1, a_0), \qquad E_2 = (a_2, a_0)$$

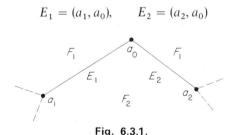

Fig. 6.3.1.

we construct a new graph G_0 by considering the arc $E_1 + E_2$ to be a single edge E_0 in G_0. Evidently G and G_0 are face colorable at the same time.

Suppose next that E_1 and E_2 have no common end points,

$$E_1 = (a_1, a_2), \qquad E_2 = (a_3, a_4).$$

The graph consists of two parts A and B connected only by the two edges E_1 and E_2 (see Fig. 6.3.2(a)).

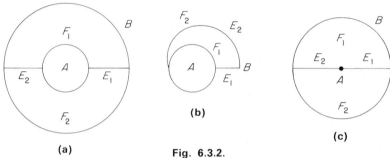

(a)   (b)   (c)

Fig. 6.3.2.

From G we derive two new graphs G_A and G_B obtained, respectively, by contracting B and A to single vertices (Fig. 6.3.2.(b, c)). It is clear that G_A and G_B are face colorable in the same colors as G. Conversely, when G_A and G_B are face colorable in $k \geq 3$ colors, the two faces F_1 and F_2 have different colors. We may name them α and β in both. Then the two colorings may be fitted together to give a face coloring for G.

Theorem 6.3.3 can be given the stronger form as follows.

Theorem 6.3.4. By a vertex coloration one can assume that G cannot be separated by two vertices a_1 and a_2 which are connected by an edge $E = (a_1, a_2)$.

By a face coloration one can assume that two faces with a common boundary edge $E = (a_1, a_2)$ have no further vertices in common.

Proof: In the case of a vertex coloration, let us suppose that G is separable into two parts A and B by the vertices a_1 and a_2 connected by the edge E as in Fig. 6.3.3. A coloration of G gives a coloration of the subgraphs $A + E$, $B + E$. Conversely, in any vertex coloration of these graphs the vertices a_1 and a_2 must have different colors and so they can be fitted together to a coloration of G.

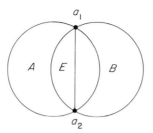

Fig. 6.3.3.

In the case of a face coloration, we suppose that the neighboring faces F_1 and F_2 in addition to the common boundary edge $E = (a_1, a_2)$ also have the corner a_3 in common (see Fig. 6.3.4).

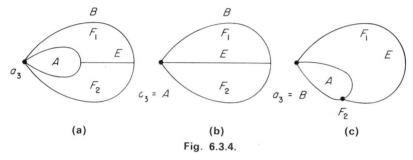

(a) **(b)** **(c)**

Fig. 6.3.4.

Here again G decomposes into two parts A and B connected by E and by the vertex a_3. As before, we obtain the graphs G_B and G_A, respectively, by contracting A and B to the single vertex a_3. Face colorations of G_A and G_B can be combined into a coloration of G.

After the preceding observations, it is natural to consider the case where G is separable by two vertices a and b into two edge disjoint components A and B.

$$G = A + B, \qquad A \cap B = \{a, b\}. \qquad (6.3.1)$$

After the reductions in Theorem 6.3.1 and Theorem 6.3.2 one may suppose that G is connected and does not have separating vertices. This implies that the components A and B are connected (see Fig. 6.3.5).

The graphs A and B may have separating edges or vertices. But the *augmented components*,

$$A' = A + E_A, \qquad B' = B + E_B, \qquad (6.3.2)$$

obtained by adjoining a new edge E_A and E_B from a to b in A and B,

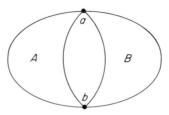

Fig. 6.3.5.

respectively, cannot be separated by a single vertex. We may draw E_A and E_B such that they lie on the boundary of the infinite face in both cases (see Fig. 6.3.6). We can now prove Theorem 6.3.5.

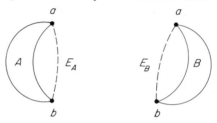

Fig. 6.3.6.

Theorem 6.3.5. When the augmented components (6.3.2) are vertex or face colorable in $k \geq 3$ colors then the recombined graph G in (6.3.1) is colorable in the same way.

Proof: When vertex colorings of A' and B' are given, the vertices a and b have different colors in each since they are connected by an edge. Thus, the colorations may be combined to a coloration of G. By a face coloring of A' and B' the faces on both sides of E_A and E_B are distinct, making it possible to combine the colorations to a coloration for G.

It should be noted in connection with this theorem that the coloring of G is not equivalent to the coloring of the component graphs since a coloring of G may not induce a coloring of A' and B'.

The fact that G is not separable by two vertices can be expressed by stating that the faces in G are *completely distinct*; that is, when F_1 and F_2 have no common boundary edge, they have, at most, one corner in common, and if they have a common boundary edge, they have no common corners not on E.

Let us make a further remark in connection with the formulation of Theorem 6.3.4. Let

$$C_n = (a_1, a_2, \ldots, a_n) \tag{6.3.3}$$

be some circuit in G. An edge $D = (a_i, a_j)$ connecting nonconsecutive vertices a_i and a_j is a *diagonal* for C_n.

Theorem 6.3.6. By vertex colorings, one can assume that no face boundary has a diagonal. Dually, by face colorings one can assume that no two nonadjoining angles at a vertex belong to faces with a common boundary edge.

Proof: If $D = (a_i, a_j)$ is a diagonal for the face boundary C_n, the two vertices a_i and a_j separate G and they are connected by an edge. The dual statement also follows from Theorem 6.3.4.

Suppose next that $\rho(a_2) = 2$ for the valence of some vertex a_0 so that there are just two edges

$$E_1 = (a_1, a_0), \qquad E_2 = (a_2, a_0)$$

at a_0. We *contract* these two edges to a single new edge $E_{12} = (a_1, a_2)$. The dual operation consists in the removal of one edge from the boundary of a face F with just two boundary edges.

Theorem 6.3.7. When the contracted graph G_1 is vertex colorable in $k \geq 3$ colors, so is the original graph and analogously for a dual contraction.

Proof: One retains the colors of the vertices in G_1 also in G, and gives a_0 a color different from those at a_1 and a_2. The dual statement is also immediate.

An important reduction for vertex colorations is based upon the *coalescence operation* on vertices. Let a_i and a_j be two nonconsecutive vertices on the boundary C_n, $n \geq 4$, in (6.3.3) for some face F. By coalescing a_i and a_j into a single vertex a one obtains a new planar graph G_1 with one fewer vertex and one more face. Suppose one has a vertex coloring for G_1. Then by the reverse operation of *splitting* or *separating* the vertex $a = a_i = a_j$ in G_1 one returns to the original graph G. When the colors of G_1 are retained in G, one obtains a coloration of G in which a_i and a_j have the same color. This is a proper coloration of G except in the case where there exists a diagonal edge (a_i, a_j) in G connecting a_i and a_j. According to Theorem 6.3.6, one can assume that the graph is already so reduced that no face diagonals exist; hence there is no restriction in the choice of a_i and a_j on the face boundary. We observe, however, that even when such a preparatory reduction has not been made a coalescence can still be achieved for any face with $n \geq 4$ edges.

When there exists a diagonal $D = (a_i, a_j)$, one selects another pair of vertices a_k and a_l, lying one each on the two sections $C_n(a_i, a_j)$ of C_n. Then there can be no diagonal $D_1 = (a_k, a_l)$ for it would have to cross D. Thus, by repeated use of the coalescence operation one can reduce the graph to the case where all faces are triangles. We mention also that the splitting of a vertex with $\rho(v) \geq 4$ edges is the dual of the coalescence operation. It can be performed with respect to two nonadjacent faces F_1 and F_2 having a corner at v provided F_1 and F_2 have no common boundary edges. When the split graph G_1 is face colored, one obtains a coloration also for G in which F_1 and F_2 have the same color.

6.4. The Five-Color Theorem

This section shall in the main be devoted to the proof of the *five-color theorem*.

Theorem 6.4.1. Any planar graph can be face (or vertex) colored in five colors.

The proof depends on a series of reductions of the face (vertex) coloring problem. In general, we shall say that a graph G is *reducible for k colors* when a coloring of G can be deduced from a coloring of a graph G_1 with a smaller number of edges in $k_1 \leq k$ colors. The first of these reductions is given by Theorem 6.4.2.

Theorem 6.4.2. A graph is reducible for $k \geq 3$ colors when it includes a face with only two boundary edges.

Proof: Let $A = (a, b)$ and $B = (a, b)$ be the two boundary edges of a face F_0 in G. These two edges lie on the boundary of two other faces F_A and F_B which may possibly coincide (see Fig. 6.4.1). The graph G_1 is obtained by eliminating A from G. Then one of the faces in G_1 will be $F_0 + F_A$ while the others will remain as in G. If the graph G_1 is colorable in $k \geq 3$ colors, the faces $F_0 + F_A$ and F_B may have the colors α and β, respectively. When the edge A is reintroduced, one can give F_0 a color γ different from α and β while the colors of the other faces of G_1 are left unchanged. This gives a k-coloration of G.

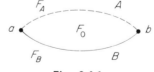

Fig. 6.4.1.

Theorem 6.4.3. A graph is reducible for $k \geq 4$ colors if it has a triangular face.

Proof: Let F_0 be a face in G with the three boundary edges $A = (a, b)$, $B = (b, c)$, $C = (c, a)$. Each of them belongs to the boundary of some other face which we denote, respectively, by F_A, F_B, F_C; they may possibly coincide. We obtain the graph G_1 by eliminating the edge A from G (Fig. 6.4.2). This merges the faces F_0 and F_A into a single face

$$F_A' = F_0 + F_A.$$

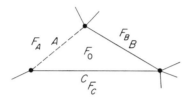

Fig. 6.4.2.

When G_1 is colored in k colors, let F_A' have the color α while F_B and F_C have the colors β and γ, respectively. When A is reintroduced, a fourth color δ different from α, β, γ may be assigned to F_0 since $k \geq 4$. The other faces retain their colors as in G_1. Through this operation a k-coloration of G is obtained.

Theorem 6.4.4. A graph is reducible for $\mathbf{k} \geq 4$ colors when it has a quadrilateral face.

Proof: The boundary edges of the quadrilateral face F_0 may be A, B, C, D. The other faces bounded by them are F_A, F_B, F_C, F_D, possibly not all different. We eliminate the edges A and C from G to obtain a graph G_1 in which F_A, F_C and F_0 coalesce into the single face

$$F_0' = F_0 + F_A + F_C.$$

Suppose there exists a k-coloration of G_1 in which the faces F_0', F_B, F_D have the colors α, β, γ, respectively. We reintroduce the edges A and C and give the face F_0 a fourth color δ while F_A and F_C retain their color α from G_1. This produces a k-coloration for G.

However, the method breaks down if F_A and F_C should happen to be faces with a boundary edge E in common because when we are not permitted to assign both faces the color α in G (Fig. 6.4.3). But when F_A

and F_C have a common boundary edge E, it is clear that this cannot occur for the two faces F_B and F_D. Thus in this case the pair of opposite edges B and D may be used to reduce G.

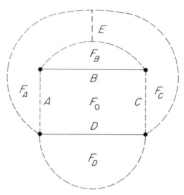

Fig. 6.4.3.

Theorem 6.4.5. A graph is reducible for $k \geq 5$ colors when it has a pentagon.

Proof: The boundary edges of the pentagonal face F_0 shall be A, B, C, D, E; the adjoining faces we denote by

$$F_A, F_B, F_C, F_D, F_E.$$

By the same argument as that used in the preceding proof it follows that for at least one pair of opposite edges, say A and C, the corresponding faces F_A and F_C have no common boundary edge. We eliminate A and C from G to obtain G_1. In G_1 the three faces F_0, F_A, F_C coalesce into a single one, $F_0' = F_0 + F_A + F_C$ (see Fig. 6.4.4). Suppose there exists a

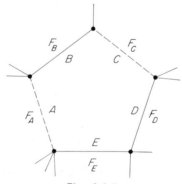

Fig. 6.4.4.

k-coloration of G_1 in which F_0' has the color α while F_B, F_D, F_E, respectively, have the colors β, γ, δ. This produces a k-coloration of G when A and C are restored and a fifth color ε is assigned to F_0.

The proof of the five-color theorem is now readily completed. According to Theorems 6.3.1 and 6.3.2 the graph to be 5-colored can be assumed to be connected and without separating vertices. Theorem 6.3.3 shows that one can suppose $\rho(v) \geq 3$ for each valence; and similarly $\rho^*(F) \geq 3$ according to Theorem 6.4.2. But then Theorem 4.1.4 establishes that the graph has at least one face with at most five boundary edges. This means that the five-coloring problem can always be reduced to the trivial case of no circuits.

6.5. The Theorem of Brooks

Let G be an arbitrary graph and

$$\rho = \max \rho(v), \qquad v \in V$$

the maximal valence. Then G can be vertex colored in $\rho + 1$ colors. To see this we construct G stepwise, in each step adding a vertex v and all those edges from v which connect it with the previously constructed part. Since one adds at most ρ edges v can be given a color $\varkappa(v)$ different from those already assigned to the end points of the added edges.

This result has been improved upon by Brooks as in Theorem 6.5.1.

Theorem 6.5.1. Let G be a connected graph, not a complete graph, and ρ its maximal valence. Then G can be vertex colored in ρ colors.

The case where G is a complete graph is evidently exceptional since $\rho + 1$ colors are required. We begin the proof of Theorem 6.5.1 by performing the reductions of Section 6.3. We can assume that G has no separating vertex v_0 since after the separation each of the two components has a valence less than ρ at v_0, hence the theorem applies to each component. The same argument applies when G is separated by two vertices connected by an edge. When the two separating vertices a and b are not connected by the edge $E = (a, b)$, we form the augmented components $A + E$ and $B + E$ as in (6.3.2). The theorem applies to each component and their colorations can be combined to a ρ-coloration of the vertices in G. The only complication arises when one of the augmented components, say $A + E$, becomes a complete graph. Then A can be colored in ρ colors such that a and b have the same colors $\varkappa(a) = \varkappa(b)$. Under these conditions there is just one edge (a, b_1) and (b, b_2) in B at the vertices a

and b, respectively. We coalesce a and b and apply the theorem to the reduced graph B'. When a and b are separated again, retaining the same color, the colorations of A and B can be combined.

After these preliminary reductions one may suppose that G cannot be separated by two vertices. According to the initial observation G can be vertex colored in $\rho + 1$ colors, $\varkappa_0, \varkappa_1, \ldots, \varkappa_\rho$. We shall perform a series of recolorations of G such that the color $\varkappa_0$ becomes superfluous. In each step of this process only the color of a single vertex is changed.

1. If $\rho(v) < \rho$ for a vertex v with the color $\varkappa(v) = \varkappa_0$, then we may select a different color at v.

2. Let $E = (a_1, a_2)$ be some edge for which $\varkappa(a_1) = \varkappa_0$. We consider the graph $G - E$. Here we can change the color at a_1 by paragraph 1 into $\varkappa(a_1) \neq \varkappa_0$. If for this new color $\varkappa(a_1) \neq \varkappa(a_2)$, the edge E can be reintroduced directly. If $\varkappa(a_1) = \varkappa(a_2)$, we recolor a_2 before adding E so that the new color $\varkappa'(a_2) \neq \varkappa(a_1)$, possibly one may have to use the color $\varkappa'(a_2) = \varkappa_0$.

3. Let $A(a_0, a_n)$ be an arc in G. By repeated applications of paragraph 2 we can recolor G such that all vertices in A except a_0 have colors different from $\varkappa_0$, while the colors of the vertices not on A remain unchanged.

4. We select an arbitrary vertex a_0. When paragraph 3 is applied to all arcs from a_0, one can achieve that a_0 is the only vertex with the color $\varkappa_0$.

5. If there should be any vertex a_0 such that $\rho(a_0) < \rho$, we can select a_0 as the only vertex with $\varkappa(a_0) = \varkappa_0$ in paragraph 4. Its color may then be changed so that G is colorable in ρ colors. It may, therefore, be assumed that G is regular with valence ρ.

6. Since G is not a complete graph, there is a pair of vertices a_0 and b_0 not connected by an edge. We arrange our coloration such that a_0 is the only vertex with $\varkappa(a_0) = \varkappa_0$. At b_0 there will be at least two edges going to vertices with the same color $\varkappa(c_1) = \varkappa(c_2)$. Since G is 3-vertex connected, there is an arc $A(a_0, b_0)$ not passing through c_1 or c_2. We recolor G with respect to A with b_0 as the only vertex of color $\varkappa_0$. Then the color at b_0 can be changed so that it is not equal to $\varkappa_0$.

Among the immediate applications of Theorem 6.5.1 we notice the following one.

Theorem 6.5.2. Every regular graph of valence 3 is vertex colorable in three colors, except for the complete graph on four vertices.

When applied to planar graphs and in the dual form, we may make the following statement.

Theorem 6.5.3. Every maximal planar graph, except the tetrahedron graph, is face colorable in three colors.

A planar graph whose faces have, at most, four boundary edges is face colorable in four colors.

CHAPTER 7

COLOR FUNCTIONS

7.1. Vertex Coloration

We suppose that a coloration of the vertices of a graph is given. The colors we may consider to be the values of a *color function* $f(v)$ defined for the vertices v. The values $f(v)$ are commonly taken to be integers. We shall extend this definition slightly and assume that the values belong to a modul, that is, an algebraic system M in which addition and subtraction are defined. We call M a *color modul* for G. We assume that the color function is *normalized*, that is $f(v_0) = 0$ for some vertex v_0. The color modul in our applications is usually finite. The number of elements in M we denote by $v(M)$.

A vertex coloring shall be called *imprimitive* when there are two color values α and β such that no vertex with the color α is connected by an edge to a vertex with the color β. When this is the case, one can identify the two colors α and β and still have a vertex coloration of G in a smaller number of colors. Thus, we may always assume that the coloration is *primitive*, that is, no such reduction is possible; in other words, for any pair of color values α and β, there exists at least one edge $E = (v_1, v_2)$ for which

$$f(v_1) = \alpha, \qquad f(v_2) = \beta.$$

From now on, a fixed direction shall be assigned to each edge in G. Any function $f(v)$ assigning a value in M to each vertex v in G shall be called a *vertex function*. Similarly, any function $g(E)$ assigning a value to each edge E in G is an *edge function*. A *directed* edge function $g(E)$ assigns the values $\pm g(E)$ to each edge where the positive sign is used for E taken in its direction in G and the negative sign for E taken in the reverse

direction. These directed edge functions we apply to edge sequences in
G. We assign to any edge sequence,

$$S = E_0, E_1, \ldots, E_{n-1}, \qquad E_i = (a_i, a_{i+1}), \qquad (7.1.1)$$

the value

$$g(S) = \sum g(E_i), \qquad (7.1.2)$$

where $g(E_i)$ is given the positive or negative sign depending on whether
E_i occurs in S with the same or the opposite direction of that in G. For
the reverse sequence S' to S in (7.1.1), one therefore has the value

$$g(S') = -g(S).$$

When $f(v)$ is a vertex function for G, it defines an *induced directed edge
function* $g(E)$ whose values are

$$g(E) = f(v_2) - f(v_1), \qquad E = (v_1, v_2) \qquad (7.1.3)$$

when E is directed from v_1 to v_2.

We make the following observation.

Theorem 7.1.1. Let $f(v)$ be a vertex function. A necessary and sufficient
condition that $f(v)$ be a color function, is that the induced edge function
be different from zero

$$g(E) \neq 0, \qquad (7.1.4)$$

for every edge E.

Proof: The definition of a color function $f(v)$ is that

$$f(v_1) \neq f(v_2), \qquad E = (v_1, v_2)$$

for every edge E. When $f(v)$ is a primitive color function, the difference of
any pair of color values $f(v)$ and $f(v')$ must occur in M.

Next denote by $g(E)$ an arbitrary directed edge function in the connected graph G. We select a fixed vertex a_0. For any vertex $a = a_n$ there
exist sequences S as in (7.1.1) from a_0 to a_n. The corresponding sequence
value (7.1.2),

$$f(a) = g(a_0, a_n; S), \qquad (7.1.5)$$

will usually depend on S. If it is always independent of S, we call $g(E)$ a
regular edge function and $f(a)$ as defined in (7.1.5) is the *induced vertex
function*. The definition shows that when $g(E)$ is a regular edge function

with the induced vertex function $f(a)$ then $g(E)$ is the directed edge function induced by $f(a)$.

Theorem 7.1.2. A necessary and sufficient condition that the directed edge function $g(E)$ be regular is that for every circuit in G,

$$g(C) = 0. \tag{7.1.6}$$

Proof: The necessity of the condition (7.1.6) is immediate. To prove the sufficiency let S_1 and S_2 be two edge sequences from a_0 to the vertex a_n. The equality

$$f(a) = g(a_0, a_n ; S_1) = g(a_0, a_n ; S_2)$$

is equivalent to

$$g(a_0, a_0 ; S_1 + S_2') = 0$$

where $S_1 + S_2'$ is the cyclic edge sequence returning to a_0 obtained by combining S_1 with the reverse sequence S_2' of S_2. Any cyclic edge sequence can be combined from circuits so that it is sufficient that (7.1.6) hold for all circuits.

We notice that the regular edge function induces a color function $f(a)$ in (7.1.5) if, and only if, (7.1.4) holds.

7.2. The Dual Theory

Suppose now that G is a planar graph. Let C be a circuit through two vertices v_1 and v_2 and $T(v_1, v_2)$ a transversal for C. Then the condition (7.1.6) will hold for C if, and only if, it is fulfilled for the two circuits

$$C_1 = C(v_1, v_2) + T(v_2, v_1),$$
$$C_2 = C(v_2, v_1) + T(v_1, v_2).$$

By repetitions of such divisions one obtains the following theorem.

Theorem 7.2.1. An edge function in a planar graph is regular if, and only if, the condition (7.1.6) holds for all minimal circuits.

One could have required instead that (7.1.6) shall hold for all face boundaries.

For a planar graph, the preceding considerations on vertex coloration have a dual form in regard to the coloring of the faces. Here we examine a *face function* $f^*(F)$ for the faces F in G. This is a color function for the faces when $f^*(F_1) \neq f^*(F_2)$ whenever F_1 and F_2 have a common boundary edge.

The original graph G had a direction assigned to its edges. This direction also induces a direction for the edges in the dual graph G^*. Each directed edge $E = (v_1, v_2)$ in G crosses a unique edge $E^* = (F_1, F_2)$ in G^*. We assign to this edge E^* a direction such that it crosses E from left to right when one proceeds in the positive direction on E. Conversely, the direction on E^* induces a unique direction in G when E is the direction from right to left when one follows E^* in its positive direction (Fig. 7.2.1).

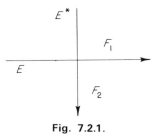

Fig. 7.2.1.

We assume in the following that this induced direction from G is used in G^*. As before, a face function $f^*(F)$ defines an edge function in G^* when one puts

$$g^*(E^*) = f^*(F_2) - f^*(F_1), \qquad E^* = (F_1, F_2) \qquad (7.2.1)$$

for neighboring faces F_1 and F_2.

Suppose now that $g^*(E^*)$ is an arbitrary edge function for G^*. Such an edge function also becomes an edge function for G when one defines

$$g(E) = g^*(E^*), \qquad (7.2.2)$$

where E is the edge in G corresponding to the dual edge E^* in G^*. The boundary C^* of a face F^* in G^* will then have a value $g^*(C^*)$ defined as in the preceding section for any edge sequence.

Under the duality correspondence the edges in C^* correspond to the edges in the star graph $St(u)$ in G, where u is the unique vertex of G lying within F^*. According to (7.2.2) one then has

$$g^*(C^*) = g(St(u)) = \sum g(E_i) \qquad (7.2.3)$$

where $E_i = (u, u_i)$ runs through the edges in $St(u)$. Here the sign of each term ± 1 depends on whether the direction of E_i from u coincides with the direction in G or not. The loops at u correspond to acyclic edges in C^*. They occur twice in the sum (7.2.3) with opposite signs so they could have been omitted in the expression.

Again one may ask when an edge function $g^*(E^*)$ is regular in the previous sense. One selects a fixed face F_0 and constructs the sum analogous to (7.1.2)

$$g^*(S^*) = \sum g^*(E^*) = f^*(F_0, F; S^*) \qquad (7.2.4)$$

from F_0 to some face F along an edge sequence S^*. The edge function $g^*(E^*)$ is regular if, and only if, the sum (7.2.4) is independent of the connecting edge sequence S^* from F_0 to F. The preceding discussion shows the following relationship.

Theorem 7.2.2. Let (7.2.2) be an edge function for G and G^*. In order that it define a regular face function $f^*(F)$ in G^* it is necessary and sufficient that for any star graph $St(u)$ in G one must have

$$g(St(u)) = 0. \qquad (7.2.5)$$

One may notice that the conditions (7.2.5) are not independent. When one takes the sum of all expressions (7.2.5), one obtains each term $g(E_i)$ twice, and with opposite signs. Loops may be disregarded as we have just observed. Thus the conditions (7.2.5) hold when they are true for all but a single vertex.

A regular edge function in G^* is a face color function when in addition to the conditions (7.2.5) $g^*(E^*) \neq 0$ for every edge E^* which is not acyclic and $g^*(E^*) = 0$ for the acyclic edges.

7.3. Color-Directed Graphs

Suppose that the color values in a coloration are ordered in some manner. Then both a vertex and a face coloration assigns a direction to the edges of G. For a vertex coloration we give an edge the direction $E = (v_1, v_2)$ when $f(v_1) < f(v_2)$ for the corresponding vertex colors. Only the loops are undirected.

Similarly for a face coloration let $f^*(F_1) < f^*(F_2)$ be the colors assigned to the two faces F_1 and F_2 on whose boundaries the edge E is located. We then give E such a direction that the face F_2 lies on the right and F_1 on the left in the positive direction (see Fig. 7.2.1). Here the acyclic edges in G remain undirected.

A directed graph is *acyclic* when it has no directed circuits; it is *cyclic* when each edge lies on a directed cyclic path [see Ore [1] (Section 8.1)].

Theorem 7.3.1. When G is a graph without loops, any vertex coloration induces an acyclic direction in G.

When G is a graph without separating edges, any face coloring induces a cyclic direction in G.

Proof: It is clear that no directed circuit can be defined by a vertex coloring since any directed arc passes through vertices with decreasing color values.

To prove the second part of the theorem we may assume that G is connected and without separating vertices. We notice that when F_0 is any face with the lowest color value β_0, the boundary edges of F_0 must all have the same cyclic direction. This observation we use to prove by induction that for any color directed edge $E = (a, b)$ there also exists a directed edge sequence $S(b, a)$. We assume that this property is established for all edges whose smallest neighboring face color is less than β. Let E be an edge lying on the boundary circuits C_1 and C_2 of two faces F_1 and F_2 having the colors β and $\alpha > \beta$, respectively (see Fig. 7.3.1).

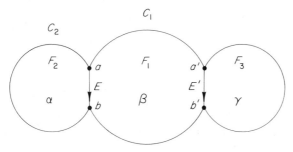

Fig. 7.3.1.

The circuit arc $C_1(b, a)$ will consist of a number of boundary edges $E' = (a', b')$ for F_1. It is then sufficient to prove the statement for all those edges E' which appear in opposite direction on C_1 from that defined by E. Such an edge E' lies on the boundary of F_1 and another face F_3 with the color γ. Since E' appears in the reverse direction on C_1, one must have $\gamma < \beta$. By the induction assumption there then exists a directed edge sequence $S'(a', b')$ as desired.

One can see that the following theorem is an immediate consequence of Theorem 7.3.1.

Theorem 7.3.2. Let G be a graph without loops or separating edges. Then the direction induced by a vertex coloration can never coincide with that induced by a face coloration.

One can sharpen the result that the direction induced by a vertex coloration is acyclic. Consider a circuit C in G with $v(C)$ edges and fix a circular direction on C. For some edges on C this direction coincides with the color direction; for others it is the reverse. Let $s(C)$ and $r(C)$ be the number of edges in each class so that

$$v(C) = s(C) + r(C). \tag{7.3.1}$$

In proceeding along C in the fixed direction each edge with the same direction increases the color value by at least one unit from one of its vertices to the other. The total number of increases is $s(C)$. Assume that G is colored in k colors $1, 2, \ldots, k$. Then the edges in the reverse direction correspond to a color decrease of at most $k - 1$. Since one returns to the starting point one must have

$$(k - 1)r(C) \geq s(C)$$

so that we conclude, as follows, from Theorem (7.3.1).

Theorem 7.3.3. Let G be a graph which is vertex colored in k colors. In the induced color direction, the number of reverse edges in any circuit must satisfy the condition

$$r(C) \geq \frac{1}{k} \cdot v(C). \tag{7.3.2}$$

Since each coloration of a graph induces a direction it is natural to pose the converse question: When does a direction on a graph induce a coloring? Let us examine the problem in the case of a directed graph G and a vertex coloring. We assume that *two directed edge functions,*

$$g_1(E), \qquad -g_2(E), \tag{7.3.3}$$

are defined for G. These are two values such that when E is taken in its positive direction, the first value (7.3.3) is assigned; when taken in its reverse direction, the second value is used. We assume in our case that the edge functions are positive,

$$g_1(E) \geq 0, \qquad g_2(E) \geq 0.$$

The edge functions (7.3.3) introduce a value $g(S)$ for each sequence (7.1.2) when one defines

$$g(S) = \sum g(E_i), \qquad i = 0, 1, \ldots, n - 1 \tag{7.3.4}$$

where each edge term is given the values

$$g(E_i) = g_1(E_i), \qquad g(E_i) = -g_2(E_i)$$

depending on whether the direction of E_i within S coincides with the direction in G or not. If one reverses S from a_n to a_0, another value $g(S')$ would result. In particular, to each circuit C there are assigned two values

$$g(C), \qquad g(C') \tag{7.3.5}$$

depending on the circular direction chosen.

We now select a fixed vertex a_0 and consider an arbitrary vertex $a = a_n$ connected to a_0 by some sequence S in (7.1.1). A vertex function $f(a)$ is introduced through the definition

$$f(a) = \max_s g(a_0, a_n ; S) \tag{7.3.6}$$

where S runs through all connecting sequences from a_0 to a. In order that such a maximum (7.3.6) shall exist it is necessary to assume that for every circuit C the quantities (7.3.5) satisfy the conditions

$$g(C) \leqq 0, \qquad g(C') \leqq 0. \tag{7.3.7}$$

If this condition did not hold, one could find sequences with arbitrarily high values $g(S)$ in (7.3.5) by including a circuit with a positive value $g(C)$ a sufficiently large number of times. We must assume also that the condition (7.3.7) applies to the special case where C consists of a single edge traversed in both directions. This implies that

$$g_1(E) - g_2(E) \leqq 0$$

so that we have

$$g_1(E) \leqq g_2(E). \tag{7.3.8}$$

When the conditions (7.3.7) and (7.3.8) hold, one need only consider connecting arcs S without circuits in the definition (7.3.6) for the vertex function $f(v)$.

When we now suppose in addition that $g(E)$ is a positive edge function, that is, according to (7.3.8),

$$0 < g_1(E) \leqq g_2(E), \tag{7.3.9}$$

then $f(a)$ is a color function for G. Suppose that $v \neq v'$ are neighboring vertices connected by the directed edge $E = (v, v')$. From the definition (7.3.6) one concludes

$$f(v') \geqq f(v) + g_1(E), \qquad f(v) \geqq f(v') - g_2(E)$$

and so

$$g_2(E) \geqq f(v') - f(v) \geqq g_1(E) \tag{7.3.10}$$

so that $f(v) \neq f(v')$.

Theorem 7.3.4. In the directed graph G let there be defined a pair of directed edge functions $g_1(E)$ and $g_2(E)$ satisfying (7.3.9) and (7.3.7) for all circuits. Then the maximal distance function $f(a)$ defined in (7.3.6) is a color function for G which induces the given direction.

To this result we add the following theorem.

Theorem 7.3.5. When $g_1(E)$ and $g_2(E)$ in Theorem 7.3.4 are positive integers and

$$m_0 = \max g_2(E), \tag{7.3.11}$$

then the values of $f(v)$ taken (mod $m_0 + 1$) define a vertex coloration of G in $m_0 + 1$ colors inducing the given directions.

Proof: According to (7.3.10) one still has $f(v') > f(v)$ for the positive remainders (mod $m_0 + 1$).

Theorem 7.3.5 readily leads to a result due to Minty.

Theorem 7.3.6. Suppose that the conditions (7.3.2) are satisfied for the circuits in a directed graph G. Then G is vertex colorable in k colors.

Proof: According to Theorem 7.3.5 it suffices to use the directed edge functions

$$g_1(E) = 1, \qquad g_2(E) = k - 1 = m_0.$$

The conditions (7.3.7) and (7.3.9) are then satisfied.

A dual exists to the preceding theory. In Section 3.1 we saw that to a circuit C^* in the dual graph G^* there corresponded a unique minimal separating family of edges $S = \{E\}$ consisting of the edges in G which separate the faces in C^*. When G is face color directed, the $v(S)$ edges in S are of two kinds: $r(S)$ edges pointing outward and $d(S)$ edges pointing inward. One finds as in Theorem 7.3.3 that when the faces in G are colored in k colors the condition

$$r(S) \geq \frac{1}{k} \cdot v(S) \tag{7.3.12}$$

must be satisfied for every such separating set S. Conversely, when this condition (7.3.12) holds for all S, there exists a face coloring for G in k colors.

Analogues to Theorems 7.3.4 and 7.3.5 can also be stated.

7.4. Some Special Applications

Let G be a connected graph directed such that it is mutually connected. We select a fixed vertex a_0 and denote by $S(a_0, a_n)$ a directed edge sequence from a_0 to a_n as in (7.1.1). The length $n(a_n, S)$ of this sequence usually depends on S. But it may happen that there is an integer $m \geq 2$ such that

$$n(a) \equiv n(a, S_1) \equiv n(a, S_2)(\mathrm{mod}\ m) \tag{7.4.1}$$

for any vertex $a = a_n$ and any pair of sequences S_1 and S_2. We shall prove Theorem 7.4.1.

Theorem 7.4.1. A necessary and sufficient condition that the directed distance remainder $n(a)(\mathrm{mod}\ m)$ in a mutually connected graph be independent of the connecting sequence S is that the number of edges in any directed circuit be divisible by the modul m. In this case, $n(a)$ is a vertex color function for G.

Proof: It is immediate that when the distance remainder is independent of S, it represents a color function with at most m colors. It is also clear that the condition for independence $(\mathrm{mod}\ m)$ is necessary. To prove the sufficiency we notice that when any directed circuit has a length divisible by m the same is true for any circular sequence. Now let $S_1(a_0, a_n)$ and $S_2(a_0, a_n)$ be two connecting sequences from a_0 to a_n of lengths n_1 and n_2, respectively. Since G is mutually connected, there also exists a returning sequence $S_3(a_n, a_0)$. When the length of S_3 is n_3, the circular sequences $S_1 + S_2, S_2 + S_3$ have lengths satisfying

$$n_1 + n_3 \equiv n_2 + n_3 \equiv 0(\mathrm{mod}\ m)$$

and so (7.4.1) follows.

Let us apply the preceding results to the simple case of a connected graph G, without separating edges, which is face colored in two colors. It is clear that all valences must be even. Conversely, suppose that this is the case. We define an edge function with the same value $g(E) = 1$ for each edge. The corresponding color modul consists of the number 0, 1 (mod 2). The function is regular in G^* if, and only if, the conditions (7.2.5) are fulfilled, that is, all valences are even. This is another proof of Theorem 6.2.3.

In the remaining part of this section, we shall assume that G has even valences and so a face coloring in two colors α and β. Since there are no separating edges each edge lies on the boundary of one α-face and one β-face. Thus, the number of edges in G can be expressed in the two forms

$$v_e(G) = \sum \rho_i{}^*(\alpha) = \sum \rho_j{}^*(\beta) \tag{7.4.2}$$

where the terms $\rho_i{}^*(\alpha)$ and $\rho_j{}^*(\beta)$ represent the number of boundary edges in the α-faces and β-faces, respectively.

Let us call an integer $m \geq 2$ a *face modul* for G when m divides the number of boundary edges for each face. According to Theorem 4.1.2 the face modul is restricted to the values $m = 2, 3, 4, 5$ when the valences in G are at least 3.

Theorem 7.4.2. Let G be a planar graph without separating edges in which the faces are colored in two colors. When G has a face modul m, then it has a vertex coloring in m colors.

Proof: According to Theorem 7.3.1 the face coloring induces a direction in G in which each component is mutually connected. Theorem 7.4.1 shows that it is sufficient to establish that any directed circuit in the face coloring has a length divisible by m. Let C be such a circuit and $I(C)$ its *interior graph* consisting of C and all edges of G lying inside C.

Since C is directed by the face coloring, all faces adjoining C on the inside must have the same color, say α, and all those adjoining C on the outside must have the color β. But this means that the graph $I(C)$ is colorable in two colors such that the exterior of C has the color β. All face boundaries inside C have lengths divisible by m by assumption. But then the relation (7.4.2) applied to $I(C)$ shows that also the remaining boundary C must have a length divisible by m.

Since every graph is colorable in five colors, and when $m = 2$ or $m = 4$ the vertices are colorable in two colors, the only case of interest for Theorem 7.4.2 is when $m = 3$. Thus, if a graph has even valences and the face boundaries all have lengths divisible by 3, then the vertices are colorable in three colors.

Theorem 7.4.3. A maximal planar graph has a vertex coloring in three colors if, and only if, it has a face coloring in two colors.

Proof: In a maximal planar graph all faces are triangles so that $m = 3$. Thus, if there is a face coloring in two colors, there exists a vertex coloring in three. Suppose, conversely, that G has a vertex coloring in three colors

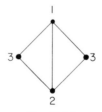

Fig. 7.4.1.

1, 2, 3. This defines a cyclic order 1, 2, 3 for each face. Correspondingly, the faces fall into two classes: those with a clockwise direction and those with a counterclockwise direction. Two neighboring faces F_1 and F_2 always have opposite character as one sees from Fig. 7.4.1, so that the two classes represent a two-coloring of the faces.

CHAPTER 8 | *FORMULATIONS OF THE FOUR-COLOR PROBLEM*

8.1. Decomposition into Three Subgraphs

We now turn to the famous *four-color problem*: Is it always possible to color the faces of a planar graph in four colors? We have already established that any graph can be face colored in five colors. On the other hand, not every graph can be face colored in three colors as one sees from the example of the tetrahedral graph (Fig. 8.1.1).

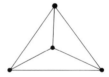

Fig. 8.1.1.

The four-color problem may be formulated in a number of different ways. Suppose that the faces in the graph G are colored in four colors, α, β, γ, δ. Since each edge is on the boundary of two neighboring faces there is associated with it a pair of colors, say α and β. The pair

$$(\alpha, \beta) = (\beta, \alpha) \qquad (8.1.1)$$

may be called the *character* of E. Thus, all edges in G fall into six *categories* according to their characters (8.1.1).

To each character (8.1.1) there exists an *opposite character* containing the two remaining colors. Let us say that the two edges E_1 and E_2 are in the same *class* when they have the same or opposite characters. In this manner, all edges in G fall into three classes, consisting, respectively, of the edges whose character belongs to one of the three types

$$(\alpha, \beta), (\gamma, \delta); \qquad (\alpha, \gamma), (\beta, \delta); \qquad (\alpha, \delta), (\beta, \gamma). \qquad (8.1.2)$$

Correspondingly one has an edge disjoint decomposition of G into three subgraphs

$$G = H_1 + H_2 + H_3. \qquad (8.1.3)$$

For some purposes, it is convenient to use the modular representation of the colors in a modul with two generators and coefficients (mod 2),

$$\alpha = 0, 0; \qquad \beta = 0, 1; \qquad \gamma = 1, 0; \qquad \delta = 1, 1.$$

In this modul the edge function $g(E)$ assigns to each edge E the sum of the color values of the adjoining faces. Thus, the three classes in (8.1.2) are characterized by the three edge values,

$$\alpha + \beta = \gamma + \delta = 0, 1,$$

$$\alpha + \gamma = \beta + \delta = 1, 0, \qquad (8.1.4)$$

$$\alpha + \delta = \beta + \gamma = 1, 1.$$

When the face color on one side of the edge is added to the edge value, one obtains the color value for the other neighboring face.

From the criterion for the regularity of the color function stated in Theorem 7.2.2 it follows: The sum of the edge values (8.1.4) at any vertex must vanish. It is easy to verify this directly also. At a vertex v the number of edges decomposes into three summands,

$$\rho(v) = \rho_1(v) + \rho_2(v) + \rho_3(v)$$

corresponding to the decomposition (8.1.3). Since the value sum at v shall be 0, 0, one obtains the congruences

$$\rho_1(v) + \rho_3(v) \equiv \rho_2(v) + \rho_3(v) \equiv 0 (\text{mod } 2).$$

This condition can be rewritten

$$\rho_1(v) \equiv \rho_2(v) \equiv \rho_3(v)(\text{mod } 2). \qquad (8.1.5)$$

On the other hand, when the conditions of (8.1.5) are fulfilled the sum of the edge values at v vanishes and a color function for the faces is defined. Thus, we have established the following result.

Theorem 8.1.1. A necessary and sufficient condition that the graph G be face colorable in four colors is that G have an edge disjoint subgraph decomposition

$$G = H_1 + H_2 + H_3 \qquad (8.1.6)$$

such that at any vertex v the number of edges from the three subgraphs either be all even or all odd.

8.2. Bipartite Dichotomy

Among the various other ways of formulating the four-color problem we mention the criterion which follows from the theorem of Minty (Theorem 7.3.6).

Theorem 8.2.1. A graph can be vertex colored in four colors if, and only if, its edges can be so directed that for every circuit and any circular direction on C the number of reverse edges is

$$r(C) \geq \tfrac{1}{4}v(C). \qquad (8.2.1)$$

If, instead of vertex coloring, one considers a face coloring in four colors, the condition (8.2.1) is replaced by an analogous condition on the number of edges in each direction in a minimal family of separating edges for the graph.

Another way of expressing the four-color conditions is by means of bipartite subgraphs. Assume that G has a face coloring in four colors α, β, γ, δ. The vertex set V^* of the dual graph G^* consists of the set of faces in G and the face coloring of G corresponds to a vertex coloring of G^* in four colors. This defines a decomposition of V^* into four disjoint sets,

$$V^* = V_\alpha^* + V_\beta^* + V_\gamma^* + V_\delta^*.$$

Each of these four-color sets is independent, that is, there are no edges in G^* joining any two of their elements. As a consequence, each of the sets $V_\alpha^* + V_\beta^*$, $V_\gamma^* + V_\delta^*$ defines a bipartite section graph in G, namely, $G^*(V_\alpha^* + V_\beta^*)$, $G^*(V_\gamma^* + V_\delta^*)$.

On the other hand, let H be a planar graph with the vertex set W. We shall say that H has a *bipartite dichotomy* when there exists a disjoint decomposition

$$W = W_1 + W_2$$

such that each of the section graphs, $H(W_1)$ and $H(W_2)$ is bipartite. It is necessary to assume that the graph have no loops. When a bipartite dichotomy exists one can color the vertices in $H(W_1)$ in two colors α and

β and the vertices in $H(W_2)$ in two other colors γ and δ to obtain a vertex coloring of H in four colors. We, therefore, can state the next theorem.

Theorem 8.2.2. A planar graph without separating edges is face colorable in four colors if, and only if, its dual has a bipartite dichotomy.

We conclude that the four color theorem is equivalent to the statement: *Any planar graph without loops has a bipartite dichotomy.*

8.3. Even Subgraphs

We shall assume, as before, that G is a graph which is face colored in four colors α, β, γ, and δ. An (α, β)-*chain* in G is a sequence of faces $F_1, F_2, \ldots, F_n$ such that each is a neighboring face to the next and the colors of the faces are alternatingly α and β. Two faces are called (α, β)-*connected* when they are both members of the same (α, β)-chain. To each given α or β-face F there exists a family $\Phi = \Phi(F; \alpha, \beta)$ consisting of all faces which are (α, β)-connected to it. We call Φ the (α, β)-*component* of F. All faces not in Φ but having a boundary edge in common with a face in Φ must be a γ or δ-face. Within each component one can therefore interchange the colors α and β of the faces and still retain a coloring of the whole graph. Such an operation shall be called an (α, β)-*interchange*. If F and F' are α or β-faces not in the same (α, β)-component, then by (α, β)-interchanges one can achieve that F and F' take any of the four-color combinations (α, α) (α, β) (β, α) (β, β).

The faces in a $\Phi(\alpha, \beta)$ component plus the boundary edges between any two of its faces form a connected domain in the plane bounded by edges in G. We may call this an (α, β)-*face*. The boundary edges for $\Phi(\alpha, \beta)$ will also be boundary edges for a (γ, δ)-*face* $\Phi(\gamma, \delta)$. Together the (α, β) and (γ, δ)-faces define a disjoint decomposition of the plane forming the faces of the subgraph H of G consisting of the boundary edges of the faces Φ. One can consider the faces in H to be colored in two colors,

$$1 = (\alpha, \beta) \qquad 2 = (\gamma, \delta).$$

As a consequence H is an even subgraph, that is, valences are even.

We shall now consider the converse problem. Given an even subgraph H of G whose faces are colored in two colors 1 and 2. When it is possible to separate this coloring further into a coloring of the faces of G in four colors? We make the preliminary observation that in an even graph all edges are circuit edges. The boundaries of the faces Φ of H are then formed by complete minimal circuits, one enclosing the whole face, the others are the boundary circuits of lobe graphs of H lying inside Φ (see Fig. 8.3.1).

A necessary condition for the faces in G lying inside of Φ to be colorable in two colors is that all vertices of G inside Φ have even valences. At a vertex v on the boundary of Φ let $\rho(\Phi, v)$ denote the number of edges of G which lie inside the face Φ. The boundary edges of Φ will in general be a

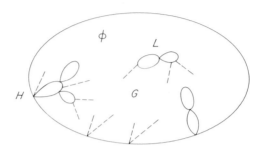

Fig. 8.3.1.

subgraph of H which falls into various disjoint components L. One of these L is defined by the edges in the minimal circuit C enclosing Φ and all the lobe graphs of H lying inside Φ but connected to C by edges in H. Another boundary component L for Φ arises from each connected component of H lying inside of Φ. When one follows any one of these boundary components L in a given direction, the α and β-faces having an edge or a vertex in common with L must follow in alternating order. Thus we conclude that when the faces of G lying inside Φ shall be colorable in two colors α and β the two conditions (8.3.1) and (8.3.2) must be fulfilled:

$$\rho(v) \equiv 0(\bmod 2) \qquad (8.3.1)$$

for each vertex v of G lying in the interior of Φ.

$$\sum \rho(\Phi; v) \equiv 0(\bmod 2), \qquad v \text{ on } L \qquad (8.3.2)$$

for each connected boundary component of Φ in H.

On the other hand we shall show that these two conditions (8.3.1) and (8.3.2) are sufficient for such an (α, β)-coloring within Φ. To illustrate the method let us suppose first that the boundary of Φ is the single minimal circuit L_0 in H. We obliterate the part of G lying outside of Φ and L_0 and select a point v_0 in this outside part of the plane. From v_0 we draw an edge to each of those vertices v on L_0 for which the number

$\rho(\Phi, v)$ is odd. We denote by G_1 the graph consisting of v_0 and its edges and that part of G which consists of L_0 and all edges on the inside of L_0. Under the given conditions G_1 is an even graph and so it can be colored in two colors α and β. This implies a corresponding coloring of the faces of G inside L_0.

A similar argument applies to the general case where there are lobe graphs of H enclosed within the minimal circuit L_0 defining Φ. Let B_1 be such a lobe graph with the boundary circuit L_1. We may select B_1 such that it is attached to the rest of H only at a single vertex v_1 (see Fig. 8.3.2.(a)).

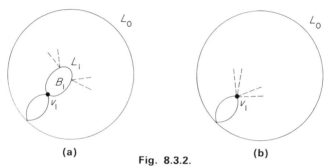

(a)   Fig. 8.3.2.   (b)

We contract the circuit L_1 to the single vertex v_1 letting each edge of G inside Φ attached to L_1 now have this attachment at v_1 (see Fig. 8.3.2.(b)). This may be done in such a way that the new graph G_1 is also planar. After the contraction the conditions (8.3.1) and (8.3.2) will remain valid for the corresponding face Φ_1 in G_1. If the faces of G_1 inside Φ_1 are colorable in two colors α and β, a similar coloring results for the faces of G inside Φ. By repeated reductions of this kind it follows that when the conditions (8.3.1) and (8.3.2) are fulfilled a two-coloring is possible.

When the two conditions (8.3.1) and (8.3.2) are satisfied for a face one may say that Φ is *totally even* with respect to G. We can then summarize in the words of Theorem 8.3.1.

Theorem 8.3.1. A necessary and sufficient condition for an even subgraph H of G to define a four coloring of the faces in G is that each face of H be totally even with respect to G.

A special case of an even subgraph is a Hamilton circuit H. It has two faces and these are totally even, since all vertices are on H and each interior or exterior edge has two end points on H. We conclude that the following theorem is true.

Theorem 8.3.2. A planar graph with a Hamilton circuit can be face colored in four colors.

When this fact is combined with the theorem of Tutte (Theorem 5.2.2), we obtain Theorem 8.3.3.

Theorem 8.3.3. A planar graph which cannot be separated by three or fewer vertices is face colorable in four colors.

8.4. Graphs with Small Face Boundaries

There are other cases in which the four-color theorem can be deduced rather easily and under fairly general conditions.

We can suppose that the graph G under consideration has been reduced as described in Section 6.3 so that it is connected and without separating vertices. These reductions, if they are possible, decrease the number of vertices, edges and faces of G. Now let F_0 be an arbitrary face with r corners

$$v_1, v_2, \ldots, v_r \tag{8.4.1}$$

and the r boundary edges

$$E_i = (v_i, v_{i+1}). \tag{8.4.2}$$

The corresponding r neighboring faces, we denote by

$$F_1, F_2, \ldots, F_r. \tag{8.4.3}$$

At each corner v_i there will be other edges different from the boundary edges of (8.4.2). We shall denote them respectively by

$$E_{i,1}, E_{i,2}, \ldots, E_{i,k_i} \qquad i = 1, 2, \ldots, r, \tag{8.4.4}$$

(see Fig. 8.4.1(a)). Their number is

$$\rho_0' = \sum_i (\rho(v_i) - 2). \tag{8.4.5}$$

Next we contract the face F_0. This contraction operation consists in drawing a new graph G' in which all the vertices v_i in (8.4.1) are replaced by a single new vertex v_0' lying inside F_0. The new edges E_{ij}' corresponding to the edges E_{ij} in (8.4.4) are given the common end point v_0' instead of the various end points v_i in (8.4.1) (see Fig. 8.4.1.(b)). The boundary edges E_i in (8.4.2) are eliminated; otherwise, the graph is left unchanged. The new graph G' is planar. It has $r - 1$ vertices and r edges fewer than G and the number of faces is decreased by one. No face valences are

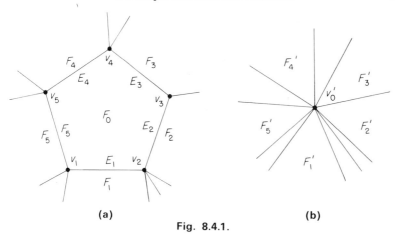

(a) (b)

Fig. 8.4.1.

increased; for the faces F_i' corresponding to F_i one has

$$\rho^*(F_i') = \rho^*(F_i) - 1$$

while $\rho(v_0')$ has the value in (8.4.5).

Next we make the observation: When it is possible to face color the contracted graph G' in four colors in the special way that the faces F_i' take only three colors, then also the original graph G can be four colored. It suffices to retain the face colors in G' when going back to G and give F_0 a fourth color different from those used to color the F_i in (8.4.3).

From this remark it follows directly that faces with two or three boundary edges can be contracted. But also every quadrilateral can be contracted. Suppose, namely, that in a graph G' one has four faces only, F_1', F_2', F_3', F_4' at a corner v_0'. In a four coloring of G' suppose that these four faces take four different colors α, β, γ, δ in this order. If there is no (α, γ)-chain connecting F_1' and F_3', one can give them both the color α by an (α, γ)-interchange. If there exists such an (α, γ)-chain between them, there can be no (β, δ)-chain connecting F_2' and F_4' and so both of these faces may be given the color β.

Theorem 8.4.1. By repeated contractions, one can reduce the four-color problem to the case of graphs in which each face has at least five boundary edges.

Our analysis shows that the reduced graph will have fewer edges, vertices, and faces than the original graph and no face valences will increase. In connection with Theorem 8.4.1 this gives Theorem 8.4.2.

Theorem 8.4.2. Any planar graph in which the faces are bounded by, at most, four edges can be face colored in four colors.

Suppose that in a graph G we have constructed a *partial coloring*, that is, some but not all of the faces in G have been correctly colored in four colors. We denote by K_0 the family of faces which have been colored. The remaining uncolored faces define a number of connected regions in the plane. Each such region D is a connected subgraph of the dual graph G^*, that is, in D one can pass from one face to any other through chains of neighboring faces.

Under certain conditions, it is possible to extend the given partial coloring to D, that is, to find another partial coloring in which the faces in D are colored in addition to those in K_0. This extension may possibly involve a change in the colors already assigned in K_0. The following theorem is due to Dirac.

Theorem 8.4.3. Let G be a graph which is partially colored in four colors and D an uncolored connected domain. If each face in D has at most five boundary edges, while one has at most four, then the partial coloring can be extended to include D.

Proof: We prove the theorem by induction with respect to the number d of faces included in D. When $d = 1$, there is a single face F_0 in D with at most four edges. If F_0 has three or fewer edges in common with the colored part K_0, it is clear that F_0 can be given a color not represented among the neighbors. When all four edges in F_0 are on the boundary of K_0, one can find the desired coloration of the graph $K_0 + F_0$ by performing a contraction of it with respect to F_0.

When $d > 1$, we denote by F_0 one of the faces with at most four boundary edges. By contracting G to G' with respect to F_0, G' is also partially colored and the number of uncolored faces is diminished by one. It is possible that the uncolored family of faces D' in G' corresponding to D in G is no longer connected since F_0 is not available in passing from one face to another. But in each connected domain of D' there is one face which originally had a boundary edge in common with F_0. After the contraction, such a face has at most four boundary edges. Thus according to the induction assumption the theorem holds in G' with respect to each of these components of D'. We conclude that there exists an extension of the coloration of G' which includes all faces in D'. From this, one returns to a coloration of G including F_0 as before.

By means of Theorem 8.4.3 one can prove the following result on four coloring due to Aarts and de Groot.

Theorem 8.4.4. A graph in which each face is bounded by at most five edges is face colorable in four colors.

Proof: The graph G may be taken to be inseparable. The reduction in Theorem 6.3.4 for face coloration does not increase the valence of any face (see Fig. 6.3.4) so we can assume that two faces with a common boundary edge have no further corners in common. The same observation holds for the contraction operations in Theorem 8.4.1 so that we may reduce the problem to a quintic graph. When there are three edges at each vertex, we have

$$\rho_0 = 3, \qquad \rho_0{}^* = 5$$

and the graph is an icosahedron according to Section 4.2. One readily verifies that the four-color theorem holds for all regular polyhedra. We may assume, therefore, that G has a vertex v_0 with $\rho(v_0) \geqq 4$. The edges at v_0 we denote by $E_1, E_2, \ldots, E_\rho$ in cyclic order. Each angle (E_i, E_{i+1}) belongs to a pentagon P_i with v_0 as a corner and E_i and E_{i+1} as boundary edges (see Fig. 8.4.2).

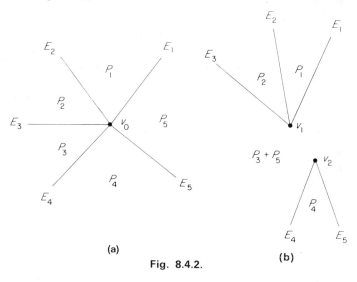

(a)

(b)

Fig. 8.4.2.

We now split the vertex v_0 into two others v_1 and v_2 by the operation described in Section 6.3. In this case we split v_0 with respect to the two faces P_3 and P_5 as indicated in Fig. 8.4.2. Since the vertex v_2 in the new graph G_1 has the valence 2, we may join the two edges E_4 and E_5 into a single one $E_4 + E_5$. This changes P_4 into a quadrangle in G_1. We now color the face $P_3 + P_5$ in G_1 in the same color to obtain a partial coloration of G_1. The remaining faces consist of one quadrangle and for the rest pentagons; they form a connected domain D for if they were separated by $P_3 + P_5$ the original graph would have a separating vertex at v_0. Thus Theorem 8.4.3 applies to G_1 and D so that G_1 is four-colorable. In turn one obtains a face coloration for G.

8.5. Angle Characters and Congruence Conditions (mod 3)

We shall now turn to certain more number theoretical formulations of the four-color problem. Our starting point is the criterion established in Theorem 8.1.1. We assume, to begin with, that G has a face coloration in four colors. By the theorem just mentioned there exists a decomposition (8.1.6) of G into three edge disjoint subgraphs H_1, H_2, H_3. To the edges of G we define a color function with the values

$$\gamma(E) = 0, 1, -1 \qquad (8.5.1)$$

depending on the graph H_i to which E belongs. We consider the values (8.5.1) to be cyclically ordered (mod 3).

It is convenient to assume in the following that G is connected. The edges at any vertex v we order in a clockwise direction. Each v is the corner of certain faces of G. Among these we select a particular one F and denote by E_1 and E_2 a pair of successive boundary edges of F at v. These two edges define an *angle* $\Psi = (E_1, E_2)$ of F. To each such angle in G we assign a *character*

$$\chi = \chi(v, E_1, E_2) \qquad (8.5.2)$$

according to the following rules

$$\chi = 0, \quad \text{when} \quad \gamma(E_1) = \gamma(E_2);$$
$$\chi = 1, \quad \text{when} \quad \gamma(E_1) < \gamma(E_2); \qquad (8.5.3)$$
$$\chi = -1, \quad \text{when} \quad \gamma(E_1) > \gamma(E_2).$$

These rules show that when the characters of all angles are known the edge colors $\gamma(E)$ are determined. One assigns a color value $\gamma(E_0)$ to some particular edge E_0. The others follow from the rule

$$\gamma(E') = \gamma(E) + \chi(E, E')$$

where E and E' are any pair of consecutive edges at a vertex.

When one proceeds along the edges of any face boundary, one returns to the original color. We conclude that for each face F the congruence

$$\sum x_i \equiv 0 (\text{mod } 3), \qquad x_i \text{ on } B(F) \qquad (8.5.4)$$

must be satisfied, where the x_i run through all characters for the corners of the face boundary $B(F)$.

To these conditions for the face boundaries there exists a corresponding set of vertex conditions.

$$\sum x_i \equiv 0 (\text{mod } 3), \qquad x_i \text{ on } St(v) \qquad (8.5.5)$$

where the x_i run through the characters belonging to the angles of an arbitrary star graph $St(v)$. This follows again from the fact that after moving through all edges around v one returns to the original color.

Finally there exists a system of congruence conditions which are consequences of the conditions on the valences of the subgraphs as stated in Theorem 8.1.1. Suppose one starts at some edge E_1 at a vertex v. The rth edge E_r then has the color

$$\gamma(E_r) = \gamma(E_1) + x_1 + \cdots + x_r. \qquad (8.5.6)$$

This expression (8.5.6) shows that one returns to the same color $\gamma(E_1)$ for the first time at the edge E_{r_1} where r_1 is the smallest index for which

$$x_1 + x_2 + \cdots + x_{r_1} \equiv 0 (\text{mod } 3).$$

The next time it happens is at the edge E_{r_2} where r_2 is the smallest index with

$$x_{r_1+1} + \cdots + x_{r_1+r_2} \equiv 0 (\text{mod } 3),$$

and so on. Thus to each edge E_1 there corresponds a series of *zero sections* for the *angle characters* defined by the smallest integers

$$r_1, r_2, \ldots, r_k$$

for which

$$x_1 + \cdots + x_{r_1} \equiv x_{r_1+1} + \cdots + r_{r_1+r_2} \equiv \cdots \equiv 0 (\text{mod } 3). \qquad (8.5.7)$$

For each edge E_1 one obtains another set of zero sections, but due to their cyclic repetition and the fact that the values $\gamma(E)$ are only defined (mod 3) it follows that there are only three essential classes of zero sections. One concludes as follows, according to Theorem 8.1.1.

ZERO SECTION CONDITIONS. When the number of zero sections (8.5.7) in each of the three classes is denoted by k_1, k_2, k_3, then these numbers satisfy the condition

$$k_1 \equiv k_2 \equiv k_3 \equiv \rho(v)(\mathrm{mod}\ 2) \tag{8.5.8}$$

for each vertex v.

The preceding discussion leads to the following theorem.

Theorem 8.5.1. A necessary and sufficient condition that the graph G be face colorable in four colors is that there exist a character system

$$\chi(E, E') = 0, \pm 1$$

defined for each angle (E, E') in G and satisfying the following conditions:

1. The congruences (8.5.4) hold for all face boundaries.
2. The congruences (8.5.5) hold for all star graphs.
3. The zero section conditions (8.5.8) are satisfied for each vertex.

Proof: We have established that the conditions of the theorem are necessary. To show that they are sufficient we need a few preliminary observations.

First, we extend the concept of an angle character to a character $\chi(E, E')$ defined for any pair of edges E and E' belonging to the same star graph $St(v)$. We put $\chi(E, E')$ equal to the sum (mod 3) of those angle characters which correspond to angles at v located between E and E' in the positive direction. From the star conditions (8.5.5) one concludes that

$$\chi(E, E') = -\chi(E', E), \qquad \chi(E, E) = 0.$$

Secondly, by means of this general angle character one obtains a definition of a character $\chi(S)$ for an arbitrary edge sequence

$$S = E_0, E_1, \ldots, E_n \tag{8.5.9}$$

by putting

$$\chi(S) = \sum \chi(E_1, E_{i+1}), \qquad i = 0, 1, \ldots, n - 1. \tag{8.5.10}$$

This yields in particular

$$\chi(S') = -\chi(S)$$

for the reverse sequence S' to (8.5.9) and

$$\chi(S) = 0, \qquad S = E + E'$$

where S is the cyclic sequence consisting of a single edge traversed first in one direction and then in the other.

Thirdly, from the conditions (8.5.4) we deduce as in Section 7.1 that the conditions analogous to them must be fulfilled also for all sums around any minimal circuit. This in turn yields the same result for any circuit. Finally, we obtain the congruence

$$\chi(S) \equiv 0 (\text{mod } 3) \qquad (8.5.11)$$

for any cyclic edge sequence S. We notice that in this statement one should consider S to be a sequence with E_0 for its first and last edge since only by this agreement will all vertex characters around S be included in the sum.

Denote by S_0 and S_1 two sequences from a vertex v_0 to a vertex v_n. The first and the last edges for the two shall be

$$E_{0,0}, E_{1,0}; \qquad E_{0,n}, E_{1,m},$$

respectively. Since $S_0 + S_1'$ is a cyclic edge sequence, we obtain

$$0 \equiv \chi(S_0 + S_1') \equiv \chi(S_0) - \chi(S_1) + \chi(E_{0,n}, E_{1,m}) - \chi(E_{0,0}, E_{1,0})(\text{mod } 3)$$

where we have taken into account the characters at v_0 and v_n; these appear in the combined sequence but not in $\chi(S_0)$ or $\chi(S_1)$. We rewrite the relation as

$$\chi(S_0) - \chi(S_1) \equiv \chi(E_{0,0}, E_{1,0}) - \chi(E_{0,n}, E_{1,m}). \qquad (8.5.12)$$

From the (8.4.12) we deduce the following lemma.

Lemma 8.5.1. When S_0 and S_1 are two edge sequences with the same end edges E_0 and E_n, then

$$\chi(S_0) \equiv \chi(S_1). \qquad (8.5.13)$$

Proof: When E_0 and E_n are traversed in the same direction in both S_0 and S_1, hence when the two sequences have the same end points, the relation (8.5.13) is immediate from (8.5.12). Suppose next that E_0 appears in the same direction in both, while E_n is traversed in opposite directions. Then by (8.5.12) we have

$$\chi(S_0) \equiv \chi(S_1 - E_n) - \chi(E_n, E_{1,m-1}) \equiv \chi(S_1).$$

The other cases follow similarly.

After these preparations the proof of Theorem 8.5.1 is readily completed. We may assume that G is connected by considering separately each of its connected components. With the edges of G we associate a three valued color function $\gamma(E)$. For this purpose, we select a particular edge E_0 and put $\gamma(E_0) = 0$. For an arbitrary edge E there exists a sequence

S in (8.5.9) connecting E_0 with $E = E_n$. We then define

$$\gamma(E) = \chi(S).$$

Lemma 8.5.1 shows that this color value is independent of the defining sequence.

Since the color function is three valued, it decomposes G into three edge disjoint subgraphs as in (8.1.6). For the colors of the edges of a star graph $St(v)$ one finds the same rule as in (8.5.6). The zero section condition (8.5.8) then expresses that the three subgraphs satisfy the parity conditions of Theorem 8.1.1.

CHAPTER 9 | *CUBIC GRAPHS*

9.1. Color Reduction to Cubic Graphs

A cubic graph, as we defined previously, is regular with the valence 3 at each vertex; its dual is a maximal graph. The importance of the cubic graphs for the coloration problem is due to the following observation.

Theorem 9.1.1. The face coloration of a graph in $k \geq 3$ colors can be reduced to the case of cubic graphs.

Proof: We may assume as usual that to be face colored the graph G has no loops, no acyclic edges and $\rho(v) \geq 3$ for all vertices. We enclose each v by a Jordan curve C_v so small that no two of them intersect and a given C_v encloses only the vertex v. We select C_v such that it intersects each of the edges E_i at v just once; this intersection we denote by a_i [Fig. 9.1.1.(a)]. If one uses the straight line representation of G, one can take the C_v as small circles with center v.

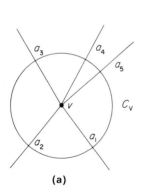

(a)

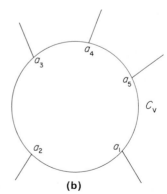

Fig. 9.1.1.

(b)

From G and the family of curves C_v we construct the cubic graph G_3 by omitting all vertices v and those parts of the edges at v which lie inside C_v. We introduce the points a_i as new vertices and the sections $C_v(a_i, a_{i+1})$ as edges in G_3 [Fig. 9.1.1.(b)]. Suppose that G_3 is face colored in k colors. By shrinking the circuits C_v back to a single vertex v and retaining the colors from G_3 one also obtains a coloration for G in k colors. We notice that the two graphs G and G_3 are not coloration equivalent in the sense that a coloration of G gives rise also to a coloration of G_3.

Many of the studies of the four-color problem have been based upon the concept of an irreducible graph. Suppose that the four-color theorem were not true. Then there would exist graphs G_0 with a minimal number of faces which cannot be four colored. Such graphs we call *irreducible graphs*. Numerous investigations of irreducible graphs have been made in the hope of proving that they cannot exist.

For face colorations the reductions in Section 6.3 all involve the coloration of a graph by means of graphs with a smaller number of faces. We conclude that an irreducible graph is connected and inseparable and no two faces with a common boundary edge can have further corners in common. It will have $\rho(v) \geq 3$ for all vertices.

We shall prove further that an irreducible graph must be cubic. However, the method used in the proof of Theorem 9.1.1 does not serve our purposes since it increases the number of faces. We proceed as follows: If G is not cubic, there is a vertex v_0 with $\rho(v_0) \geq 4$. This vertex we split with respect to two nonadjoining faces F and F' having a corner at v_0 (Section 6.3). The splitting increases the number of vertices by one, leaves the number of edges unchanged, and joins F and F' into a single face with a valence equal to the sum of their valences. As we noticed a face coloring of the split graph G_1 leads to a coloring of the original graph G by coalescence. We conclude that the irreducible graph is cubic.

We shall go one step further in our reduction of irreducible graphs. In connection with the proof of the five-color theorem in Section 6.4 we noticed that when a graph has a face bounded by $\rho^* = 2, 3, 4$ edges its coloration in $k \geq 4$ colors can be reduced to the coloration of graphs with a smaller number of faces.

Theorem 9.1.2. A graph which is irreducible with respect to face coloring is inseparable, cubic, and the face valences satisfy $\rho^*(F) \geq 5$.

There are irreducible graphs also for the dual problem of vertex coloring in four colors. These are graphs with a minimal number of vertices which cannot be vertex colored in four colors. Such graphs must be maximal planar such that $\rho(v) \geq 5$ for each vertex.

9.2. Configurations in Cubic Graphs

Due to their importance for the four-color theorem a considerable number of investigations have been made on the special cubic graphs which satisfy the condition

$$\rho^*(F) \geq 5 \qquad (9.2.1)$$

for all faces F. We shall reproduce some of the results here.

Our starting point is Euler's formula in the form (4.3.1) introduced by Lebesgue. Let us suppose first that our graph has only *isolated pentagonal faces*, that is, no pentagon has a boundary edge in common with another pentagon. For a pentagon P, we denote by

$$(x_1, x_2, x_3, x_4, x_5) \qquad (9.2.2)$$

the valences of its five neighboring faces in this cyclic order. In the left-hand sum in (4.3.1) we gather into groups all the angle contributions corresponding to those angles which have their vertices on the boundary of P. Among them there are five inner angles and ten outer angles. The sum of the inner angle contributions yields the face contribution (4.3.3) for P; in this special case it has the value $\frac{1}{6}$. The outer angles occur in pairs, two for each neighboring face. The angle value for each is as in (4.3.2)

$$\frac{1}{3} + \frac{1}{x_i} - \frac{1}{2}.$$

The total sum of all the desired angle contributions for P is found to be

$$2 \cdot \sum \frac{1}{x_i} - \frac{3}{2}. \qquad (9.2.3)$$

All angles in G with positive contributions must be inner angles in pentagons so that the pentagon sums (9.2.3) include all positive terms in (4.3.1). The maximal value for the expression (9.2.3) is $\frac{1}{6}$ and it occurs when $x_i = 6$ for all i. We conclude that there must be at least twelve pentagons in G for which the sums (9.2.3) are positive. The corresponding quintuplets of valences (9.2.2) may then be computed from the inequality

$$\sum \frac{1}{x_i} > \frac{3}{4}. \qquad (9.2.4)$$

As in Section 4.3 it is only necessary to determine and list all maximal solution sets majoring all others. The calculations show that there are only the following three types:

No pentagonal neighbors:

$$(6, 6, 7, 7, \quad 7),$$

$$(6, 6, 6, 7, \quad 9), \qquad (9.2.5)$$

$$(6, 6, 6, 6, 11).$$

All permutations of these are also maximal sets since the condition (9.2.4) is symmetric. An immediate consequence of the form (9.2.5) of the majoring sets (9.2.5) is a theorem due to Wernickle.

Theorem 9.2.1. In a cubic graph satisfying (9.2.1) there must exist a pentagon touching another pentagon or a hexagon.

Next we turn to the case where each pentagon P has at most one pentagonal neighbor P_1. As before one computes the contributions of the angles with their vertex on the boundary of P. Since we wish to determine the contribution per pentagon those angle contributions which belong both to P and P_1 are counted only with half value. The total contribution for P is then found to be

$$2\left(\frac{1}{x_2} + \frac{1}{x_3}\right) + \frac{3}{2}\left(\frac{1}{x_1} + \frac{1}{x_4}\right) - 1.$$

This expression is positive when

$$4\left(\frac{1}{x_2} + \frac{1}{x_3}\right) + 3\left(\frac{1}{x_1} + \frac{1}{x_4}\right) > 2.$$

As before we determine the maximal solutions which we now write in the order

$$(5; x_2, x_3; x_1, x_4)$$

so that the values x_2, x_3 can be permuted and similarly x_1, x_4.

One pentagonal neighbor:

$$
\begin{array}{ll}
(5; 6, 6; 6, 17) & (5; 6, 7; 6, 11) \\
(5; 6, 6; 7, 12) & (5; 6, 8; 6, \ 8) \\
(5; 6, 6; 8, 10) & (5; 6, 9; 6, \ 7) \\
\multicolumn{2}{c}{(5; 7, 7; 6, 8)}
\end{array}
\qquad (9.2.6)
$$

In the last symbol the numbers can be permuted at random.

When G is a graph in which each pentagon has at most one pentagonal neighbor, the valences of the neighboring faces must be included in one of the maximal types enumerated in (9.2.5) and (9.2.6). From these tables one reads off a result which is due to Franklin.

Theorem 9.2.2. In a cubic graph satisfying (9.2.1) there is at least one pentagon touching two faces with at most six boundary edges.

The same kind of analysis can be carried out when there are two or more pentagons touching a given one. We shall omit the enumeration of the results. The complete lists of possible pentagonal neighborhoods are included in the paper by Lebesgue.

9.3. Four-Color Conditions in Cubic Graphs

In Chapter 8 we discussed various formulations of the conditions for the existence of a face coloration in four colors. For cubic graphs these conditions in many instances take simpler forms. From theorem 8.1.1 we conclude the following theorem.

Theorem 9.3.1. A cubic graph can be face colored in four colors if, and only if, it can be edge colored in three colors; in other words, G has an edge disjoint decomposition

$$G = H_1 + H_2 + H_3 \tag{9.3.1}$$

into subgraphs H_i of valence 1, that is, each graph H_i has exactly one edge at each vertex.

This condition can also be expressed in the following form.

Theorem 9.3.2. A necessary and sufficient condition for a cubic graph to have a face coloring in four colors is that it have a subgraph

$$H_0 = \sum C_i \tag{9.3.2}$$

which is the sum of disjoint circuits C_i of even length, one passing through each vertex of G.

Proof: From (9.3.1) one obtains such a subgraph (9.3.2) by putting

$$H_0 = H_2 + H_3. \tag{9.3.3}$$

This graph has one edge of H_2 and one edge of H_3 at each vertex; hence it is the disjoint sum of even circuits. Conversely when a subgraph (9.3.2) is given, one finds a representation (9.3.3) by letting the edges in each C_i belong alternatingly to H_2 and H_3. There remains at each vertex just a single edge not in H_0 and these form the third subgraph H_1 in (9.3.1).

One could also have derived Theorem 9.3.2 directly as a consequence of Theorem 8.3.1 connecting four coloring with the even subgraphs.

The coloring condition stated in Theorem 8.2.1 does not simplify in the case of cubic graphs. Theorem 8.2.2 reads, in this special case, as seen in Theorem 9.3.3.

Theorem 9.3.3. The four-color theorem is true if, and only if, every maximal planar graph has a bipartite dichotomy.

The conditions for a four coloring given in Section 8.5 simplify considerably for cubic graphs. In Theorem 8.5.1 there are now just three edges at each vertex and when G is four colored each belongs to a different subgraph H_i in (9.3.1). This shows that the angle characters (8.5.2) can only have the two values ± 1. The only zero section is

$$x_1 + x_2 + x_3 \equiv 0 \,(\text{mod } 3) \qquad (9.3.4)$$

and this is the same as the star graph condition (8.5.5).

The congruence (9.3.4) shows that at a vertex v only two types of sets of angle characters are possible, namely

$$(+1, +1, +1), \qquad (-1, -1, -1).$$

In the first case the edge colors at v follow in increasing cyclic order; in the second case the order is decreasing. We may, therefore, describe the edge distribution at v simply by a single character ± 1. This leads us to the criterion of the next theorem.

Theorem 9.3.4. A cubic graph can be face colored in four colors if, and only if, a character $\chi(v) = \pm 1$ can be assigned to each vertex such that the vertices of any minimal circuit satisfy the condition

$$\sum \chi(v) \equiv 0 \,(\text{mod } 3). \qquad (9.3.5)$$

This theorem can be reformulated as follows.

Theorem 9.3.5. A cubic graph can be face colored in four colors if, and only if, the family of congruences (9.3.5) defined by the minimal circuits has a solution set $\{x_i\}$ with $x_i \not\equiv 0 \,(\text{mod } 3)$ for all i.

These last results are due to Heawood. They seem well fitted for use in connection with an exploration of the four-color problem by means of computers. For a given planar graph one would have to assign values $\chi(v) = \pm 1$ to each vertex. The machine would then have to examine whether for some such choice the corresponding set of face congruences were solvable in values $\pm 1 \pmod 3$. Even for a single graph of some size the number of choices is immense. However, even if this problem could be resolved, there remains the question of finding an automatic generation of all planar graphs with a given number of vertices.

One often hears discussed among mathematicians this computer approach to the four-color problem, but no one seems to have done anything about it. It is possible, of course, that a complete solution could be found in the negative sense that the machine would exhibit a graph which could not be colored in four colors. However, in view of the fact that it is known that all planar graphs with up to 35 faces can be colored it seems unlikely that even the most extensive computer analysis would be capable of pushing this limit up further.

Heawood has made considerable efforts to analyze the preceding congruence conditions theoretically; a number of his results are very interesting. He takes his starting point in a somewhat more general problem: To each face F_i there is assigned arbitrarily a number

$$\varphi_i = 0, 1, 2 : \pmod 3$$

and the congruences (9.3.5) are replaced by

$$\sum \chi(v) \equiv \varphi_i \pmod 3. \tag{9.3.6}$$

Each time one assigns characters ± 1 to the vertices such a set of congruences will occur. But for congruences obtained this way the values φ_i must satisfy a condition. In the congruences (9.3.6) each vertex appears exactly three times; hence by adding them one finds

$$\sum \varphi_i \equiv 0 \pmod 3. \tag{9.3.7}$$

Thus, one can restrict the values φ_i by assigning them only to the finite faces, leaving the value of F_∞ to be determined by (9.3.7). When the number of faces of the graph is n, there are only $n - 1$ congruences to be considered.

As a consequence, the number of choices of face values is 3^{n-1}. The corresponding number of vertices is $2n - 4$; hence the number of sets of vertex values is

$$2^{2n-4} = 4^{n-2}.$$

Thus, when $n \geq 6$, the number of face choices is less, usually considerably less than the number of vertex choices ± 1. This might inspire the hope that for sufficiently large values of n one could find solutions for the congruences (9.3.6) for all choices of the φ_i.

Heawood examined these congruences in detail for certain graphs, in particular, the dodecahedron graph with $n = 12$. He showed that for such a graph there are, due to symmetry, essentially only six choices of face values for which there are no solutions. For a dodecahedron with faces marked as in Fig. 9.3.1 these cases have been listed in the subsequent table.

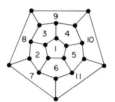

Fig. 9.3.1.

	1	2	3	4	5	6	7	8	9	10	11
I	2	1	0	0	0	0	0	0	0	0	0
II	2	1	0	0	0	0	0	0	1	0	2
III	2	1	0	1	1	0	2	2	0	0	0
IV	0	0	2	1	2	1	2	1	0	0	0
V	2	1	0	0	0	0	0	0	1	2	1
VI	2	1	0	0	0	0	0	0	2	2	0

In each of these cases the values 1 and 2 may be interchanged.

Heawood also developed some systematic methods for the analysis of the general graph congruences (9.3.6). One of the consequences of these is that there will always exist some systems which are not solvable. This is the case, in particular, for choices of the face values all zero, except for a pair of adjoining faces with the values 1 and 2 (Case I for the dodecahedron).

In connection with the Heawood congruences one should also mention papers by Veblen and Franklin.

9.4. The Interchange Graph and the Color Problems

In Section 3.5 we defined the *medial graph* $M(G)$ of a given graph G in the following manner. On each edge E of G a midpoint $m(E)$ is selected.

When E_1 and E_2 are consecutive edges on the boundary of a face, we draw the edge in $M(G)$,

$$(m(E_1), \qquad m(E_2)).$$

The properties of the medial graph are evident from Fig. 9.4.1. Here we suppose that $E = (v_1, v_2)$ is a common boundary edge of the two faces F_1 and F_2 in the inseparable graph G. The three consecutive boundary edges on F_1 including E we denote by E_1', E, E_1'', and analogously for F_2 by E_2', E, E_2''. The midpoints of these edges are, respectively, m_1', m, m_1''; m_2', m, m_2''.

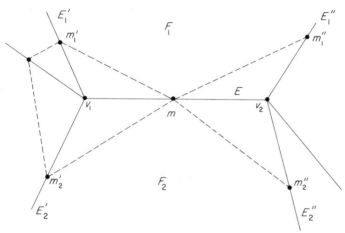

Fig. 9.4.1.

From Fig. 9.4.1 one reads off the following properties of the medial graph: $M(G)$ is planar and regular with valence $\rho_M = 4$, that is, it is the dual of a maximal bipartite graph. This dual is the radial graph $R(G)$ defined in Section 3.5. The vertices in $M(G)$ are in one-to-one correspondence with the edges in G. The faces in $M(G)$ fall into two color classes, each edge in $M(G)$ lying on the boundary of one face in each category:

α-*faces* $F_M(v)$, each enclosing a single vertex v in G' and having $\rho(v)$ boundary edges,

β-*faces* $F_M(F)$, each lying within a face F of G and having $\rho^*(F)$ boundary edges.

These medial graphs are closely related to the *interchange* graphs introduced for arbitrary graphs in Section 1.5. (Ore, [1]) Here we considered the edges of a graph G to be the vertices of a new graph $I(G)$ in which two edges $E_1 \neq E_2$ were connected by an edge in $I(G)$ if, and only if, the two had a common end point. It was supposed that G had no multiple edges. From this definition it is evident that the medial graph $M(G)$ can be considered to be a subgraph of the interchange graph $I(G)$.

For cubic graphs we have simply Theorem 9.4.1.

Theorem 9.4.1. In the case of a cubic planar graph the interchange graph and the medial graph are the same.

We assume in the following that the cubic graph has no loops; then the interchange graph is seen to have no multiple edges. For such a cubic graph G the α-faces in $I(G)$ all have $\rho(v) = 3$ boundary edges. We say for short that a graph with even valences is *triangle colored* when it can be face colored in two colors α and β such that all α-faces are triangles. We conclude as shown in the following theorem.

Theorem 9.4.2. A graph with single edges is the interchange graph of a cubic graph if, and only if, it is a dual maximal bipartite graph which can be triangle colored.

The importance of these considerations for the four-color problem is evident from Theorem 9.4.3.

Theorem 9.4.3. A cubic planar graph G without loops is face colorable in four colors if, and only if, its interchange graph $I(G)$ is vertex colorable in three colors, or dually, if its radial graph $R(G)$ is face colorable in three colors.

Proof: Suppose that the cubic graph G is face colorable in four colors. According to Theorem 9.3.1 there exists a decomposition (9.3.1) of G into three subgraphs H_1, H_2, H_3, each having just one edge at each vertex. We assign a color value i to an edge E when it belongs to the graph H_i, hence a color value i to the midpoint $m(E)$ of E. This represents a vertex coloration of $I(G)$ in three colors since any edge, $(m(E_1), m(E_2))$ in $I(G)$ connects edges E_1 and E_2 with a common end point so that $m(E_1)$ and $m(E_2)$ have different colors. Conversely, when $I(G)$ has a vertex coloration in three colors one also has a decomposition of the edges in G into three edge disjoint subgraphs H_i. At a vertex in G the three edges belong to different graphs H_i since their midpoints are connected by edges in $I(G)$.

This discussion brings us to the following formulation of the four-color problem.

Theorem 9.4.4. The four-color problem is equivalent to the proposition: Let G be a planar triangle colored graph with single edges and regular with valence 4. Then G is vertex colorable in three colors.

It is necessary to require single edges as one sees from the graph in Fig. 9.4.2, which cannot be vertex colored in three colors.

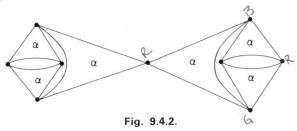

Fig. 9.4.2.

9.5. Planar Interchange Graphs

In connection with the applications of interchange graphs in the preceding it is of interest to investigate when an interchange graph is planar. This problem has been considered by Sedlacek and we shall reproduce his results here.

Theorem 9.5.1. A finite planar graph G has a planar interchange graph $I(G)$ if, and only if, it has the following property. All valences in G satisfy $\rho(v) \leq 4$ and when $\rho(v) = 4$ then v is a separating vertex.

Proof: We show first that the conditions are necessary. If $\rho(v) \geq 5$ for some vertex, then $I(G)$ includes a simplex ρ_n, $n \geq 5$ and so it is not planar. Consider a vertex $v \in G$ with $\rho(v) = 4$. Let the four edges at v be

$$E_i = (v, v_i), \qquad i = 1, 2, 3, 4.$$

These edges correspond to four vertices

$$e_i, \qquad i = 1, 2, 3, 4$$

in $I(G)$ spanning a tetrahedral graph S_4 in $I(G)$; since $I(G)$ is planar S_4 divides the plane into four triangular domains.

Suppose now that v is not a separating vertex in G; we shall show that this leads to a contradiction. There would then exist connecting arcs in G

$$P_{ij} = P_{ij}(v_i, v_j), \qquad i, j = 1, 2, 3, 4$$

connecting any pair of different vertices v_i and v_j and not passing through v. Let us consider the two arcs P_{12} and P_{13} from v_1 to v_2 and v_3, respectively. We may assume that they coincide up to a last vertex t and from then on they are disjoint. The next edges in the two arcs may be E' and

E''. Corresponding to them are the vertices e' and e'' and these are connected by an edge (e', e'') in $I(G)$ since E' and E'' have a common end point. To each P_{ij} there corresponds an arc p_{ij} in G connecting e_i and e_j and having no vertices in common with S_4 except these end points. But the two arcs p_{12} and p_{13} must lie within the same face of S_4 since the two first vertices in the arcs which are different are connected by an edge (e', e''). We conclude from this argument that all arcs p_{ij} lie within the same face. This, however, is not possible since each face in S_4 is separated from one of the vertices e_i.

To prove the sufficiency of the condition we observe that when G is planar and $\rho(v) \leqq 3$ for all vertices also $I(G)$ can be drawn in the plane by joining midpoints of adjacent edges. Thus we can prove the theorem by induction with respect to the number of separating vertices with $\rho(v_0) = 4$. Such a vertex separates G into two components and by assumption the interchange graph of each can be drawn in the plane. Two cases may occur:

(a) G_1 and G_2 each has two edges at v_0.
(b) G_1 has three edges and G_2 has one edge at v_0.

In Fig. 9.5.1(a) and (b) it has been indicated how in each case the graphs $I(G_1)$ and $I(G_2)$ can be fitted together to give a planar representation of $I(G)$.

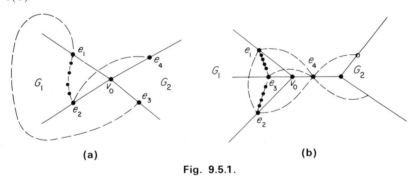

(a)   (b)

Fig. 9.5.1.

Theorem 9.5.2. When G is a nonplanar graph, then $I(G)$ is nonplanar.

Proof: The analysis is carried out on each of the two types of Kuratowski graphs. One can show that any graph conformal to S_5 or $K = (3, 3)$ has an interchange graph conformal with one of the original type, hence the interchange graph cannot be planar when G is not planar. We leave the details to the reader.

1. When is the second interchange graph of a planar graph planar? The same question for the nth interchange graph.
2. When are all the repeated interchange graphs of a planar graph planar?
3. Try to extend the previous results to infinite graphs.

9.6. Construction of Cubic Graphs

For any even number v there exists a regular graph on v vertices with valence ρ when $1 \leq \rho \leq v - 1$. This is a consequence of the fact that any complete graph S_v on v vertices is the edge direct sum of v graphs of valence 1. In particular there exist cubic graphs for each even $v \geq 4$. For $v = 4$ there is only one such graph, namely, S_4. For $v = 6$ there are two of them, namely, the 6-vertex Kuratowski graph and the graph in Fig. 9.6.1.

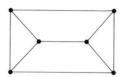

Fig. 9.6.1.

There exists a successive construction of cubic graphs due to E. L. Johnson which we shall now present. It makes it possible to construct any cubic graph on $v + 2$ vertices from a cubic graph on v vertices. For this purpose we need a couple of auxiliary results. A subgraph with six vertices and five edges as in Fig. 9.6.2 we call an H-graph.

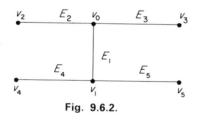

Fig. 9.6.2.

Lemma 9.6.1. Any vertex v_0 in a cubic graph with $v \geq 6$ lies on an H-graph.

Proof: Let the three edges at v_0 be

$$E_1 = (v_0, v_1), \qquad E_2 = (v_0, v_2), \qquad E_3 = (v_0, v_3).$$

Not all edges v_i, $i = 1, 2, 3$ can be connected by edges for this is only possible when $G = S_4$. If, at most, one pair of these vertices are connected by an edge, we can assume that at v_1 there are no edges to v_2 and v_3. Then the edges E_1, E_2, E_3, E_4, E_5 form an H-graph [Fig. 9.6.3(a)].

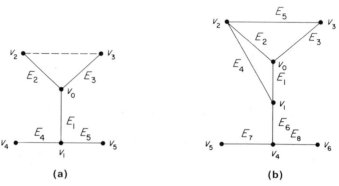

(a)   (b)

Fig. 9.6.3.

When there are two edges connecting the vertices v_i, $i = 1, 2, 3$, we assume that there are edges [see Fig. 9.6.3(b)]

$$E_4 = (v_1, v_2), \qquad E_5 = (v_2, v_3).$$

There is a third edge $E_6 = (v_1, v_4)$ at v_1 and at v_4 there are two other edges

$$E_7 = (v_4, v_5), \qquad E_8 = (v_4, v_6).$$

One of the vertices v_5 and v_6 may or may not coincide with v_3 but in either case E_1, E_4, E_6, E_7, E_8 form an H-graph.

Let us denote an H-graph as in Fig. 9.6.2. It shall be called *restricted* when it has the properties: No vertex v_2 or v_3 is edge connected both to v_4 and v_5; no vertex v_4 and v_5 is edge connected both to v_2 and v_3.

Lemma 9.6.2. Any connected cubic graph with $v \geq 8$ contains a restricted H-graph.

Proof: We take an H-graph as in Fig. 9.6.2. There cannot be four edges from $\{v_2, v_3\}$ to $\{v_4, v_5\}$ for G would have to be a cubic graph with $v = 6$. Suppose that there are three connecting edges. We select the notations as in Fig. 9.6.4 where there is no edge (v_2, v_4) and put $E_6 = (v_2, v_5)$. The third edge incident to v_2 shall be $E_7 = (v_2, v_6)$. The two other edges at v_6 are $E_8 = (v_6, v_7)$ and $E_9 = (v_6, v_8)$.

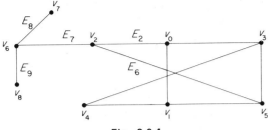

Fig. 9.6.4.

We see that there cannot be any edges from v_7 or v_8 to v_0 or v_5 since there are already three edges at these vertices. We conclude that E_2, E_6, E_7, E_8, E_9 is a restricted H-graph.

There remains the case where there are two connecting edges, both from the same vertex v_3 as in Fig. 9.6.5 At v_2 there are two other edges

$$E_6 = (v_2, v_6), \qquad E_7 = (v_2, v_7)$$

where v_6 and v_7 cannot coincide with v_i, $i = 0, \ldots 5$. Then E_1, E_2, E_3, E_6, E_7 form a restricted H-graph because edges from $\{v_1, v_3\}$ have their other end point in $\{v_0, v_4, v_5\}$.

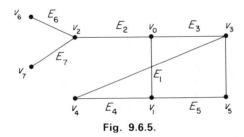

Fig. 9.6.5.

In Fig. 9.6.2 we have drawn a restricted H-graph. A new graph G' can be obtained from G by an H-*reduction*. This consists in eliminating the vertices v_0 and v_1 and their edges and replacing them by a pair of edges $(v_2, v_4), (v_3, v_5)$ or $(v_2, v_5), (v_3, v_4)$. One of these pairs is not in G since H is restricted.

To this H-reduction there exists a converse operation, the H-*expansion*. Let

$$F_1 = (u_2, u_4), \qquad F_2 = (u_3, u_5)$$

be two edges in G where all end points are distinct. The H-expansion of G

with respect to F_1 and F_2 is obtained by eliminating F_1 and F_2 and adjoining two vertices u_0 and u_1 with edges

$$(u_0, u_1)(u_0, u_2)(u_0, u_5)(u_1, u_3)(u_1, u_4)$$

or also by

$$(u_0, u_1)(u_0, u_2)(u_0, u_3)(u_1, u_4)(u_1, u_5).$$

We are now ready to prove Theorem 9.6.1.

Theorem 9.6.1. For $v \geq 6$ every connected cubic graph on $v + 2$ vertices is an H-expansion of a connected cubic graph on v vertices.

Proof: The reduced graph G' obtained from G by an H-reduction is cubic. It remains to show that the reduction can be made such that G' is connected. We assume first that by the reduction with respect to H in Fig. 9.6.2 the edges at v_0 and v_1 are replaced by

$$E_1' = (v_2, v_4), \qquad E_2' = (v_3, v_5)$$

If G' should not be connected, there would exist vertices a and b not connected by an arc in G'. On the other hand, in G there is an arc $P(a, b)$ and this arc must include v_0 or v_1 or both since otherwise P would also lie in G'.

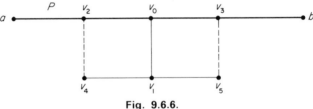

Fig. **9.6.6.**

Suppose that P includes only v_0 (Fig. 9.6.6). Then in G every arc from v_2 to v_3 must pass through v_0 or v_1; hence v_0 and v_1 is a separating pair of vertices in G. For the same reason v_0 and v_1 must separate v_2 and v_5, v_3 and v_4 as well as v_4 and v_5.

Next suppose that P includes both v_0 and v_1. Since they are adjacent in G they may be taken as consecutive vertices in P (Fig. 9.6.7). Let v_2 be the vertex preceding v_0 in P. In P one cannot have the section $P(v_2, v_0, v_1, v_4)$ for it could be replaced by the edge (v_2, v_4) in G'. We conclude that P includes the section $P(v_2, v_0, v_1, v_5)$. For the same reason as in the preceding case the vertices v_0, v_1 must separate v_2 and v_5, also v_2 and v_3 as well as v_4 and v_3 and also v_4 and v_5.

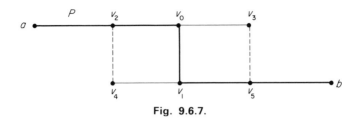

Fig. 9.6.7.

Under these conditions there can be no edges (v_2, v_5) and (v_3, v_4) in G so in the H-reduction of G one could have added these edges instead of (v_2, v_4) and (v_3, v_5). If the graph G'' obtained this way should not be connected, it follows as before that v_2 is separated also from v_3 by the vertices v_0, v_1 and similarly for the other v_i. Thus under these conditions each of the vertices v_i $i = 1, 2, 3, 4$, is separated from the others by the pair (v_0, v_1). This implies that each of the edges in the H-graph is acyclic; hence they are separating edges in G and this graph must have the form drawn in Fig. 9.6.8.

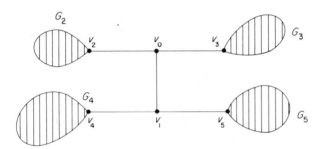

Fig. 9.6.8.

Every separating edge in G can be taken as the middle edge in a restricted H-graph. Thus in Fig. 9.6.8 one could have taken (v_0, v_2) instead of (v_0, v_1) for the reduction. If this does not give a connected graph G', one can continue further into the component G_2. Since G is finite, one must finally arrive at the desired H-reduction.

CHAPTER 10

HADWIGER'S CONJECTURE

10.1. Contractions and Subcontractions

In this chapter we shall, in general, consider finite, nonplanar graphs; they shall have single edges and no loops. Let G be such a graph with the vertex set $V = V(G)$. By τ we denote a correspondence of V into another set $V_1 = \tau(V)$. In V_1 we define a graph $G_1 = \tau(G)$ by introducing an edge

$$E_1 = \tau(E) = (\tau(a), \tau(b))$$

whenever there exists an edge $E = (a, b)$ in G. We then call τ a *homomorphism* of G_1 onto G_1 while G_1 is a *homomorphic image* of G or G is *homomorphic* to G_1 (see Ore [1], Section 5.3).

A homomorphism is *connected* when all $a \in V$ with the same image $\tau(a)$ in G_1 define a connected section graph in G. A connected homomorphism shall be called a *contraction*; we also say that the image G_1 is a *contraction* of G. Any contraction can be executed stepwise by means of *edge contractions*, consisting in the identification of the end points of an edge $E = (a, b)$. Loops and multiple edges resulting from this operation are eliminated. A contraction of a connected graph is connected; the contraction of a planar graph is planar. The contraction operation is transitive.

When B is a bridge in G with respect to some set of vertices S, there will be a certain attachment set

$$A = \{a_1, \ldots, a_k\} \leqq S$$

for B. When B is nonsingular, let b be a vertex in B, not an attachment. From b there is an arc in B to each a_i so by contraction of edges in B one can reduce B to a graph consisting of b and edges (b, a_i). We shall say that B has been *contracted to a vertex*. In a second step one can identify b with one of the attachments, say a_1. The result of this *complete contraction* is to reduce G to $G - B$ plus those edges (a_1, a_i) which do not already occur in G.

When

$$\tau^{-1}(a_1) \subset V$$

is the inverse image set of a vertex a_1 in the contraction G_1, then by definition the section graph $G(\tau^{-1}(a_1))$ is connected. The edges touching it connect this graph with other inverse image graphs. If in each graph $G(\tau^{-1}(a_1))$ one selects a vertex $a' \in V$, one obtains a *contraction* G' of G into itself isomorphic to G_1. Thus one can always conceive of a contraction of G as such an *inner contraction*.

A graph H is a *subcontraction* of a graph G when there exists a contraction τ of G to a graph $G_1 = \tau(G)$ such that G_1 has a subgraph isomorphic to H. We express this by writing

$$G \succ H. \tag{10.1.1}$$

It is usually assumed that both G and H are connected graphs. We leave it to the reader to verify the following properties of subcontractions:

1. When $G \succ H$ and $H \supset H_1$, then $G \succ H_1$.
2. When $G' \supset G$ and $G \succ H$, then $G' \succ H$.
3. When $G \succ G'$ and $G' \succ G''$, then $G \succ G''$.

In particular, when A is any subgraph of G or A is conformal to a subgraph of G then $G \succ A$. For a simplex $H = S_n$ the property of being a contraction or a subcontraction is the same.

When a relation (10.1.1) holds, one can assume that one deals with inner contractions so that

$$V(G) \supseteq V(G_1) \supseteq V(H). \tag{10.1.2}$$

If here $V(H)$ should be a proper subset of $V(G_1)$, one could have continued the contraction taking some contraction which takes $V(G_1)$ into $V(H)$. For this double contraction G_2 of G one would also have $G_2 \supset H$. Thus in (10.1.2) one may assume that $V(G_1) = V(H)$. A corresponding contraction τ with

$$\tau(V) = \tau(V(H))$$

is a *defining contraction* for the subcontraction H.

When H is a subcontraction of G, one cannot usually assert that G has a subgraph H_1 conformal to H. In the following special case it is true (Halin).

Theorem 10.1.1. When G has a subcontraction H with valences $\rho_H(v) \leqq 3$, then G has a subgraph conformal to H.

Proof: Let τ be a defining contraction. An inverse image set

$$A_0 = \tau^{-1}(h_0)$$

is then connected by edges in H to, at most, three other such sets

$$A_i = \tau^{-1}(h_i), \qquad i = 1, 2, 3.$$

For each connection we select an edge (A_0, A_i) in G. Their end points in A_0 shall be a_1, a_2, a_3. If there are two different vertices a_1 and a_2, we connect them by an arc $P(a_1, a_2)$ of G lying in the connected graph

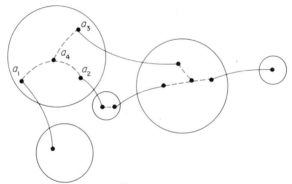

Fig. 10.1.1.

$G(A_0)$. If there is a third vertex a_3, we add an arc $Q(a_3, a_4)$ to a first vertex a_4 on P. We then construct a graph H_1 consisting of all selected edges (A_0, A_i) for all pairs of inverse image sets; to these edges we add for each A_0 the arc $P(a_1, a_2)$ when there are two end points and the arcs

$$P(a_4, a_1), P(a_4, a_2), P(a_4, a_3)$$

when there are three end points. One verifies that H_1 is conformal to H (see Fig. 10.1.1).

A similar argument may be used to show the following theorem according to Halin.

Theorem 10.1.2. When $G \succ S_5$, then either G contains a subgraph conformal to S_5 or $G \succ L$ where L is the graph in Fig. 10.1.2.

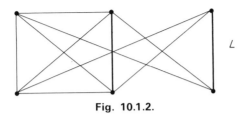

Fig. 10.1.2.

Proof: When $G \succ S_5$, there exist five inverse image sets

$$A_i = \tau^{-1}(v_i), \qquad i = 1, 2, 3, 4, 5$$

for the vertices v_i of the simplex S_5. Each of these is connected by edges in G to the four others. Let

$$a_2, a_3, a_4, a_5 \in A_1$$

be the end points of four such edges from A_1. Suppose $a_2 \neq a_3$. In $G(A_1)$ there is a connecting arc $P(a_2, a_3)$ and also connecting arcs $Q(a_4, a_4')$ and $R(a_5, a_5')$ to first vertices a_4' and a_5' on P. When $a_4' \neq a_5'$, we contract all other sets A_i to single vertices. This gives a graph S_4 which together with the four edges to A_1 and the arcs P, Q, R produces a graph conformal to L. If $a_4' = a_5'$ for any choice of the connecting arc $P(a_2, a_3)$ and for every set A_i we obtain a graph conformal to S_5. The same is true when $a_2 = a_3 = a_4 = a_5$ for all A_i.

Let us also point out that the Kuratowski theorem may be given the following form (Halin; Harary and Tutte).

Theorem 10.1.3. A graph is nonplanar if, and only if, it has one of the Kuratowski graphs as subcontraction.

Proof: A graph G is nonplanar if, and only if, it has a subgraph conformal to S_5 or the hexagonal Kuratowski graph K. Then it also has these graphs as subcontractions. On the other hand when $G \succ K$ it also has a subgraph conformal to K according to Theorem 10.1.1. When $G \succ S_5$ it either has a subgraph conformal to S_5 or

$$G \succ L \succ K = (3, 3)$$

according to Theorem 10.1.2.

Finally we observe:

Theorem 10.1.4. When $G \neq S_5$ is a three-vertex connected graph which contains a subgraph conformal to S_5, then

$$G \succ L, G \succ M.$$

Proof: Here M is the graph drawn in Fig. 10.1.3.

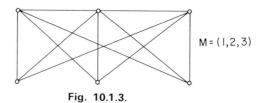

M = (1, 2, 3)

Fig. 10.1.3.

Suppose first that G contains a subgraph S_5. By assumption, there is a vertex v_0 not on S_5. It belongs to a bridge with respect to S_5 attached at at least three vertices. Consequently, there are three disjoint arcs from v_0 to three attachments. When these arcs are contracted to edges, one obtains a graph on six vertices and one readily sees that it contains L and M subgraphs.

Secondly, let G have a subgraph S_5' conformal, but not equal to S_5. Since G is three-vertex connected there exists an arc $Q(v_0, v_1)$ having only its end points on S_5' and connecting an inner vertex v_0 of one of the S_5'-arcs with a vertex v_1 not on this arc. The graph $S_5' + Q$ can be contracted to a graph S_5 with an added edge from one of the vertices to the midpoint of one of its opposite edges. Also this graph contains L and M as subgraphs.

10.2. Maximal Graphs and Simplex Decompositions

Any graph A defines a division of the family of all graphs into two classes $K(A)$ and $K^*(A)$ consisting respectively of the graphs satisfying

$$G \succ A, \qquad G \not\succ A.$$

Usually we consider only finite connected graphs A and G. The graph A shall be called the *image graph*. A *maximal graph* G in $K^*(A)$ is a graph such that

$$G + E \in K(A)$$

for any new edge E added to G between two vertices not previously edge connected. The *maximal class* $K_0^*(A)$ consists of all maximal graphs in $K^*(A)$.

A *simplex* S_v is a complete graph on v vertices. Let the number of vertices in A be $n = v_v(A)$. Any simplex $S_v, v \geqq n$, belongs to $K(A)$; any graph with fewer than n vertices belongs to $K^*(A)$. Since no edge can be added to a simplex, we include all $S_v, v < n$, in the maximal class $K_0^*(A)$. By this special definition any finite graph in $K^*(A)$ is contained in some maximal graph with the same vertex set.

A *decomposition* or *separation* of a graph G by means of a subgraph H is a representation of G in the form

$$G = G_1 + G_2, \qquad G_1 \cap G_2 = H \qquad (10.2.1)$$

where the *components* G_1 and G_2 are section subgraphs, hence the *separating graph* H also has this property. It is usually assumed that the separation (10.2.1) is *proper*, that is, both G_1 and G_2 include vertices not in H.

When H is a subgraph with vertex set $V(H)$, there will, in general, be a certain number of bridges B in G with respect to H (or $V(H)$). A *broad bridge* is a bridge B for which the attachment set $A(B)$ is the whole set $V(H)$. In (10.2.1) each component consists of a number of bridges with respect to H. A *broad separation* is one in which both components G_1 and G_2 include broad bridges.

When the separation (10.2.1) is not broad, let B be a bridge with an attachment set

$$A(B) = V(B) \cap V(H) \subset V(H).$$

Then one obtains a separation

$$B = G_1' + G_2', \qquad G_1' \cap G_2' = H' \subset H,$$

where G_1' is the section graph spanned by $V(B)$ and H' the graph spanned by

$$V(B) \cap V(H).$$

By repeated reductions of this kind one obtains:

Theorem 10.2.1. From a separation (10.2.1) one can deduce another with a separating graph $H' \subset H$ such that all bridges with respect to H' are broad.

Denote by η the vertex connectivity of G, that is, the smallest number of vertices in any separating set for G. Then Theorem 10.2.1 shows, in particular, that all bridges with respect to a minimal separating graph H with η vertices are broad.

A *simplex decomposition* is a representation (10.2.1)

$$G = G_1 + G_2, \qquad G_1 \cap G_2 = S_v \qquad (10.2.2)$$

in which the separating graph $H = S_v$ is a simplex.

A K_0^*-*decomposition* of a graph $G \in K_0^*(A)$ is a simplex decomposition (10.2.2) in which the components G_1 and G_2 both belong to K_0^*. When no such representation exists, we call G a K_0^*-*indecomposable graph*. From this definition it follows that the following theorem is true.

Theorem 10.2.2. Every graph $G \in K_0^*$ has a representation

$$G = G_1 + \cdots + G_2 \qquad (10.2.3)$$

as the sum of K_0^*-indecomposable graphs obtained by repeated K_0^*-decompositions.

A representation (10.2.3) is a *basis representation* for G. The totality of all K_0^*-indecomposable graphs is a *basis* for $K_0^*(A)$. It should be noted that the basis representation need not be unique; it is also possible that one basis element may contain another.

For a given image graph A we shall investigate the K_0^*-decompositions in some further detail. The vertex connectivity of A is denoted by δ. Suppose $G \succ A$ where G is some arbitrary graph with a simplex decomposition (10.2.2). Let γ be a defining contraction for $G \succ A$. From γ we derive its *restriction* γ_1 to G_1 by defining the inverse image sets of γ_1 to be the intersections.

$$\gamma_1^{-1}(a) = \gamma^{-1}(a) \cap V(G_1), \qquad a \in A. \qquad (10.2.4)$$

A set in (10.2.4) is void when

$$\gamma^{-1}(a) \subset V(G) - V(G_1).$$

The remaining sets (10.2.4) are disjoint. Their section graphs in G_1 are connected since any two vertices in S_v are connected by an edge. For the same reason, when two sets, $\gamma^{-1}(a)$, $\gamma^{-1}(b)$, are connected by an edge in G the corresponding sets in (10.2.4) are connected by an edge in G_1. This shows that γ_1 defines a contraction $G_1 \succ A_1$ where A_1 is a section subgraph of A.

In the same way one obtains a restriction γ_2 of γ to G_2 such that $G_2 \succ A_2$. From A_1 and A_2 one returns to A

$$A = A_1 + A_2, \qquad A_1 \cap A_2 = D \qquad (10.2.5)$$

where D is the section graph of A defined by those vertices $d \in A$ for which

$$\gamma_1^{-1}(d) \cap \gamma_2^{-1}(d) \neq \phi. \tag{10.2.6}$$

This intersection lies in S_v so that (10.2.5) represents a separation of A by at most v vertices. From this, we conclude the following theorem.

Theorem 10.2.3. When a graph $G \in K(A)$ has a simplex decomposition (10.2.2) with $v \leq \delta - 1$, *then either* $G_1 \succ A$ *or* $G_2 \succ A$ *or both.*

When $v \geq \delta$, the situation is more complicated. Let us consider only the case $v = \delta$. If any intersection (10.2.6) should include more than one vertex, then D in (10.2.5) would have fewer than δ vertices and one of the relations

$$G_1 \succ A_1, \qquad G_2 \succ A_2 \tag{10.2.7}$$

must again hold. When each intersection (10.2.6) has a single vertex, D has δ vertices. We conclude that either (10.2.7) holds or there exists some defining contraction γ for $G \succ A$ such that its restrictions to G_1 and G_2 yield

$$G_1 \succ A_1, \qquad G_2 \succ A_2$$

where A_1 and A_2 are the components in some separation (10.2.5) of A by δ vertices.

From Theorem 10.2.3 one obtains the next theorem.

Theorem 10.2.4. When $G \in K_0^*$ has a simplex decomposition (10.2.2) with $v \leq \delta - 1$, then this is also a K_0^*-decomposition.

Proof: We shall have to show that both components in (10.2.2) belong to K_0^*. We consider G_1. When it is a simplex there is nothing to prove. Thus a new edge $E_1 = (a_1, b_1)$ can be added to G_1 and we have the simplex decomposition

$$G + E_1 = (G_1 + E_1) + G_2, \qquad (G_1 + E_1) \cap G_2 = S_v.$$

Since

$$G + E_1 \in K(A), \qquad G_2 \in K^*(A)$$

it follows from Theorem 10.2.3 that

$$G_1 + E_1 \in K$$

and we conclude

$$G_1 \in K_0^*.$$

In connection with Theorem 10.2.4 we observe that in the special case where $A = S_n$ is a simplex it cannot be separated so we may formally put $\delta = \infty$. Then Theorem 10.2.4 holds without restriction on v. The same remark applies to the next theorem.

Theorem 10.2.5. Let $G \in K_0{}^*$ have a simplex decomposition (10.2.2) where $v \leq \delta - 2$. Then S_v cannot be a proper subgraph of a simplex both in G_1 and G_2 except when

$$A = S_n, \qquad v = n - 2. \tag{10.2.8}$$

Proof: The conditions of the theorem say that there exist vertices $a_i \in G_i$, $i = 1, 2$ such that a_i is connected by edges to each vertex in S_v. We denote by

$$S_{v+1}(a_1), S_{v+1}(a_2), S_{v+2}(a_1, a_2)$$

the three simplexes spanned by $V(S_v)$ and the vertices a_1, a_2 and a_1, a_2 respectively. When the edge $E = (a_1, a_2)$ is added to G, one has

$$G + E \succ A$$

by assumption. Consider the simplex decomposition

$$G + E = G_1 + (G_2 + S(a_1, a_2))$$
$$S(a_1) = G_1 \cap (G_2 + S(a_1, a_2)). \tag{10.2.9}$$

Theorem 10.2.3 together with $v \leq \delta - 2$ shows that one of the components in (10.2.9) must have A as a subcontraction. Since $G_1 \in K_0{}^*$

$$G_2 + S(a_1, a_2) \succ A.$$

This graph has the simplex decomposition

$$G_2 + S(a_1, a_2), \qquad G_2 \cap S(a_1, a_2) = S(a_2)$$

and we conclude again from Theorem 10.2.3

$$S_{v+2}(a_1, a_2) \succ A.$$

This implies $v + 2 \geq n$. If A were not a simplex it would be a subgraph of

$$S(a_1) + S(a_2) \subset G$$

which is impossible. Thus $A = S_n$ and since $S(a_1)$ cannot contain A we must have $v = n - 2$ and (10.2.8) follows.

As an application we find Theorem 10.2.6.

Theorem 10.2.6. When $G \in K_0^*$ has a separating vertex, then either A can be separated by one or two vertices or $A = S_3$ and G is a tree.

Proof: Let $S_1 = (s)$ be a separating vertex in G. Since s is the end point of an edge both in G_1 and G_2 the simplex S_1 is a subgraph of a larger simplex S_2 in both G_1 and G_2. If A is not separable by two vertices, it follows from Theorem 10.2.5 that $A = S_3$. Since any graph with a circuit is contractible to S_3 we conclude that G is a tree.

10.3. Indecomposable Graphs

The properties of the graphs in $K_0^*(A)$ depend on those of the indecomposable graphs according to Theorem 10.2.2. Therefore, we shall examine these basis graphs in further detail.

Suppose $G \supset G_1$ are two graphs in K_0^*. Then $G - G_1$ decomposes into bridges with respect to G_1. For any such bridge B the attachment set must span a simplex S_B in G_1. To see this let s_1 and s_2 be two attachments. By contracting B completely to s_1 one obtains a contracted graph containing G_1 and having an edge (s_1, s_2). Since G and G_1 belong to K_0^* this is only possible when the edge already occurs in G_1.

The simplex S_B defines a decomposition of G in which one component is $B + S_B$; the other consists of G_1 and all other bridges to it. If the number v of vertices in S_B satisfies $v \leq \delta - 1$, it follows from Theorem 10.2.4 that G_1 decomposes into two components in K_0^* one of which contains G.

Theorem 10.3.1. A K_0^*-indecomposable graph $G \in K_0^*$ can have no subgraph $G_1 \in K_0^*$ with any bridge having fewer than δ attachments. In particular, when $A = S_n$ is a simplex G can have no subgraphs in K_0^*.

The last statement is a consequence of the fact that for a simplex $\delta = \infty$.

In Theorem 10.2.6 we established conditions under which a graph $G \in K_0^*$ can have a separating vertex. For the separation of K_0^*-indecomposable graphs one has a stronger result.

Theorem 10.3.2. Let A be 3-vertex connected and $A \neq S_3$. Then no K_0^* indecomposable graph $G \in K_0^*$ can be separated by two vertices.

Proof: Under the given conditions G has no separating vertices according to Theorem 10.2.6. Suppose G is separated by two vertices u_1 and u_2

$$G = G_1 + G_2, \qquad G_1 \cap G_2 = \{u_1, u_2\}. \qquad (10.3.1)$$

There can be no edge $E = (u_1, u_2)$ in G for G would become K_0*-decomposable by $S_2 = E$ contradicting Theorem 10.2.4. In (10.3.1) each component is connected since G has no separating vertices. Thus by contracting G_1 and G_2 to an edge E one obtains the two graphs

$$G_1' = G_1 + E, \qquad G_2' = G_2 + E.$$

Both belong to K* by assumption but their sum $G + E$ is in K, contradicting Theorem 10.2.3.

This argument can be generalized. Let H be a subgraph of G. A *contraction of G to H* is a contraction in which G is contracted to the vertices in H, contracting all edges except those which connect vertices in H. The result is a graph H_1 having H as a subgraph.

Theorem 10.3.3. Let $G \in K_0$* have a separation (10.2.1) by a graph H with $v \leq \delta - 1$ vertices. If both G_1 and G_2 are contractible to a simplex S on H, then $S = H$.

Proof: If H were not a simplex, one could add an edge E to it. Then by assumption $G + E \succ A$ with the defining contraction γ. The vertices $a \in A$ with

$$\gamma^{-1}(a) \cap V(H) \neq \phi$$

cannot separate A since $v < \delta$. Thus one may suppose that every set $\gamma^{-1}(a)$ has a nonvoid intersection with $V(G_1)$. There is also a defining correspondence φ for the contraction of G_2 to a simplex S_v on H. Here all sets

$$\varphi^{-1}(h), \qquad h \in V(H)$$

are connected by edges in G_2 since the graph $\varphi(G_2)$ is a simplex. From these two correspondences γ and φ we derive a new correspondence ψ with the inverse image sets

$$\psi^{-1}(a) = \gamma^{-1}(a) \cap V(G_1) + \sum_i \varphi^{-1}(h_i)$$

where in the sum

$$h_i \in V(H) \cap \gamma^{-1}(a).$$

One verifies that χ defines a contraction $G \succ A$ contrary to the condition $G \in K_0$*.

Theorem 10.3.4. Suppose $\delta \geq 4$ and $A \neq S_3$. When an indecomposable graph $G \in K_0$* has a separation by three vertices

$$U = \{u_1, u_2, u_3\}, \tag{10.3.2}$$

then no two vertices in U can be connected by edges. The vertices in U define just two bridges B_1 and B_2 where B_1 consists of three edges from a common vertex b_1 with $\rho(b_1) = 3$

$$B_1 = (b_1, u_1) + (b_1, u_2) + (b_1, u_3). \tag{10.3.3}$$

The bridge B_2 is not of this type.

Proof: G cannot be separated by one or two vertices according to Theorems 10.2.6 and 10.3.2. Since U is a minimal separating set any bridge for U is attached at all three vertices. If there should be any edge connecting the vertices in (10.3.2), any bridge could be contracted to a simplex S_3 on U. We see that Theorem 10.3.3 implies that there can be no such edges.

Let B_1 be some bridge for U. There exists a vertex $b_1 \in B_1$ connected by disjoint arcs.

$$Q_1(b_1, u_1), \qquad Q_2(b_1, u_2), \qquad Q_3(b_1, u_3) \tag{10.3.4}$$

to U. As we observed there must be one bridge not contractible to S_3 on U, so let B_1 be such a bridge. Suppose there exists some intermediate vertex q_1 on the arc Q_1 in (10.3.4). Since $Q_1(b_1, u_1)$ cannot be separated from the rest of the graph by the two vertices b_1 and u_1, there must be some arc $P(q_1, p)$ disjoint from b_1 and u_1 going to some vertex p lying on one of the other arcs Q_2 or Q_3 (Fig. 10.3.1). But then B_1 is contractible to S_3 on U as one readily sees. We conclude that in B_1 the arcs (10.3.4) are single edges. If there should be other arcs $Q(b_1, u_i)$ in B_1, a contraction to S_3 on U could again be found. We conclude that B_1 has the form (10.3.3). If there should be more than two bridges, all but one of them must be of this type.

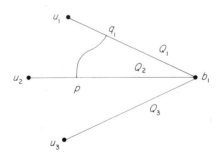

Fig. 10.3.1.

Two bridges (10.3.3) together can be contracted to S_3. Hence, if there exists a bridge B_2 not of this type, there can only be one bridge B_1. Similarly, if there is no bridge B_2, there can at most be three bridges B_1. This leaves us only with the two graphs in Fig. 10.3.2. The reader may verify that there exists no graph A with $\delta \geq 4$ such that

$$G \in K_0{}^*(A), \qquad G + E \in K(A) \qquad \text{for every added edge } E.$$

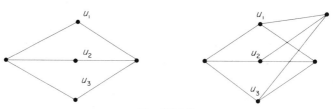

Fig. 10.3.2.

10.4. Hadwiger's Conjecture

There exists for the vertex coloration of a graph a general and very interesting conjecture due to Hadwiger.

Hadwiger's conjecture. When G is an arbitrary graph with chromatic number $\varkappa(G) = k$, then G can be contracted to S_k,

$$G \succ S_k.$$

This conjecture has been the object of a number of recent studies on graph coloration; let us mention especially the papers by Wagner, Halin, and Dirac (see bibliography). The importance of this conjecture for the four-color problem is evident from the following theorem.

Theorem 10.4.1. Hadwiger's conjecture for $k = 5$ implies the four-color theorem.

Proof: If there should exist some planar graph G with chromatic number $k = 5$, it would imply that G was contractible to S_5. For a planar graph this is not possible by the Kuratowski criterion.

The main result which has been obtained in connection with Hadwiger's conjecture is as follows.

Wagner's equivalence theorem: Hadwiger's conjecture for $k = 5$ is equivalent to the four-color theorem.

In view of Theorem 10.4.1 it remains to show that when the four-color theorem holds for planar graphs then for $k = 5$ Hadwiger's conjecture is true for arbitrary graphs. The proof of this fact is one of the principal objects of this and the next section (Wagner).

Let us make clear the relation of this demonstration to the preceding discussion of the maximal graphs in a class $K_0*(A)$. In this case we take $A = S_k$. If one can show that all graphs in the class $K*(S_k)$ can be colored in $k - 1$ colors, it follows that all graphs with the chromatic number k must be contractible to S_k. It suffices to prove this for the graphs in the maximal class $K_0*(S_k)$. In turn, it suffices to show that all $K_0*(S_k)$-indecomposable graphs can be colored in $k - 1$ colors since then the coloration of an arbitrary graph in $K_0*(S_k)$ in $k - 1$ colors will follow from Theorem 10.2.2. Thus our problem leads directly to the explicit determination of the basis graphs for the class $K_0*(S_5)$. In general, one sees for an arbitrary graph A that if all basis graphs of the class $K_0*(A)$ are colorable in $k - 1$ colors then all graphs with $\varkappa(G) = k$ must satisfy $G \succ A$.

For the smallest values of k Hadwiger's conjecture can be proved.

Theorem 10.4.2. Hadwiger's conjecture is true for $k < 5$ (Dirac).

Proof: $k = 2$. The graphs in $K*(S_2)$ are the graphs without edges; hence they are colorable in one color, so a graph with $\varkappa(G) = 2$ is contractible to S_2.

$k = 3$. The graphs in $K*(S_3)$ are the graphs without circuits. Since trees are bipartite they can be colored in two colors, hence graphs with $\varkappa(G) = 3$ must be contractible to S_3.

The remaining case $k = 4$ follows from Theorem 10.4.3.

Theorem 10.4.3. The $K_0*(S_4)$-indecomposable graphs are the simplexes $S_i, i \leq 3$.

Proof: Suppose that G is a basis graph which is not a simplex. According to Theorem 10.3.2 it cannot be separated by two vertices. In G we select vertices $p \neq q$ not connected by an edge. By Menger's theorem there exist three disjoint arcs

$$A_1(p, q), \qquad A_2(p, q), \qquad A_3(p, q).$$

We may assume that A_1 includes an intermediate vertex a_1. The edges in A_1 belong to a bridge B with respect to the circuit

$$C = A_2 + A_3.$$

Here B cannot only have the attachments p and q. Suppose a_2 is an attachment on A_2. Then there is an arc $B_1(a_1, a_2)$ in B and the subgraph consisting of the arcs A_1, A_2, A_3, B_1 is contractible to S_4 contradicting $G \in K_0{}^*(S_4)$.

Since S_2 and S_3 are colorable in 3 colors, the remaining case $k = 4$ in Theorem 10.4.2 is a consequence of Theorem 10.4.3.

Let us introduce a special type of graph composition. When G and H are disjoint graphs, then their *composite* $G \circ H$ is the graph consisting of G and H and in addition the totality of all edges connecting a vertex in G with a vertex in H. For such a composition we have:

Theorem 10.4.4. When S_v is a simplex, then the relation $G \succ A$ is equivalent to

$$G \circ S_v \succ A \circ S_v \qquad (10.4.1)$$

Proof: It is evident that when $G \succ A$, then also (10.4.1) holds. Suppose on the other hand that (10.4.1) is fulfilled and denote by γ some defining contraction. We shall show that from γ a defining contraction ψ for $G \succ A$ can be constructed.

The vertices $a \in V(A)$ fall into two categories: The vertices $a' \in S'$ such that

$$\gamma^{-1}(a') \subset V(G) \qquad (10.4.2)$$

and the vertices $a'' \in S''$ such that

$$\gamma^{-1}(a'') \cap V(S_v) \neq \phi. \qquad (10.4.3)$$

Let there be t vertices a''

$$a_1'', \ldots, a_t''.$$

Then there are at most $v - t$ vertices in $V(S)$ which do not belong to any of the sets (10.4.3). Thus in S' there must exist at least t vertices,

$$s_1', \ldots, s_t'$$

such that

$$\gamma^{-1}(s_i') \subset V(G). \qquad (10.4.4)$$

Since the s_i' are all connected by edges in S' the sets (10.4.4) are all connected by edges in G.

The contraction ψ for G is obtainable as follows: For a vertex a' in (10.4.2) we put

$$\psi^{-1}(a') = \gamma^{-1}(a').$$

For each vertex a_i'' in (10.4.3) we select a corresponding vertex s_i' and put

$$\psi^{-1}(a_i'') = \gamma^{-1}(s_i').$$

The sets $\psi^{-1}(a)$ are all disjoint and their section graphs are connected since they are inverse image sets of γ lying in $V(G)$. For two vertices a' the sets $\psi^{-1}(a')$ are connected by an edge in G when a_1' and a_2' are connected by an edge in A. The sets $\psi^{-1}(a'')$ are all connected by edges in G. The same is true for any pair of vertices a' and a'' by the construction of the composite $A \circ S'$. We conclude that ψ defines $G \succ A$.

We conclude from Theorem 10.4.4 that $G \in K_0{}^*(A)$ implies

$$G \circ S \in K^*(A \circ S)$$

and vice versa. An edge added to G is also an added edge for $G \circ S$ and conversely since in $G \circ S$ the only vertices which are not edge connected must belong to G. From this we conclude that $G \in K_0{}^*(A)$ implies

$$G \circ S \in K_0{}^*(A \circ S).$$

Theorem 10.4.4 yields the next theorem.

Theorem 10.4.5. When Hadwiger's conjecture is true for some k, it is true for all $h < k$.

Proof: By assumption, the chromatic number of any graph $G \in K^*(S_k)$ satisfies

$$\varkappa(G) \leqq k - 1.$$

Suppose now that $G \in K^*(S_h)$. Then

$$G \circ S_{k-h} \in K^*(S_h \circ S_{k-h}) = K^*(S_k)$$

and so

$$\varkappa(G \circ S_{k-h}) \leqq k - 1.$$

But since

$$\varkappa(G \circ S_{k-h}) = \varkappa(G) + k - h,$$

this implies

$$\varkappa(G) \leqq h - 1.$$

The proof of Hadwiger's conjecture evidently involves great difficulties. A simpler related question has been proposed by Halin: For any integer k does there exist some other integer $\varphi(k)$ such that every graph

G with chromatic number

$$\varkappa(G) \geq \varphi(k)$$

satisfies

$$G \succ S_k?$$

The answer is in the affirmative, as shown by Wagner.

Theorem 10.4.6. A function $\varphi(k)$ as described does exist for all k and it is bounded by the inequalities

$$\varphi(k + 1) \leq 2\varphi(k) - 1. \tag{10.4.5}$$

Proof: Hadwiger's conjecture would be equivalent to $\varphi(k) = k$. According to Theorem 10.4.2 such a function exists for $k < 5$ with

$$\varphi(k) = k, \qquad k = 2, 3, 4.$$

Thus the existence of the function for subsequent values may be deduced by induction.

Suppose that G is a graph with

$$\varkappa(G) \geq 2\varphi(k) - 1 \tag{10.4.6}$$

and the theorem is true for all $k' \leq k$. We shall show that $G \succ S_{k+1}$. In G we select a fixed vertex v_0. The vertex set decomposes into disjoint sets

$$V(G) = v_0 + V_1 + V_2 + \ldots$$

where V_i consists of the vertices whose distance from v_0 is i. By $G_i = G(V_i)$ we denote the section graph defined by V_i. For these graphs one cannot have

$$\varkappa(G_i) < \varphi(k), \qquad i = 1, 2, 3, \ldots$$

for each G_i would be colorable in at most $\varphi(k) - 1$ colors; by using one color set for the even numbered G_i and a completely different set for the odd numbered G_i one would obtain a coloration of G in at most $2\varphi(k) - 2$ colors, contradicting (10.4.6).

Therefore, we can select a graph G_i with

$$\varkappa(G_i) \geq \varphi(k).$$

By the induction assumption $G_i \succ S_k$. From v_0 there exist connecting arcs to each vertex $v_i \in V_i$. These arcs can be contracted to single edges from v_0. When this contraction is combined with the contraction $G_i \succ S_k$, one sees that G has a subgraph contractible to S_{k+1}.

Another result also due to Wagner establishes that for $k = 5$ Hadwiger's conjecture is nearly correct. Let us write

$$S_v^* = S_v - E$$

for the graph obtained by removing a single edge E from a simplex S_v. Then we have, according to Wagner, the next theorem.

Theorem 10.4.7. Any graph with chromatic number $\varkappa(G) = 5$ satisfies

$$G \succ S_5^*.$$

The proof is based upon a determination of the basis graphs of the class $K_0^*(S_5^*)$. It will be clear from the form of these graphs that they are all colorable in four colors, so the theorem follows.

Theorem 10.4.8. The only nonplanar basis graph in $K_0^*(S_5^*)$ is the Kuratowski graph $K = (3, 3)$.

Proof: We leave it to the reader to verify that K is a basis graph, that is, K is not contractible to S_5^* but any graph $K + E$ has this property.

On the other hand let P be a nonplanar basis graph for $K_0^*(S_5^*)$. Since P is not contractible to S_5 the Kuratowski criterion shows that P contains a subgraph K' conformal to K. The principal vertices in K' we denote by

$$a_1, a_2, a_3; b_1, b_2, b_3.$$

Their connecting arcs in K' are

$$T_{ij} = T_{ij}(a_i, b_j).$$

We shall prove that all T_{ij} must be edges. Take c as an intermediate vertex on T_{11}. There can be no arcs from c disjoint from K' to vertices in K' not on T_{11} for by contraction one would obtain a graph

$$K' + E' \succ S_5^*.$$

Thus the two vertices a_1 and b_1 separate P. But S_5^* has $\delta = 3$ so this would contradict Theorem 10.3.2. We conclude that $K' = K$. But for similar reasons there can be no further edges in P and so $P = K$.

Theorem 10.4.9. The planar basis graphs for $K_0^*(S_5^*)$ are

1. The simplexes S_2, S_3, and S_4.
2. The prism graph in Fig. 10.4.1.
3. The wheel graph in Fig. 10.4.2 with an arbitrary number of spokes.

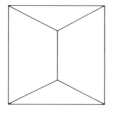 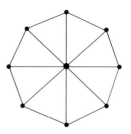

Fig. 10.4.1.   Fig. 10.4.2.

Proof: The reader may verify also here that none of these graphs have S_5^* as a subcontraction, but any added edge will give them this property. They cannot be separated by a simplex. Denote by P some planar basis graph. We may assume that it has at least five vertices when the simplexes S_3 and S_4 are excluded. Since

$$P + E \succ S_5^*,$$

there exists some circuit C in P. We select C minimal and take it as the boundary of the infinite face. Since P cannot be separated by an edge there are no interior diagonals for C. Nor can there be any bridge B for C with only two attachments.

As a consequence there will be an interior vertex a_0 in C from which there are three disjoint arcs

$$A_1(a_0, c_1), \qquad A_2(a_0, c_2), \qquad A_3(a_0, c_3) \tag{10.4.7}$$

to different vertices $c_i \in C$. We select these arcs such that their total length is minimal. Then two non-neighboring vertices on an arc A_i cannot be connected by an edge. Theorem 10.3.2 shows that $\rho(v) \geq 3$ for each vertex in P. The arcs (10.4.7) divide C into three sections

$$C_1 = C(c_1, c_2), \qquad C_2 = C(c_2, c_3), \qquad C_3 = C(c_3, c_1)$$

with corresponding circuits (Fig. 10.4.3)
$$D_1 = A_1 + A_2 + C_1, \qquad D_2 = A_2 + A_3 + C_2, \qquad D_3 = A_3 + A_1 + C_3.$$

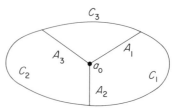

Fig. 10.4.3.

Case 1. All vertices in P lie on the circuits D_i. Suppose first that there are more than three edges at a_0. By our assumption every edge E_0 at a_0 not included in the arcs A_i must have its other end on C. If any A_i should have more than one edge, we could replace it by the edge E_0 making the sum of the lengths of the A_i shorter. We conclude that P is a wheel graph.

Secondly, let there be just three edges at a_0. There is an intermediate vertex on one of the arcs A_i, say $a_1 \in A_1$, since otherwise one would have $P = S_4$. At a_1 there is some edge not in A_1, say $E_1 = (a_1, b_1)$. We suppose that E_1 lies in the interior of D_1. The end point b_1 is then either c_2 or on one of the arcs C_1 or A_2. Under these conditions there are no edges in P lying in the interior of D_2 or D_3 for by checking the various alternatives one finds that this would imply $P \succ S_5{}^*$. Since there are at least three edges at each vertex, we conclude that the arcs A_3, C_2, C_3 are edges.

When b_1 is an interior vertex of C_1, we select a_1 and b_1 as close to c_1 as possible. Then there can be no other edges in the interior of D_1 from the arc $A_1(a_0, a_1)$ for it would follow that $P \succ S_5{}^*$. Thus in this case P is a prism graph as in Fig. 10.4.1. When $b_1 = c_2$ and there exists an edge from $A_1(a_0, a_1)$ to an interior vertex of A_2, we again have $P \succ S_5{}^*$. Thus in this case we obtain a wheel graph with four spokes and center c_2. There remains the case where b_1 is an interior vertex of A_2 and here one sees without difficulty that P is a prism graph.

Case 2. There are vertices in P which do not lie on any of the circuits D_i.

Under the given conditions this case cannot arise. To verify this let v_1 be a vertex in the interior of D_1. It belongs to some bridge B_1 with respect to this circuit. We may assume as before that B has at least three attachments. None of these can be intermediate vertices on C_1. If, namely, there were such an attachment $b_1 \in C_1$, then not all attachments could be on C_1 for P would be separable by two vertices. If there is an attachment $a_1 \in A_1$, one finds again $P \succ S_5{}^*$, and the same for an attachment $a_2 \in A_2$. When there are no attachments of B_1 at intermediate vertices of C_1, one also readily obtains $P \succ S_5{}^*$.

The graphs in Theorem 10.4.8 and 10.4.9 are all colorable in at most four colors so that the proof of Theorem 10.4.7 is completed.

10.5. Wagner's Equivalence Theorem

We turn to the proof of Wagner's result to the effect that Hadwiger's conjecture for $k = 5$ is equivalent to the four-color problem. The original proof by Wagner is quite complicated. A somewhat simpler proof was given by Halin. Here we shall simplify the proof still further, making use of some of the ideas in Halin's proof.

Our main object is to establish a basis for the class $K_0^*(S_5)$. The planar basis graphs are readily found. Such a basis graph must be maximal planar. Theorem 2.7.2 shows that such a graph actually belongs to $K_0^*(S_5)$. The only simplexes which can separate a maximal planar graph are the triangles S_3.

Lemma 10.5.1. The planar basis graphs in $K_0^*(S_5)$ are the maximal planar graphs without separating triangles.

To examine the nonplanar basis graphs we introduce the special graph W drawn in two forms in Fig. 10.5.1. It is a nonplanar graph with

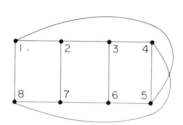
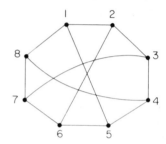

Fig. 10.5.1.

eight vertices and twelve edges; it is regular with valence 3. One can consider W to be a Möbius strip divided into four rectangles or also as an octagon in which opposite vertices are connected by edges. W cannot be contracted to S_5 since this would involve the coalition of three vertices so the resulting graph would have at most nine edges while S_5 has ten edges. Since $L \succ S_5$ we see that W cannot be contracted to the graph L in Fig. 10.1.2. The same holds for the graph $M = (1, 2, 3)$ drawn in Fig. 10.1.3. Let us add an edge E to W. Due to the symmetries of W we need only consider the cases where E connects vertices 1, 6 or 1, 7. We leave it to the reader to verify that in either case

$$W + E \succ L \succ S_5, \qquad W + E \succ M \succ S_5.$$

Thus we can state the following lemma.

Lemma 10.5.2. The graph W is a basis graph for each of the classes

$$K_0^*(L), K_0^*(M), K_0^*(S_5).$$

In the following we shall consider graphs which have a subgraph K' conformal to the Kuratowski graph $K = (3, 3)$. As before we denote the principal vertices of K' by

$$a_1, a_2, a_3; \qquad b_1, b_2, b_3;$$

and their connecting arcs in K' by $T_{ij}(a_i, b_j)$. Two connecting arcs form an angle when they have an end point or *summit* in common. These are a-angles or b-angles depending on the character of the summit.

The following lemma is due to Halin.

Lemma 10.5.3. Let the graph $G \nsucc L$ contain a subgraph K' conformal to K. Then either G includes a subgraph W' conformal to W or one of the classes of principal vertices in K' separates each pair of such vertices in the other.

Proof: Suppose that the vertices a_1 and a_2 are not separated by the $\{b_i\}$ nor b_1 and b_2 by the $\{a_i\}$. Then in G there exist arcs

$$A(a_1, a_2), \qquad B(b_1, b_2)$$

such that A includes no vertex b_i and B no vertex a_i. We select A and B such that they have a minimal number of edges outside K'. An *outer section* of these arcs is a section having only its end points on K'. Let us consider the possible locations of such a section $A(p, q)$ in regard to K'.

1. $A(p, q)$ cannot have its end points p and q on the same arc T_{ij} for then it could be replaced by an arc in K'.

2. $A(p, q)$ cannot connect two legs of an a-angle for then it could be replaced by an arc along these legs.

3. When $A(p, q)$ does not connect the legs of any angle, then p and q must be intermediate vertices on two arcs T not forming an angle. One verifies that then

$$K' + A(p, q) \succ W.$$

The same argument applies to the arc $B(b_1, b_2)$. This leaves us with the case where all outer sections $A(p, q)$ connect legs of b-angles and all $B(p', q')$ connect legs of a-angles. We shall show that this situation cannot arise since it implies $G \succ L$.

We select the notations such that $B(p', q')$ connect the legs of an angle with summit a_1 and $A(p, q)$ the legs of an angle with summit b_1. Two cases can occur:

1. The legs of the two angles do not include the connecting arc T_{11}. Then T_{12}, T_{13} is one pair of legs, T_{21}, T_{31} the other. The outer sections

are

$$B(p', q'), \qquad p' \in T_{12}, \qquad q' \in T_{13}$$
$$A(p, q), \qquad p \in T_{21}, \qquad q \in T_{31}.$$

When the two sections are disjoint, we contract the vertex pairs

$$(p, a_2)(q, a_3)(p', b_2)(q', b_3)$$

along their connecting arcs T in K'. The resulting graph is conformal to L.

When A and B are not disjoint, we contract them to a single vertex t with edges to p, q, p', q'. Then the same contraction as above is applied. The result is a graph K' to which has been added four edges from a new vertex t to a_2, a_3, b_2, b_3. When finally a_1 and b_2 are contracted along T_{12}, one obtains a graph with a subgraph conformal to L.

2. The legs of the two angles are

$$T_{11}, T_{12}; \qquad T_{11}, T_{21}.$$

We begin by contracting (q, a_2) and (q', b_2) along their connecting T-arcs.

(a) Both p and q are intermediate vertices on T_{11}. We contract them to p along T_{11}; this may be done such that the arcs $A(p, a_2)$ and $B(p, b_2)$ are contracted along T_{13}. The resulting graph has a subgraph conformal to L.

(b) $p = a_1$. If A and B are disjoint, we contract p' to b_1 to obtain a graph L'. When A and B are not disjoint, we contract them to a vertex t with edges to a_1, a_2, b_1, b_2. Finally, a_1 is contracted to b_3 to obtain L'.

A consequence of Halin's lemma is Theorem 10.5.1.

Theorem 10.5.1. A nonplanar graph G which is 4-vertex connected and has at least six vertices satisfies

$$G \succ L \succ S_5.$$

Proof: This follows from Theorem 10.1.4 in case G contains a subgraph conformal to S_5. Therefore, we may suppose that G has a subgraph conformal to K. Lemma 10.5.3 shows that G includes a subgraph W' conformal to W. From any principal vertex in W' there are four disjoint arcs to the other principal vertices. This leads to the existence of an arc not in W' connecting two of its branches. From Lemma 10.5.2 we conclude

$$G \succ W + E \succ L \succ S_5.$$

We are now ready to prove the next theorem.

Theorem 10.5.2. The only nonplanar basis graph for $K_0^*(S_5)$ is W.

Proof: Let $P \in K_0^*(S_5)$ be a nonplanar basis graph. Since P cannot be contracted to S_5, we must have $P > K$ so P has a subgraph K' conformal to K and Lemma 10.5.3 can be applied.

Suppose P contains a subgraph W' conformal to W. We shall establish that this is only possible when $P = W$. We begin by showing that $W' = W$. Assume that there is an intermediate vertex v on an arc $W(a, b)$ in W' joining two principal vertices a and b. Since a and b do not separate P according to Theorem 10.3.2, there exists an arc $T(v, u)$ not including a and b to some vertex u lying on one of the other arcs of W'. But this is impossible since it implies

$$P \supset W' + T > W + E > L > S_5.$$

Also when $W = W'$, one cannot have $P \neq W$ for no edge or arc in P can connect two vertices in W according to the same argument.

We are left with the case where P cannot be contracted to S_5 or W. It shall be shown that this alternative cannot occur. Since $L > S_5$ we may apply Lemma 10.5.3, indeed the proof of this lemma is considerably simpler on the stronger assumption $G \nsucc S_5$. We conclude that there exists in P a set of three vertices $A = \{a_1, a_2, a_3\}$ which separate three other vertices in pairs. This means that there are at least three bridges B in P for A. But this contradicts Theorem 10.3.4.

The proof of Wagner's equivalence theorem can now readily be completed. We saw that for $k = 5$ Hadwiger's conjecture implies the four-color theorem. Suppose, on the other hand, that the four-color theorem is true. This means that the planar basis graphs for $K_0^*(S_5)$ can be colored in four colors. The only nonplanar basis graph W can be colored in three colors as one verifies. Thus all graphs in $K_0^*(S_5)$ can be colored in four colors; hence all graphs requiring five colors must belong to $K(S_5)$, that is, be contractible to S_5.

From a basis for $K_0^*(S_5)$ one also obtains a basis for $K_0^*(L)$ as one sees from the following observation by Halin (personal communication).

Theorem 10.5.3. Let G be a 3-vertex connected graph with at least six vertices. Then $G \in K_0^*(L)$ if, and only if, $G \in K_0^*(S_5)$.

Proof: Suppose $G \in K_0^*(L)$. Then G cannot contain a subgraph S_5' conformal to S_5 according to Theorem 10.1.4. In turn it follows from Theorem 10.1.2 that $G \in K^*(S_5)$; hence $G \in K_0^*(S_5)$ since $L > S_5$. On the other hand, suppose that $G \in K_0^*(S_5)$. We add an arbitrary edge E to G.

If
$$G + E \supset S_5',$$ (10.5.1)

we conclude from Theorem 10.1.4 that

$$G + E \succ L.$$

When (10.5.1) does not hold, we obtain the same result from Theorem 10.1.2. This shows that $G \in K_0^*(L)$ and we may state the following theorem.

Theorem 10.5.4. The basis graphs for $K_0^*(L)$ are W and the simplexes $S_i, i \leq 5.$

Wagner's equivalence theorem may be given other forms as indicated by Halin, for instance we have Theorem 10.5.5.

Theorem 10.5.5. The four-color theorem is equivalent to the statement: One has $G \succ S_5$ for any 5-chromatic nonplanar graph with vertex connectivity 3 and not containing a subgraph W' conformal to W.

Proof: When the four-color theorem is true, $G \succ S_5$ follows from Wagner's theorem. Conversely, suppose that the statement of the theorem is correct. We can then show that there is no planar graph G which is 5-chromatic. If there were such a graph G, we can suppose that it is maximal, hence $G \in K_0^*(S_5)$. From G we derive a nonplanar graph $G' \in K_0^*(S_5)$ which is also 5-chromatic by adding two graphs S_4 at one of the triangles of G. Here G' cannot be 4-vertex connected and it cannot be separated by two vertices. Nor can it contain a subgraph W' as one readily verifies. According to the statement of the theorem one should have $G' \in K(S_5)$ which is impossible.

There are other ways in which the equivalence theorem can be stated. One can make use of the graph $M = (1, 2, 3)$ in Fig. 10.1.3. Thus, for every 5-chromatic graph G

$$G \supseteq S_5' \qquad \text{or} \qquad G \in K(M)$$

or also

$$G \supseteq S_5' \qquad \text{or} \qquad G \in K(L), \qquad G \in K(M).$$

10.6. Contractions to S_4

The importance of Hadwiger's conjecture has induced a number of studies of the contraction of graphs to simplexes, notably by Dirac. Let us first consider the case of a simplex S_4. We found in Theorem 10.4.3 that the basis graphs for the class $K_0*(S_4)$ are the simplexes S_2 and S_3. This means that the graphs in $K_0*(S_4)$ can be constructed successively by means of triangles, attaching each along an edge to the previously constructed part of the graph. Since a graph is contractible to S_4 if, and only if, one of its lobe graphs has this property, we need only consider 2-vertex connected graphs.

The graphs which cannot be contracted to S_4 are very special. Both S_5 and $K = (3, 3)$ belong to $K(S_4)$ so that all graphs in $K*(S_4)$ are planar. Since each graph in $K_0*(S_4)$ is composed of triangles, it follows by induction that it must have at least two vertices with $\rho(v) = 2$. This yields Theorem 10.6.1.

Theorem 10.6.1. A graph G with $\rho(v) \geq 3$ for all vertices with at most a single exception must belong to $K(S_4)$.

In the construction of a graph $G \in K_0*(S_4)$ each added triangle contributes one new vertex and two edges so one obtains the following theorem by induction.

Theorem 10.6.2. When the number of edges in a graph G is at least $2v_v - 2$, then $G > S_4$.

In connection with Theorem 10.6.1 let us examine the graphs in $K*(S_4)$ which have exactly two vertices with $\rho(v) = 2$. Take first $G \in K_0*(S_4)$. We begin our construction of G with some triangle T_0 with one of its corners at a 2-vertex in G. In each step we add a triangle T_{i+1} to the preceding triangle T_i. It is not possible to attach some later triangle T_j also to T_i for it would lead to a graph G with more than two 2-vertices. We conclude that our graph must be a *chain of triangles* as drawn in Fig. 10.6.1.

Fig. **10.6.1.**

Suppose next that $G \in K*(S_4)$ is 2-vertex connected. Since G is a subgraph of some $G_1 \in K_0*(S_4)$, it follows that G_1 must also have exactly two 2-vertices. We conclude that G is a subgraph of a chain of triangles Fig. 10.6.1, obtained by eliminating some of the edges connecting pairs of vertices with $\rho \leq 4$. Finally, a general graph in $K*(S_4)$ with only two 2-vertices must consist of a string of lobe graphs of this kind.

Let us add a few remarks about graphs contractible to S_4.

Theorem 10.6.3. Let G be a 2-vertex connected graph with valences $\rho(v) \geq 3$. When a_0 is an arbitrary vertex and $E = (a_1, a_2)$ an arbitrary edge, then there exists a subgraph S_4' conformal to S_4 which includes a_0 and E.

Proof: In an inseparable graph there exists a circuit C passing through a_0 and E. We select C of maximal length and shall construct a graph S_4' including C. Let v_0 be a vertex on C different from the end points of E. From v_0 we can find a *chord* for C, that is an arc $A(v_0, v_1)$ having only its end points $v_0 \neq v_1$ on C. This is an immediate consequence of the fact that there is an edge at v_0 not in C and G is inseparable. The other end v_1 cannot be a neighbor of v_0 on C for it would lead to a longer circuit including a_0 and E.

Each chord divides C into two sections, one including E and the other not. We select a chord $A(v_0, v_1)$ such that the section S not including E is as short as possible. We noted that S must have at least one intermediate vertex s_0. At s_0 there is a chord $B(s_0, s_1)$. Under the given conditions s_1 is not a vertex on S, nor can $A(v_0, v_1)$ and $B(s_0, s_1)$ have a vertex in common. Then the subgraph S_4' consisting of C and the arcs A and B has the desired property.

Theorem 10.6.4. Let G be 3-vertex connected and

$$A_1(a, b), \qquad A_2(a, b), \qquad A_3(a, b)$$

three disjoint arcs connecting two arbitrary vertices a and b. Then there exists a subgraph S_4' conformal to S_4 including these arcs.

Proof: At most one of the three arcs is a single edge. Since G is 3-vertex connected there exists an arc B from an intermediate vertex on one arc A_1 to an intermediate vertex on another arc A_2 not passing through a or b. The four arcs B, A_1, A_2, A_3 form S_4'.

10.7. Multiply-Connected Graphs

We return to the study of contractions of graphs to S_5 and $S_5^* = S_5 - E$. We may assume that G has at least five vertices. In the following G shall be 3-vertex connected. Then a graph $^*G \in K_0^*(S_5^*)$ has no simplex decomposition

$$G = G_1 + G_2, G_1 \cap G_2 = S_v.$$

By assumption $v \geq 3$; when this is the case we select two vertices

$v_i \in G_i$, $i = 1, 2$ not in S_v. From each v_i there are three disjoint arcs to S_v and this would yield $G \succ S_5^*$.

We conclude that when $G \in K_0^*(S_5^*)$ is 3-vertex connected, it must be a basis graph. These basis graphs were determined in Theorem 10.4.9 so we obtain Theorem 10.7.1.

Theorem 10.7.1. When G is 3-vertex connected, then $G \succ S_5^*$ except when G is one of the following three graphs.

    1. The Kuratowski graph $K = (3, 3)$.
    2. The prism graph in Fig. 10.4.1.
    3. The wheel graph in Fig. 10.4.2.

A consequence of this theorem is a result obtained differently by Dirac.

Theorem 10.7.2. For a 3-vertex connected graph one has $G \succ S_5^*$ if it has more than one vertex satisfying $\rho(v) \geq 4$.

Proof: The exceptional graphs in Theorem 10.7.1 have valences $\rho(v) = 3$ except for the central vertex in the wheel graph.

We turn next to the 4-vertex connected graphs. When such a graph is nonplanar, it is contractible to S_5 according to Theorem 10.5.1. Hence we shall consider the planar graphs especially. Since the graph is 4-vertex connected, one has $\rho(v) \geq 4$ for every vertex. According to Theorem 10.7.2 one has $G \succ S_5^*$ in this case. This property is preserved in most cases when an arbitrary vertex v_0 and its edges are removed from G. To see that

$$G_1 = G(V - v_0) \succ S_5^* \qquad (10.7.1)$$

we need only observe that G_1 is 3-vertex connected and apply Theorem 10.7.2.

An exception to (10.7.1) can only occur when $\rho_1(u) = 3$ for all vertices in G_1 or when there is a single exception v_4 with $\rho_1(v_4) \geq 4$. We note that the first case where G_1 is regular with valence 3 can be excluded. It would imply that in G there is an edge from v_0 to every vertex in G_1. Since G is planar one sees that G_1 has a Hamilton circuit C and all other edges are diagonals to C. Suppose v_0 lies outside C. Then there can only be inner diagonals in G_1 and such a graph must have some vertices with $\rho_1 = 2$.

When there exists a vertex v_4, we arrive at an exceptional type of graph. Then there is an edge from v_0 to every vertex in G_1 except possibly v_4. When also the edges from v_4 are removed, we obtain as before a graph

G_2 consisting of a circuit C and possibly some outer diagonals. When there are outer diagonals, there will be two vertices in G_2 with $\rho_2 = 2$ which are separated on C by one of the diagonals. We replace v_0 and its edges inside C. But then it is not possible to replace v_4 and its edges in such a manner that G is planar and all its vertices have valences ≥ 4.

We conclude that there can be no diagonals for C. Then G becomes a *double wheel graph* as drawn in Fig. 10.7.1. It consists of a circuit C and two vertices a and b connected by edges to each vertex on C. There can be no edge $E = (a, b)$ for G would not be planar.

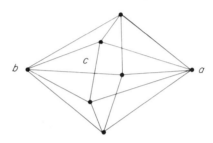

Fig. 10.7.1.

Theorem 10.7.3. A 4-vertex connected graph G satisfies $G \succ S_5$ when it is not planar. When it is planar, then

$$G(V - a) \succ S_5{}^*$$

for all vertices a except when G is a double-wheel graph.

We now turn to the 5-vertex connected graphs. Here we shall show Theorem 10.7.4 to hold true.

Theorem 10.7.4. Let G be a graph which can be contracted to a 5-vertex connected graph. Then $G \succ S_5$ when G is not planar and when G is planar then

$$G(V - a - b) \succ S_5{}^* \qquad (10.7.2)$$

$$G(V - a - b - c) \succ S_4 \qquad (10.7.3)$$

for all choices of the vertices a, b, c.

Proof: We prove the theorem first for the case where G is actually 5-vertex connected. We can assume G planar. When a vertex v_0 and its edges are removed from G, the resulting graph G_1 cannot be a double wheel graph (Fig. 10.7.1). In such a graph the vertices on C have valences $\rho_1 = 4$, hence there would have to be edges from v_0 to each of them.

However, this is not possible when G is planar. Thus the relations (10.7.2) follow from Theorem 10.7.3.

To prove the relations (10.7.3) we remove three vertices v_0, v_1, v_2 and their edges from G. The resulting graph G_3 is 2-vertex connected. From Theorem 10.6.1 we conclude that the relations (10.7.3) will hold except when G_3 has two or more vertices with $\rho_3 = 2$. We shall show that this cannot occur. Each of the 2-vertices must be connected by an edge to v_0, v_1, v_2 since $\rho \geq 5$ in G. If there were three or more 2-vertices, G would include a Kuratowski graph $K = (3, 3)$ and this is impossible since G is planar. The considerations in Section 10.6 show that when there are just two 2-vertices G_3 is a subgraph of a triangle chain as in Fig. 10.6.1. But one verifies that for such a graph it is impossible to add the three vertices v_i with $\rho(v_i) \geq 5$ and edges to both 2-vertices in such a manner that G is planar.

Suppose, finally, that G is a graph with vertex set V contractible into a 5-vertex connected graph G_1 with vertex set V_1. We have shown that the relations (10.7.2) and (10.7.3) hold in G_1. To prove them for G denote by γ the defining correspondence for $G > G_1$. It suffices to show that for any vertex a

$$G(V - a) > G_1(V_1 - a_1), \qquad a_1 = \gamma(a). \qquad (10.7.4)$$

To obtain the contraction (10.7.4) we consider the connected section graphs

$$G(\gamma^{-1}(b_1)), \qquad b_1 \in V_1.$$

When a is removed from G, these graphs remain connected except possibly for $b_1 = a_1$ where $G(\gamma^{-1}(a_1))$ may decompose into components. We contract all these components into neighboring graphs $G(\gamma^{-1}(b_1))$ and then contract the resulting graph, defining the correspondence by the $\gamma^{-1}(b_1)$ sets. This yields the relation (10.7.4).

It is evident that one has a theorem analogous to Theorem 10.7.4 for $k \geq 5$-connected graphs, when $k - 3$ and $k - 2$ vertices are removed.

CHAPTER 11 | *CRITICAL GRAPHS*

11.1. Types of Critical Graphs

Dirac has made use of another approach to the coloration problem through the introduction of the *critical graphs*. Instead of examining the class of all graphs with a given chromatic number k one studies those graphs of this class which are minimal in some respect. These critical graphs can then be shown to have special properties of various kinds.

Let G be an arbitrary k-chromatic graph. We say that G is *vertex critical* (v-critical) when for any vertex v the section graph

$$G_1 = G(V - v) \qquad (11.1.1)$$

has the chromatic number $k - 1$. One can also state the definition in the form that any proper section subgraph of G shall have a smaller chromatic number. Any k-chromatic graph contains a k-chromatic section subgraph.

The definition shows that a v-critical graph must be connected and without separating vertices. More strongly, a v-critical graph can have no simplex decomposition. If there were some decomposition by a simplex S_v, then one would have $v \leq k - 1$ since G is k-chromatic. But then a $(k - 1)$-coloration of the two components could be combined to a $(k - 1)$-coloration of G which is not possible. If a v-critical graph should contain some simplex S_v, then there can only be a single bridge in G with respect to S_v since otherwise G would have a simplex separation. For the same reason the bridge with respect to S_v must be broad. This implies that if a v-critical graph contains a simplex S_v then it is contractible to S_{v+1}.

The valences of a v-critical k-chromatic graph must satisfy

$$\rho(v) \geq k - 1. \qquad (11.1.2)$$

164

If for some vertex one has $\rho(v) < k - 1$, then G_1 in (11.1.1) is $(k - 1)$-chromatic and v could be added to G_1 in such a manner that G would become colorable in $k - 1$ colors. The property (11.1.2) can be extended.

Theorem 11.1.1. Any v-critical k-chromatic graph G is $(k - 1)$-edge connected.

Proof: Suppose G has a decomposition into two section subgraphs

$$G = G(A) + G(\bar{A}) + G(A, \bar{A}), \qquad A + \bar{A} = V$$

where the connecting graph has fewer than $k - 1$ edges. The graphs $G(A)$ and $G(\bar{A})$ have color functions f and $\bar{f}$ with values $1, \ldots, k - 1$. We obtain a contradiction by showing that they can be combined into a coloration of G in $k - 1$ colors. Denote by $a_1, a_2, \ldots, a_s$ the vertices in A from which there are connecting edges to $\bar{A}$. We take their color values to be $1, 2, \ldots, r$ and order the vertices such that

$$1 = f(a_1) \leqq f(a_2) \leqq \cdots \leqq f(a_s) = r.$$

Next we order the edges $(a_i, \bar{a}_j)$ in the graph $G(A, \bar{A})$ with nondecreasing i. For $E_1 = (a_1, \bar{a}_1)$ we arrange the values of $\bar{f}$ such that $\bar{f}(\bar{a}_1) = 2$. For the subsequent edges $E_t = (a_i, \bar{a}_j)$ we put

$$\bar{f}(\bar{a}_j) = t + 1.$$

This naming of the color at $\bar{a}_j$ may require a change in the previous numbers but in any case the color value will be higher than before, so we have

$$f(a_i) < f(\bar{a}_j).$$

A graph shall be called *edge-critical* (*e*-critical) when the removal of any edge E produces a graph $G - E$ with the chromatic number $k - 1$. Every *e*-critical graph is v-critical; every k-chromatic graph contains a k-chromatic *e*-critical subgraph.

In general, it is not simple to recognize when a graph is critical.

Theorem 11.1.2. A k-chromatic graph is *e*-critical when its valences satisfy $\rho(v) \leqq k - 1$ with a single exception.

Proof: It is readily seen that any proper subgraph G_1 of G has at least one vertex with $\rho(v) \leqq k - 2$. The condition (11.1.2) shows that no such graph can be k-chromatic and *e*-critical. On the other hand, G must include some *e*-critical subgraph so this can only be G itself.

According to (11.1.2) the number of edges in a v-critical or e-critical graph must satisfy

$$2v_e \geqq (k-1) \cdot v_v.$$

For e-critical graphs Dirac has sharpened this result to

$$2 \cdot v_e \geqq (k-1) \cdot v_v + k - 3, \qquad k \geq 4, \qquad G \neq S_k.$$

A third class of critical graphs is defined as follows. A connected k-chromatic graph G is *contraction critical* (c-critical) when any proper contraction $G_1 \neq G$ of G has a chromatic number $k_1 < k$.

Let us consider the effect on the chromatic number of a single edge contraction with respect to an edge $E = (u, v)$ whose end points are contracted to a single vertex $u_1 = v_1$. The resulting graph G_1 can be colored as G except one may possibly have to give the contracted vertex $u_1 = v_1$ a new color. On the other hand, when a coloration for G_1 is given, the same coloration can be used for G when a new color is introduced for one of the vertices u or v. We conclude that the chromatic numbers for the two graphs satisfy

$$\varkappa(G_1) - 1 \leqq \varkappa(G) \leqq \varkappa(G_1) + 1.$$

Thus the contraction of an edge changes the chromatic number of G and any of its contractions by at most one unit.

The chromatic number of some contractions of G may exceed k. But repeated contractions lead to graphs with a smaller number of edges, finally to a single vertex. We conclude that there exist minimal contractions G_1 with chromatic number k while all proper contractions of G_1 have smaller chromatic numbers.

Theorem 11.1.3. Every k-chromatic graph can be contracted into a c-critical k-chromatic graph.

We shall also define: G is a *subcontraction critical graph* (*s.c.*-critical) when $\varkappa(H) < k$ for the chromatic number of every subcontraction $H \neq G$. A graph which is *s.c.*-critical is c-critical but not always conversely. When H is a subcontraction with

$$V(G) \supset V(H)$$

we can contract G to a graph $G_1 \supseteq H$ with the same vertex set as H so that

$$\varkappa(G_1) \geqq \varkappa(H).$$

Hence for such a subcontraction H of a c-critical graph the condition for an *s.c.*-critical graph is satisfied. But G may have subgraphs with

$$V(G) = V(H), \qquad \varkappa(G) = \varkappa(H).$$

Consequently, in order that a graph be *s.c.*-critical is it necessary and sufficient that it be both *c*-critical and *e*-critical. Such a graph we shall call *irreducible*. From any *k*-chromatic graph one obtains a *k*-chromatic irreducible graph by repeated applications of the two operations of forming *e*-critical subgraphs and *c*-critical contractions.

We point out that some writers have used the term irreducible in a different sense, namely, as a graph which is both *c*-critical and *v*-critical. This is a weaker condition than the previous one. To distinguish between them one could talk about *e-irreducible* and *v-irreducible* graphs. From any *k*-chromatic graph one can construct a *k*-chromatic *v*-irreducible graph by repeated formation of *v*-critical subgraphs and *c*-critical contractions.

11.2. Contraction-Critical Graphs

We shall consider the separation of contraction-critical graphs. When T is a separating set for the graph G, then one has a representation

$$G = G_1 + G_2, \qquad G_1 \cap G_2 = H,$$
$$H = G(T), \qquad T = V(H). \tag{11.2.1}$$

The edges in G fall into bridges with respect to H. A *minimal separating set* T has no proper subset separating G; this may be stated equivalently that all bridges with respect to H are broad. The bridges with respect to H we denote by $\{B_i\}$. To each of these there is an *augmented bridge*

$$B_i^+ = B_i + H. \tag{11.2.2}$$

In a *k*-chromatic graph G we shall derive a number of coloration properties for these bridges. We already noticed that H cannot be a simplex since it would imply that G could be colored in $k - 1$ colors. Thus T always includes an independent set of G containing at least two vertices.

We shall prove Theorem 11.2.1.

Theorem 11.2.1. Denote by T a minimal separating set for the *k*-chromatic *c*-critical graph G and let $T' \subseteq T$ be an independent set in $G(T)$. Then there exists a coloration in $k - 1$ colors of any augmented bridge B^+ such that all vertices in T' have the same color.

Proof: We select a bridge $B_1 \neq B$ and contract it to a single vertex b_1 with edges (b_1, t) to each $t \in T$. Next we contract all vertices $t' \in T'$ to b_1 to obtain a proper contraction G_1 of G. Thus by assumption G_1 is colorable in $k - 1$ colors. We consider the subgraph of G_1 which consists of B^+ with the vertices in T' contracted to b_1. We separate b_1 again to the set T' and obtain the desired coloration of B^+.

Theorem 11.2.2. Among the colorations of an augmented bridge B^+ in $k - 1$ colors there must exist one in which a given pair of vertices t_1, $t_2 \in T$ not joined by an edge have different colors.

Proof: This is evident when the chromatic number of B^+ is less than $k - 1$. Suppose $\varkappa(B^+) = k - 1$ and that t_1 and t_2 have the same colors in any $(k - 1)$-coloring of B^+. We contract another bridge B_1 such that we obtain a proper subcontraction of G which contains the graph $B^+ + (t_1, t_2)$. This contraction could then not be colorable in $k - 1$ colors, contrary to the fact that G is c-critical.

Theorem 11.2.3. No c-critical graph can be separated by an independent set.

Proof: If such a separation should exist, there would be a minimal separating set T. But then all augmented bridges B^+ could be colored such that the vertices in T all have the same color. These $(k - 1)$-colorations could be combined to a $(k - 1)$-coloration of G which is impossible.

    The preceding results imply: *No c-critical graph can be separated by two vertices.* Thus we may assume that any separating set T has at least three vertices.

Theorem 11.2.4. Let G be a c-critical k-chromatic graph with a minimal separating set T. Then $G(T)$ can have no maximal independent set $T' \subset T$ such that the graph $G(T - T')$ is colorable in essentially one way.

Proof: We recall that the term colorable in essentially one way means that all colorations are the same except for the names of the colors. When T' is a maximal independent set, there is an edge from each vertex $t \in T - T'$ to some vertex $t' \in T'$. According to Theorem 11.2.1 we can color each augmented bridge B^+ in $k - 1$ colors such that all vertices in T' have the same color α while the vertices in $T - T'$ have colors different from α. If $G(T - T')$ is colorable in essentially one way, the colors in the various augmented bridges could be named such that they coincide on $G(T)$; hence G would be colorable in $k - 1$ colors.

An instance of Theorem 11.2.4 occurs when $G(T - T')$ is a simplex. As a special case $G(T - T') = t_0$ can be a single vertex so $G(T)$ consists of a star graph at v_0 and isolated vertices. This observation implies the following statement.

No c-critical graph has a separating set of three vertices.

Proof: We know that $G(T)$ cannot be a simplex on three vertices nor three independent vertices. But if it has one or two edges, these must form a star graph.

Let us mention the following result.

Theorem 11.2.5. Let G be a c-critical, k-chromatic graph, T a minimal separating set, and $t_0 \in T$. Then no contraction of $G(T - t_0)$ can have a chromatic number exceeding $k - 3$.

Proof: We contract two bridges for T into two star graphs with centers b_1 and b_2 having edges (b_1, t_i) and (b_2, t_i) to all $t_i \in T$. Assume that some contraction H_1 of $G(T - t_0)$ has a chromatic number $k_1 \geq k - 2$. We contract $G(T - t_0)$ to H_1 and next the edge (b_1, t_0) to t_0 to obtain a contraction G_1 of G. In G_1 there is a subgraph H_2 consisting of H_1, the edge (t_0, b_2) and edges from t_0 and b_2 to every vertex in H_1. The chromatic number of this graph is $k_1 + 2 \geq k$ which is impossible. By the same series of contractions one proves that when $G(T - t_0)$ is contractible to a simplex S_v then G is contractible to S_{v+2}.

We turn to the following result due to Dirac.

Theorem 11.2.6. When G is c-critical with $\varkappa(G) \geq 5$, it cannot be separated by fewer than five vertices.

Proof: According to the preceding it is sufficient to examine the separation by four vertices. Suppose

$$T = \{t_1, t_2, t_3, t_4\}$$

is such a separating set. By examining the various possibilities for the separating graph $G(T)$ we shall show that they all lead to a contradiction. We have already eliminated the case where $G(T)$ has no edges or is a simplex S_4. Theorem 11.2.4 eliminates the case where $G(T)$ has one edge or $G(T) = S_4 - E$. Consequently, there remain only three alternatives.

1. $G(T)$ *has four edges.* The case where $G(T)$ includes a triangle is again excluded by Theorem 11.2.4. We may assume that

$$G(T) = (t_1, t_2, t_3, t_4) \tag{11.2.3}$$

is a circuit. We established in Theorems 11.2.1 and 11.2.2 that there exist $(k-1)$-colorations of any augmented bridge $B_1{}^+$ such that t_1 and t_3 have the same color and also colorations in which the colorations of these two vertices are different. For t_2 and t_4 the same is true.

In this case as well as in the two remaining ones we obtain a contradiction by showing that a coloration of G in $k-1$ colors will result. To treat case 1 where $G(T)$ is a circuit (11.2.3) we divide the augmented bridges (11.2.2) into two classes:

    a. Bridges B^+ which can be colored in $k-1$ colors such that the vertices t_i have four different colors. Their sum graph M can be colored in the same way.

    b. Bridges B^+ not colorable in this fashion. When one colors them such that t_1 and t_3 have different colors the vertices t_2 and t_4 must have equal colors. Their sum N is $(k-1)$-colorable in this way.

Evidently one has

$$G = M + N, \qquad M \cap N = G(T). \tag{11.2.4}$$

We shall show that the two components can be so $(k-1)$-colored that such a coloration results also for G. In N any coloration with different colors for t_1 and t_2 must have equal colors for t_2 and t_4 and vice versa. Thus for any coloration of the graph

$$N' = N + (t_1, t_3) + (t_2, t_4) \tag{11.2.5}$$

at least k colors are required.

Take a coloration of M in which the vertices t_i have the colors $i = 1, 2, 3, 4$. In M we consider the subgraph consisting of all vertices with colors 1 and 3 and the edges connecting them. In this subgraph t_1 and t_3 are connected. If this were not true, one could interchange the colors 1 and 3 in the component including t_1. This gives a coloration of M in which t_1 and t_3 have the same color 3 while t_2 and t_4 have the colors 2 and 4. But then the colorations of M and N can be combined to a $(k-1)$-coloration of G. Thus we may assume that there exists an arc $A_1(t_1, t_3)$ in M whose vertices have the colors 1 and 3 alternatively. The length of A_1 is at least 3 since there is no edge (t_1, t_3) in G. The same argument applies to t_2 and t_4 so there also exists an arc $A_2(t_2, t_4)$ whose vertices have alternating colors 2 and 4.

We now contract G with respect to A_1 and A_2 such that the arcs become single edges (t_1, t_3) and (t_2, t_4). But the contracted graph includes a subgraph N' in (11.2.5) which is not colorable in $k-1$ colors. This is not possible since G is c-critical.

2. $G(T)$ *has three edges.* According to Theorem 11.2.4 we may assume that these edges form an arc $(t_1, t_2)(t_2, t_3)(t_3, t_4)$. For each B^+ there is a coloring with the same color for t_1 and t_4; hence t_2 and t_3 have two different colors. All these colorations can be combined to a coloration for G in $k - 1$ colors.

3. $G(T)$ *has two edges.* We may suppose that the two edges (t_1, t_2) and (t_3, t_4) have no common endpoint. Here we divide the augmented bridges into the classes:

    a. Bridges B^+ colorable such that t_1 and t_3 have the same color and also t_2 and t_4. Their sum M is colorable in $k - 1$ colors in the same way.

    b. Bridges B^+ not so colorable. We can color them all such that t_1 and t_3 have equal colors; hence t_2 and t_4 have different colors. Their sum N is colorable in the same way.

As before we have a decomposition (11.2.4). We shall show that it is possible to color M and N such that the coloration can be combined to a $(k - 1)$-coloration of G. We color M such that t_1 and t_3 have the color 1 and t_2 and t_4 the color 2. We consider the subgraph of M consisting of all vertices with the colors 1 and 3 and the edges connecting them. In this subgraph there must exist an arc $A_1(t_1, t_3)$. If this were not the case, one could change the color of t_1 to 3 while t_3 still has the color 1 and t_2 and t_4 the color 2. But then one could combine a coloration of M and N to a coloration of G in $k - 1$ colors. Similarly there must exist an arc $A_2(t_2, t_4)$ in M whose vertices alternatingly have the colors 2 and 4.

We construct the subgraph of G

$$N' = N + A_1(t_1, t_3) + A_2(t_2, t_4)$$

and contract the arcs A_1 and A_2 to single vertices t_1' and t_2'. By the defining property of N the resulting graph N'' cannot be colorable in $k - 1$ colors, for by separating the vertices t_1' and t_2' again one would obtain a coloration of N in which t_1 and t_3 and also t_2 and t_4 have equal colors. But since G is c-critical, it cannot have a subcontraction N'' not colorable in $k - 1$ colors. This completes the proof of Theorem 11.2.6.

From this theorem we conclude that for a k-chromatic graph, $k \geq 5$, the conditions of Theorem 10.7.4 are satisfied and so the contraction properties of this theorem are fulfilled for such graphs.

11.3. Edge-Critical Graphs

We shall examine the edge-critical graphs in some further detail to give an exposition of various results obtained by Dirac and Gallai.

We suppose as before that the e-critical graph G has the chromatic number $k = \varkappa(G)$. The vertices in G then satisfy the condition (11.1.2). A vertex v shall be called *minor* when $\rho(v) = k - 1$. The *minor graph* G_0 in G is the section graph of G defined by the minor vertices. For this subgraph one can prove the following result.

Theorem 11.3.1. The minor graph G_0 of an e-critical graph G consists of lobe graphs which are simplexes and odd circuits.

For the proof of this theorem we shall apply a method related to the one used in Section 6.5 to derive the theorem of Brooks. Since G is v-critical as well as e-critical, the section graph $G(V - v_0)$ is colorable in $k - 1$ colors for any given vertex v_0. We say that a color function $f(v)$ belongs to the vertex v_0 when the color $f(v_0)$ is different from the $k - 1$ colors at the other vertices. For a minor vertex v_0 the colors at all its $k - 1$ neighbors must be different since otherwise G could be colored in $k - 1$ colors.

Suppose next that v_0 and v_1 are neighbors and $f_0(v)$ a color function belonging to v_0 such that $f_0(v_1)$ is different from the colors $f_0(v_i)$ of all other neighbors of v_0. One can then *interchange* the colors at v_0 and v_1 leaving all other colors unchanged to obtain a coloration $f_1(v)$ of G belonging to the vertex v_1. When v_0 is a minor vertex, such an interchange can always be made according to a preceding observation.

A *minor circuit*

$$C_0 = (v_0, v_1, \ldots, v_{n-1}) \tag{11.3.1}$$

is a circuit in the minor graph G_0, that is, all its vertices are minor. We then have Lemma 11.3.1.

Lemma 11.3.1. When $f_0(v)$ is a color function belonging to a vertex v_0 on a minor circuit C_0 in (11.3.1), then the values (11.3.2) on C_0

$$f_0(v_0), f_0(v_2), \ldots, f_0(v_{n-1}), f_0(v_1) \tag{11.3.2}$$

also define a color function $\bar{f}_0(v)$ belonging to v_0 and coinciding with $f_0(v)$ on all vertices outside C_0.

Proof: This follows by repeated interchanges of the type just defined along the vertices of C_0 until one returns to v_0. One sees that (11.3.2) represents a cyclic permutation of the colors on C_0 for all vertices different from v_0.

Suppose now that in the minor circuit C_0 in (11.3.1) there are no diagonals for C_0 at v_0, that is, the only neighbors of v_0 lying on C_0 are v_1

and v_{n-1}. The other $k - 3$ neighbors

$$n_1, n_2, \ldots, n_{k-3}$$

do not lie on C_0. None of these vertices can have the same color as any vertices on C_0 in any color function belonging to v_0. This is evident for v_1 and v_{n-1} since v_0 is minor. By using the cyclic permutation of the lemma one can achieve a coloration in which an arbitrary vertex color on C_0 becomes a neighbor color to v_0.

Since there are $k - 3$ colors defined on the neighbors of v_0, there are only two colors available for the vertices on C_0, that is, C_0 must be an odd circuit.

Lemma 11.3.2. When G is an e-critical graph, then at each vertex in an even minor circuit there is at least one diagonal.

Next we shall establish Theorem 11.3.2.

Theorem 11.3.2. Let G be an arbitrary graph with the property that every even circuit has at least two diagonals. Then the lobe graphs of G are simplexes and odd circuits.

The proof proceeds in several steps. We may suppose that G is 2-vertex connected, hence it includes circuits.

1. When G contains an even circuit

$$C = (a_1, a_2, \ldots, a_n), \tag{11.3.3}$$

then G contains the simplex spanned by C.

If this were not true, there would be a shortest circuit C without this property. For $n = 4$ the statement holds so we may suppose in (11.3.3) that $n \geq 6$. A diagonal (a_i, a_j) for C shall be called *odd* or *even* depending on the length of the two sections $C(a_i, a_j)$ and $C(a_j, a_i)$ into which it divides C.

We show that a minimal C must include at least one odd diagonal. Suppose that we have a pair of even diagonals

$$D_1 = (a_1, a_j), \qquad D_2 = (a_i, a_k).$$

When the vertices a_1, a_j separate a_i, a_k on C [Fig. 11.3.1(a)], we consider the circuits

$$C_1 = C(a_1, a_i) + D_2 + C(a_k, a_j) + D_1,$$

$$C_2 = C(a_i, a_j) + D_1 + C(a_1, a_k) + D_2.$$

Both are even and at least one is shorter than C. Since this circuit has the property 1 by assumption, it follows readily that one of neighboring edges (a_1, a_{j-1}) or (a_1, a_{j+1}) to D_1 is in G and so is an odd diagonal for C. When a_1, a_j do not separate a_i, a_k on C [Fig. 11.3.1(b)], we consider the circuit

$$C_1 = D_1 + C(a_j, a_i) + D_2 + C(a_k, a_1)$$

and apply the same argument.

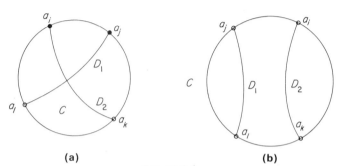

(a)

(b)

Fig. 11.3.1.

We may suppose, therefore, that C has an odd diagonal $D_1 = (a_1, a_j)$. Then the circuits

$$C_1 = C(a_1, a_j) + D_1, \qquad C_2 = D_1 + C(a_j, a_1) \qquad (11.3.4)$$

are both even; hence by assumption all possible diagonals exist for them in G. Also any diagonal (a_i, a_k) must exist when a_i, a_k separate a_1 and a_j on C. In this case we know that we have a quadrangle

$$(a_1, a_i)(a_i, a_j), \qquad (a_j, a_k)(a_k, a_1)$$

hence also its diagonal (a_i, a_k).

2. When C in (11.3.3) is an odd circuit with at least one diagonal $D_1 = (a_1, a_j)$, then G contains the simplex spanned by C.

In this case one of the circuits (11.3.4), say C_1 is even, hence all its diagonals exist. The diagonal $D_2 = (a_1, a_{j-1})$ defines an even circuit

$$C_3 = D_2 + C(a_{j-1}, a_j, \dots, a_1)$$

hence all diagonals for C_3 and also for C_2 must exist. By the quadrangle argument used above it follows that all diagonals for C exist.

We are now in a position to complete the proof of Theorem 11.3.2. We select C in (11.3.3) as a maximal circuit in G. If G should contain all possible diagonals for C then

$$G_1 = G(C) = S_n.$$

Suppose there were a vertex v in G not on C. Then one could find disjoint arcs

$$A_1(v, a_i), \qquad A_2(v, a_j) \qquad (11.3.5)$$

from v to different vertices a_i and a_j on C with no other vertices on C. If $a_j = a_{i+1}$ one would find a larger circuit C. The same is true when a_i and a_j are not neighbors on C; one need only take

$$C_1 = A_2 + C(a_j, a_{i+1}) + (a_{i+1}, a_{i-1}) + C(a_{i-1}, a_{j+1}) + (a_{j+1}, a_i) + A_1.$$

When G does not include all possible diagonals of C, we have seen that C is odd and has no diagonals. If there should be a vertex v in G not on C, we construct the same arcs (11.3.5) as before. Again a_i and a_j cannot be neighbors on C. The arcs (11.3.5) together with the two arcs $C(a_i, a_j)$ define two circuits, one odd and the other even since C is odd. The even one has all possible diagonals and this leads to the existence of diagonals for C, contrary to our assumption.

The combination of Theorem 11.3.2 with Lemma 11.3.2 yields the desired proof of Theorem 11.3.1.

An immediate consequence is Theorem 11.3.3.

Theorem 11.3.3. The only *e*-critical graphs having only minor vertices are the simplexes and the odd circuits.

If an *e*-critical graph has only one nonminor vertex v, the graph $G_1 = G(V - v)$ has the form described in Theorem 11.3.2. To construct G one need only add the edges from v to G_1. In order that G be an *e*-critical graph it is necessary that G_1 satisfy certain special conditions which have been determined by Dirac and Gallai.

A consequence of Theorem 11.3.3 is also the coloration theorem of Brooks (Theorem 6.5.1).

When G is a connected graph, not a simplex or an odd circuit with valences $\rho(v) \leqq \rho_0$, then G can be colored in ρ_0 colors.

If this were not true, there would be an *e*-critical subgraph G_1 of G with chromatic number $\rho_0 + 1$. But then all vertices in G_1 would be minor and G_1 would have the form of Theorem 11.3.3. But one cannot have $G_1 = S_{\rho_0+1}$ for it would lead to vertices in G with valences $\rho > \rho_0$.

11.4. Construction of *e*-Critical Graphs

We turn to methods of constructing *e*-critical k-chromatic graphs. Suppose that such a graph has a separation by two vertices a and b

$$G = G_1 + G_2, \qquad H = G_1 \cap G_2 = \{a, b\}. \qquad (11.4.1)$$

The edge $E = (a, b)$ cannot occur in G for this would give a simplex separation. Furthermore, there can only be two bridges B_1 and B_2 with respect to $\{a, b\}$. Suppose there were several bridges $\{B_i\}$. In the various $(k - 1)$-colorations of a bridge B_i it cannot occur that in one coloration $\varkappa(a) = \varkappa(b)$ and in another $\varkappa_1(a) \neq \varkappa_1(b)$ for it would lead to a $(k - 1)$-coloration of G. Thus all bridges fall into two classes, depending on the colors at a and b in any $(k - 1)$-coloration. All bridges cannot belong to the same class for this would again make G colorable in $k - 1$ colors. If there should be more than two bridges, we select B_1 and B_2 from different classes. But then $B_1 + B_2$ would also be $(k - 1)$-colorable, which is impossible.

We now select the notations in (11.4.1) such that in each $(k - 1)$-coloration of G_1 the vertices $\{a, b\}$ have the same color while in G_2 they have different colors. We can then construct two e-critical k-chromatic graphs K_1 and K_2 from G_1 and G_2 as follows:

1. $K_1 = G_1 + E$. Evidently this graph is colorable in k but not in $k - 1$ colors. To see that it is e-critical we remove from it an edge $E_1 \neq E$. By assumption there exists a coloration of $G - E_1$ in $k - 1$ colors. Since this is also a $(k - 1)$-coloration of G_2 in which the vertices a and b have different colors it is also a $(k - 1)$-coloration of $K_1 - E_1$.

2. The graph K_2 is obtained by identifying the two vertices a and b in G_2. Again K_2 is seen to be k-colorable, but not $(k - 1)$-colorable. To prove that K_2 is e-critical we remove an edge E_2 from it. This corresponds to a unique edge E_2' in G so that $G - E_2'$ has a $(k - 1)$-coloration. This is also a coloration of G_1 in which a and b must have the same color. These vertices can, therefore, be identified to give a $(k - 1)$-coloration of K_2.

To this *decomposition procedure* for the construction of e-critical graphs there also exists a reverse *composition procedure*. Let K_1 and K_2 be two disjoint e-critical k-chromatic graphs. We remove an edge $E_1 = (a, b)$ from K_1 to obtain the graph $G_1 = K_1 - E_1$. This is a connected graph since K_1 has no separating vertices. In K_2 we select a vertex c and divide the edges at c into two disjoint nonvoid classes A and B. This is possible since there are at least $k - 1 \geqq 2$ edges at c. We separate c into two new vertices c_1 and c_2 letting the edges in A go to c_1 and the edges in B to c_2. The resulting graph is denoted by G_2; it is also connected. Finally, we obtain the composed graph

$$G = G_1 + G_2 \qquad (11.4.2)$$

by identifying a and c_1 as well as b and c_2 (Fig. 11.4.1).

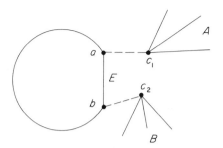

Fig. 11.4.1.

Theorem 11.4.1. The composed graph G in (11.4.2) is e-critical and k-chromatic provided the graph G_2 can be colored in $k - 1$ colors.

Proof: Since K_1 is e-critical G_1 is colorable in $k - 1$ colors, but only such that a and b have the same color. By assumption G_2 is also $(k - 1)$-colorable and since K_2 is e-critical and k-chromatic the vertices c_1 and c_2 must have different colors. We conclude that G is k-colorable but not $(k - 1)$-colorable.

To prove that G is e-critical we remove an edge from it; this may be either an edge $E_1' \subset G_1$ or $E_2' \subset G_2$. In the first case we know that $K_1 - E_1'$ is colorable in $k - 1$ colors such that $\varkappa_1(a) \neq \varkappa_1(b)$. Any $(k - 1)$-coloration for G_2 must have

$$\varkappa_2(a) \neq \varkappa_2(b)$$

so the two may be combined to a coloration of G in $k - 1$ colors. When an edge $E_2' \subset G_2$ is removed, it corresponds to a unique edge E_2'' in K_2. The graph $K_2 - E_2''$ is $(k - 1)$-colorable and this gives a coloration of G_2 with $\varkappa_2(c_1) = \varkappa_2(c_2)$. The graph G_1 is $(k - 1)$-colorable with $\varkappa_1(a) = \varkappa_1(b)$ so again the two colorations can be combined to a $(k - 1)$-coloration of $G - E_2'$.

Suppose one selects the family B of c-edges in K_2 such that it contains at most $k - 2$ edges. Then G_2 can always be colored in $k - 1$ colors so that Theorem 11.4.1 holds without restriction. To verify this we observe that the graph obtained by removal of the B-edges from c_2 in G_2 is a subgraph of K_2, hence colorable in $k - 1$ colors. This coloration in $G_2 - c_2$ can evidently be extended to include a coloration of c_2.

The preceding observations are due to Hajos. We shall add some further results by the same author.

Theorem 11.4.2. Let K_1 and K_2 be disjoint graphs with chromatic numbers

$$\varkappa(K_1) \geq k, \qquad \varkappa(K_2) \geq k.$$

We select a vertex $a_1 \in K_1$ and divide the edges at a_1 into two nonvoid classes A_1 and B_1 and analogously for $a_2 \in K_2$. The sets of end points other than a_1 and a_2 for the edges in B_1 and B_2 we denote, respectively, by

$$U_1 = \{b_1^{(i)}\}, \qquad U_2 = \{b_2^{(j)}\}. \qquad (11.4.3)$$

When the edges in B_1 and B_2 are omitted from K_1 and K_2, then the vertices a_1 and a_2 are identified and each $b_1^{(i)}$ joined by an edge to each $b_2^{(j)}$; the resulting graph G also satisfies $\varkappa(G) \geq k$.

Proof: (see Fig. 11.4.2): Suppose G were $(k-1)$-colorable. In G we reseparate $a_1 = a_2$ into two disjoint vertices a_1 and a_2 where both have the same color in the $(k-1)$-coloration. In U_1 all vertices $b_1^{(i)}$ have colors

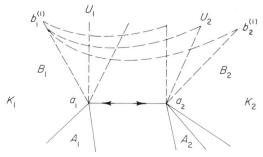

Fig. 11.4.2.

different from those of $b_2^{(j)} \in U_2$. If one $b_2^{(j)}$ should have the same color as a_1, one could restore the edges in B_1 and obtain a $(k-1)$-coloration of K_1. When none of the vertices in U_1 and U_2 have the color of a_1, the same is true.

Theorem 11.4.2 may be supplemented as follows:

Theorem 11.4.3. When the graphs K_1 and K_2 in Theorem 11.4.2 are k-chromatic and e-critical, the combined graph G has the same property provided the set $U_1 + U_2$ in (11.4.3) has at most $k-1$ vertices.

Proof: We must show that $G - E$ is colorable in $k-1$ colors for each of its edges E. We first take $E = E_1$ as an edge corresponding to an edge in K_1. The graph $K_1 - E_1$ is colorable in $k-1$ colors by assumption.

In this coloration the vertices in U_1 must have colors different from the color at $a_1 = a_2$. From K_2 we eliminate the edge $E_2 = (a_2, b_2^{(1)})$. In the resulting $(k - 1)$-coloration all vertices in $U_2 - b_2^{(1)}$ must have colors different from that of a_2 while $b_2^{(1)}$ and a_2 have the same color since K_2 is not $(k - 1)$-colorable.

The two colorations can be combined to a $(k - 1)$-coloration of $G - E_1$. The edges from U_1 to $b_2^{(1)}$ can be added immediately. In the $(k - 1)$-coloration of $K_2 - E_2$ we select the colors on $U_2 - b_2^{(1)}$ such that they are different from those on U_1. This is possible since the set

$$U_1 + U_2 - b_1^{(1)}$$

has at most $k - 2$ vertices by assumption. But then the edges connecting U_1 and U_2 can be added and one has a $(k - 1)$-coloration for $G - E_1$.

Secondly, let us eliminate from G one of the edges connecting U_1 and U_2, say,

$$E = (b_1^{(1)}, b_2^{(1)})$$

and write

$$E_1 = (b_1^{(1)}, a_1), \qquad E_2 = (b_2^{(1)}, a_2), \qquad a_1 = a_2.$$

When one eliminates the corresponding edges from K_1 and K_2, one obtains $(k - 1)$-colorations for $K_1 - E_1$ and $K_2 - E_2$. In these $b_1^{(1)}$ and a_1 as well as $b_2^{(1)}$ and a_2 must have the same color since K_1 and K_2 are e-critical. The two colorations can be combined to give a $(k - 1)$-coloration of $G - E$. To achieve this it is only necessary to select the colors on $U_2 - b_2^{(1)}$ in the second coloration different from those on $U_1 - b_1^{(1)}$ and $a_1 = a_2$ in the first. This is always possible by our assumption on the number of elements in $U_1 + U_2$.

Let us apply these results to the case where the e-critical graphs are simplexes

$$K_1 = S_k^{(1)}, \qquad K_2 = S_k^{(2)}. \tag{11.4.4}$$

The combined graph G is obtained by identifying a single vertex $a_1 = a_2$ in the two, then eliminating the edges from a_1 in the families B_1 and B_2 and replacing them by all edges connecting U_1 and U_2 in (11.4.3). The set $U_1 + U_2$ spans a simplex in G so we obtain the following theorem.

Theorem 11.4.4. By the composition of two simplexes (11.4.4) one obtains an e-critical graph if, and only if, the set $U_1 + U_2$ contains fewer than k vertices.

When $U_1 = b_1$ is a single vertex, this condition is always fulfilled.

11.5. Conjunctions and Mergers

Denote by G_1 and G_2 two disjoint graphs and by

$$E_1 = (a_1, b_1), \qquad E_2 = (a_2, b_2) \tag{11.5.1}$$

edges in G_1 and G_2, respectively. We construct a new graph G_0 by identifying the vertices a_1 and a_2 to a single vertex a_0, then eliminating the edges (11.5.1) from the joined graph, replacing them by a new edge

$$E_0 = (b_1, b_2). \tag{11.5.2}$$

The resulting graph

$$G_0 = K(G_1, G_2) \tag{11.5.3}$$

we call a *conjunction* of the components G_1 and G_2 (Fig. 11.5.1). A conjunction is a special case of the graph construction introduced in Theorem 11.4.1.

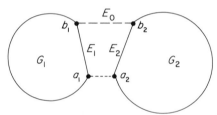

Fig. 11.5.1.

We examine the effect of forming conjunctions upon the chromatic numbers. In (11.5.3) we denote the chromatic numbers of the three graphs, respectively, by

$$k_0, k_1, k_2; \qquad k_1 \geqq k_2, k_1 \geqq 3 \tag{11.5.4}$$

and prove Theorem 11.5.1.

Theorem 11.5.1. For a conjunction (11.5.3) with chromatic numbers (11.5.4) one has $k_0 = k_1$ except when $k_1 > k_2$ and

$$k_1' = \varkappa(G_1 - E_1) = k_1 - 1;$$

in this case

$$k_0 = k_1 - 1.$$

Proof: Consider first the case $k_1 > k_2$. One cannot have $k_1' \leqq k_1 - 2$ since G_1 would become $(k_1 - 1)$-colorable. Suppose $k_1' = k_1 - 1$. In any

$(k_1 - 1)$-coloration of $G_1 - E_1$ the vertices a_0 and b_1 must have the same color since G_1 is k_1-chromatic. For G_2 as well as $G_2 - E_2$ there exists a $(k_1 - 1)$-coloration in which a_0 and b_2 have different colors. The two colorations of the graphs

$$G_1 - E_1, \qquad G_2 - E_2 \qquad (11.5.5)$$

can be combined with different colors at b_1 and b_2; hence the edge E_0 can be added to give a $(k_1 - 1)$-coloration of G_0. In the last case $k_1' = k_1$ there is a k_1-coloration of G_1 and $G_1 - E_1$ in which a_0 and b_1 have different colors. Since $k_1 > k_2$ we can select a k_2-coloration of G_2 such that the color at b_2 is different from those at a_0 and b_1. By combination one obtains a k_1-coloration of G_0.

Secondly, let

$$k_1 = k_2 = k \geq 3.$$

If G_0 should have a $(k - 1)$-coloration, the two graphs (11.5.5) would be $(k - 1)$-colorable. But these colorations must be such that a_0 and b_1 as well as a_0 and b_2 have the same color, hence the addition of E_0 would make G_0 k-chromatic, which is impossible. Thus it remains only to show that G_0 is k-colorable. We have a k-coloration of G_1 and $G_1 - E_1$ with different colors at a_0 and b_1 and similarly for G_2 and $G_2 - E_2$. Since $k \geq 3$ one can select these colorations such that b_1 and b_2 have different colors, hence G_0 is k-colorable.

It follows from Theorem 11.5.1 that

$$\varkappa(G_i) \geq k, \qquad i = 1, 2$$

implies for any conjunction

$$\varkappa(G_0) \geq k.$$

For the following analysis we need a more general graph operation. All graphs under consideration shall have single edges and no loops. In a graph G let

$$A_1 = (a_1, b_1, \ldots), \qquad A_2 = (a_2, b_2, \ldots), \qquad |A_1| = |A_2| \quad (11.5.6)$$

be two sets of vertices with the same number of elements and such that there are no edges from A_1 to A_2. Denote by μ some 1-1 correspondence from A_1 to A_2. A μ-coalition of G is the independent homomorphism obtained by identifying pairs of corresponding vertices. When two vertices should become connected by two edges, under this operation they are reduced to a single edge.

By coalescing two vertices not connected by an edge the chromatic number is not decreased as one readily sees. As a consequence the operation of forming a μ-coalition does not decrease the chromatic number.

Now let G_1 and G_2 be two disjoint graphs with vertex sets V_1 and V_2. We first construct a conjunction G_0 of the two as in (11.5.3). We then select two sets A_1 and A_2 as in (11.5.6) such that

$$a_i \in A_i \subseteq V_i, \quad i = 1, 2, \quad |A_1| = |A_2| = \alpha. \tag{11.5.7}$$

Denote by μ a 1–1 correspondence from A_1 to A_2 such that

$$\mu(a_1) = a_2$$

while in case

$$b_1 \in A_1, \quad b_2 \in A_2$$

these vertices do not correspond under μ. A *merger*

$$G_0' = M(G_1, G_2) \tag{11.5.8}$$

is the graph obtained from a conjunction G_0 in (11.5.3) by applying to it a μ-coalition defined by a pair of sets (11.5.7). A conjunction is a special merger with

$$A_1 = a_1, \quad A_2 = a_2, \quad \alpha = 1.$$

Since a merger is a conjunction followed by a coalition one sees that

$$\varkappa(G_0') \geq k$$

provided

$$\varkappa(G_1) \geq k, \quad \varkappa(G_2) \geq k.$$

When n_1 and n_2 are the number of vertices in G_1 and G_2, the number of vertices in the merger is given by

$$n_0' = n_1 + n_2 - \alpha.$$

One can also introduce the merger in a slightly different way. Let G_1 and G_2 be disjoint graphs and A_i subsets as in (11.5.7) connected by a 1–1 correspondence μ. The *μ-sum*, $G_1 \mu G_2$, is obtained by identifying A_1 and A_2 to a single set A_0 retaining all edges in G_1 and G_2 except that all edges lying in A_0 shall remain simple. Then the merger (11.5.8) can be written

$$G_0' = E_0 + (G_1 - E_1)\mu(G_2 - E_2). \tag{11.5.9}$$

We shall derive some properties of mergers.

Theorem 11.5.2. Let G_0' be an e-critical k-chromatic graph which is a merger (11.5.9) of graphs G_1 and G_2 with

$$\varkappa(G_1) \geqq k, \qquad \varkappa(G_2) \geqq k_2.$$

If the graphs

$$G_1 - E_1, \qquad G_2 - E_2 \qquad\qquad (11.5.10)$$

are proper subgraphs of G_0', then both G_1 and G_2 are e-critical and k-chromatic.

Proof: The graphs (11.5.10) can be $(k - 1)$-colored since they are proper subgraphs of an e-critical graph; thus G_1 and G_2 are k-colorable, hence k-chromatic. To show that G_1 is e-critical we remove an edge E from it and verify that $G_1 - E$ is $(k - 1)$-colorable. When $E = E_1$, there is nothing to prove. Suppose $E \neq E_1$. If $G_1 - E$ were k-chromatic, the graph $G_1 - E_1 - E$ as a proper subgraph of G_0' would be $(k - 1)$-colorable but only such that a_0 and b_1 have the same color. The graph $G_2 - E_2$ is $(k - 1)$-colorable as a subgraph of G_0' but only such that a_0 and b_2 have the same color since G_2 is k-chromatic. This produces a contradiction since in the $(k - 1)$-coloration of $G_0' - E$ the two vertices b_1 and b_2 would have to have the same color in spite of the fact that it contains the edge $E_0 = (b_1, b_2)$.

Theorem 11.5.2 applies in particular to a conjunction G_0. Here the graphs (11.5.10) are always proper subgraphs.

One may ask conversely when a merger of two e-critical k-chromatic graphs has the same property. This, however, is only the case under very special conditions. For conjunctions Theorem 11.5.3 is true.

Theorem 11.5.3. A conjunction of e-critical k-chromatic graphs is e-critical k-chromatic.

We leave the simple proof to the reader. It may also be considered to be a special case of Theorem 11.4.3.

11.6. Amalgamations

Let

$$G_1, G_2, \ldots, G_r \qquad\qquad (11.6.1)$$

be a family of disjoint graphs. Any graph derived from these by repeated mergers we call an amalgamation of the G_i. The obervations in Section

11.5 show that when

$$\varkappa(G_i) \geqq k, \qquad i = 1, 2, \ldots, r,$$

then $\varkappa(G) \geqq k$ for any amalgamation.

When all graphs in (11.6.1) are k-simplexes, that is, complete graphs S_k on k vertices, the corresponding amalgamations shall be called k-amalgamations.

Theorem 11.6.1. For any k-amalgamation

$$\varkappa(G) \geqq k. \qquad (11.6.2)$$

A k-amalgamation is *minimal* when it contains no proper subgraph which is a k-amalgamation.

A basic result is the following.

Theorem 11.6.2. A graph G has chromatic number $\varkappa(G) \geqq k$ if, and only if, it has a subgraph which is a k-amalgamation.

Proof: According to Theorem 11.6.1 it suffices to show that any graph G which contains no k-amalgamation is colorable in fewer than k colors. When G contains no k-amalgamation, one can add edges to it, keeping the vertex set the same, until one arrives at a graph G' which is maximal with respect to this property, that is, G' contains no k-amalgamation, but the addition of any further edge produces such a subgraph. Clearly, it is sufficient to establish that a maximal graph G' is colorable in fewer than k colors.

In G' we select a vertex a_0 and denote by b_1 and b_2 two vertices not connected to a_0 by edges. Suppose that for no choice of such three vertices does there exist an edge. $E_0 = (b_1, b_2)$. Then the binary relation "not edge connected" is a transitive relation in the vertex set V' of G'; hence it is an equivalence relation. Thus any two vertices which are not equivalent are connected by an edge. Let

$$V' = B_1 + B_2 + \cdots + B_s \qquad (11.6.3)$$

be the corresponding decomposition into equivalence blocks. These are independent sets in G' and this graph consists of all possible edges connecting a vertex in one block with a vertex in a different block. Then G' must contain a simplex S_s. Since there are no k-amalgamations in G' one must have $s < k$. But then G' is colorable in s colors such that each block in (11.6.3) is one of the color sets.

It remains to consider the case where there exists some edge $E_0 = (b_1, b_2)$. This we shall show cannot occur under our conditions on G'. By assumption the graph

$$G' + E_1, \qquad E_1 = (a_0, b_1)$$

contains a k-amalgamation K_1 which must include E_1. Since G' contains no k-amalgamation we can, if we wish, assume that K_1 is a minimal k-amalgamation. Similarly,

$$G' + E_2, \qquad E_2 = (a_0, b_2)$$

contains a k-amalgamation K_2 including E_2 which may also be taken minimal. We draw the graphs K_1 and K_2 in a disjoint manner and form their conjunction K_0 by identifying $a_1 = a_2 = a_0$ and adding the edge E_0 as in Fig. 11.5.1. From K_0 we form a merger K_0' of K_1 and K_2 by identifying their common vertices in G' under the natural correspondence μ. Then K_0' is a k-amalgamation and a subgraph of G', contradicting the definition of this graph.

Theorem 11.6.2 gives a sharper form of a result obtained by Hajós. The theorem of Hajós states that for any graph G one has $\varkappa(G) \geq k$ if, and only if, G contains a subgraph derived from simplexes S_k by repeated conjunctions and arbitrary independent homomorphisms. For some of the applications it is essential to use the more specific form derived above.

Theorem 11.6.2 permits us to reformulate Hadwiger's conjecture.

Theorem 11.6.3. Hadwiger's conjecture is equivalent to the statement: Every k-amalgamation can be contracted to a simplex S_k.

Proof: We saw in Theorem 11.6.1 that the chromatic number of a k-amalgamation is at least k. Thus if Hadwiger's conjecture is true, every k-amalgamation is contractible to S_k. Conversely, let every k-amalgamation be contractible to S_k. Theorem 11.6.2 shows that every k-chromatic graph is contractible to S_k.

This formulation of Hadwiger's conjecture is noteworthy since it contains no reference to chromatic numbers.

We also point out the next theorem.

Theorem 11.6.4. The four-color conjecture is equivalent to the statement: No 5-amalgamation is planar.

Proof: Suppose that the four-color conjecture is true so there exists no planar 5-chromatic graph; hence no 5-amalgamation is planar. On the other hand, when this is true, the four-color conjecture follows since a 5-chromatic planar graph would have to contain a planar 5-amalgamation.

We also point out Theorem 11.6.5.

Theorem 11.6.5. An edge critical k-chromatic graph is a minimal k-amalgamation. Conversely, every k-chromatic minimal k-amalgamation is edge critical.

Proof: Every e-critical k-chromatic graph G contains a minimal k-amalgamation K according to Theorem 11.6.2. Theorem 11.6.1 shows that $\varkappa(K) \geq k$ so $G = K$. On the other hand, let K be a minimal k-chromatic k-amalgamation. Since it must contain an e-critical k-chromatic subgraph, it is itself e-critical.

11.7. Mergers of Simplexes

We investigate the properties of mergers of simplexes. The notations are the same as before. Denote by G_0' the merger of the two k-simplexes G_1 and G_2. The coalesced sets A_1 and A_2 in (11.5.7) have $\alpha \leq k$ vertices. In case $\alpha = k$ all pairs of vertices are merged. Since there exists an edge $(a_0, \mu(b_1))$ in G_2 it follows that $G_0' = S_k$. In the following we exclude this special case and assume $\alpha \leq k - 1$.

Theorem 11.7.1. The merger of two k-simplexes is k-chromatic.

Proof: According to Theorem 11.6.1 it suffices to show that G_0' is k-colorable.

Case 1.
$$b_1 \notin A_1, \qquad b_2 \notin A_2.$$
After the merger the two graphs
$$G_1 - E_1, \qquad G_2 - E_2$$
have the simplex S_α in common. Each of them is $(k - 1)$-colorable such that a_0 and b_1 and a_0 and b_2 have the same color. The two $(k - 1)$-colorations can be combined to a $(k - 1)$-coloration of $G_0' - E_0$; hence we have a k-coloration of G_0'.

Case 2.
$$b_1 \in A_1, \qquad b_2 \notin A_2.$$
Here b_1 corresponds to $\mu(b_1)$ under the merger and since there is an edge $(a_0, \mu(b_1))$ in G_2 there must exist subgraphs
$$G_1, G_2 - E_2, \qquad G_1 \cap (G_2 - E_2) = S_\alpha.$$

in $G_0' - E_0$. Here G_1 has a k-coloration with different colors at a_0 and $\mu(b_1)$ while $G_2 - E_2$ has a $(k - 1)$-coloration with the same color at a_0 and b_2. This yields a k-coloration of G_0'.

Case 3.

$$b_1 \in A_1, \qquad b_2 \in A_2.$$

Here G_0' is composed of the two graphs

$$G_1, G_2, \qquad G_1 \cap G_2 = S_\alpha$$

and so it is k-colorable.

Theorem 11.7.2. G_0' can only be e-critical when

$$b_1 \notin A_1, \qquad b_2 \notin A_2. \tag{11.7.1}$$

Proof: If, for instance, $b_1 \in A_1$, then after the merger G_0' contains a graph isomorphic to G_1 and also edges E from b_2 not belonging to this subgraph. After the removal of an edge E the graph $G_0' - E$ is not $(k - 1)$-colorable; hence G_0' is not e-critical.

We assume in the following that the condition (11.7.1) is fulfilled. Then we have

$$G_0' - E_0 = (G_1 - E_1) + (G_2 - E_2), \qquad (G_1 - E_1) \cap (G_2 - E_2) = S_\alpha. \tag{11.7.2}$$

We investigate when a graph $G_0' - E$ is $(k - 1)$-colorable. According to (11.7.2) this is immediate when $E = E_0$. Assume next

$$E \subset G_0' - (G_2 - E_2) - E_0. \tag{11.7.3}$$

The graphs

$$G_1 - E, \qquad G_1 - E - E_1$$

are $(k - 1)$-colorable with different colors at a_0 and b_1. The graph $G_2 - E_2$ is $(k - 1)$-colorable with the same color at a_0 and b_2. In G_0' the two graphs

$$G_1 - E - E_1, \qquad G_2 - E_2$$

have S_α as their intersection so their $(k - 1)$-colorations can be combined and E_0 added so $G_0' - E$ is $(k - 1)$-colorable.

There remains only the case

$$E \subset S_\alpha, \qquad E = (a, b). \tag{11.7.4}$$

To handle this alternative we need an auxiliary result on the coloration of simplexes.

Lemma 11.7.1. A graph,

$$S_k - E - E', \qquad E = (a, b), \qquad E' = (a', b'), \qquad (11.7.5)$$

is $(k - 2)$-colorable when E and E' have no common end point. It is $(k - 1)$-chromatic when $a = a'$ and then an arbitrarily chosen vertex b or b' must have the same color as a.

Proof: In the first case one obtains a $(k - 2)$-coloration of the graph (11.7.5) by giving a and b the same color, a' and b' a second color, and the remaining vertices $k - 4$ other colors. In the second case where $a = a'$, the section graph on $V - a$ is a simplex S_{k-1}; hence it requires $k - 1$ colors. The color at a can be taken arbitrarily as that of b or b'.

We consider the removal from G_0' of an edge E satisfying (11.7.4). Assume first that E does not have a_0 as an end point. According to the lemma the graphs

$$G_1 - E_1 - E, \qquad G_2 - E_2 - E \qquad (11.7.6)$$

are $(k - 2)$-colorable such that both ends of E have the same color. By combination this gives a $(k - 2)$-coloration of

$$G_0' - E_0 - E; \qquad (11.7.7)$$

hence a $(k - 1)$-coloration of $G_0' - E$. Secondly, let $E = (a_0, b)$. By the lemma there exist $(k - 1)$-colorations of the graphs (11.7.6) such that both ends of E have the same color while the color at a_0 is different from that of b_1 or b_2. The two colorations can be combined to give a $(k - 1)$-coloration of the graph $G_0' - E_0 - E$.

When $\alpha \leqq k - 2$, there are at least two choices of colors at b_1 different from those on S_α so we may assume that in the combined coloration b_1 and b_2 have different colors; hence $G_0' - E$ is $(k - 1)$-colorable. This is not true when $\alpha = k - 1$ as one sees from the fact that when a_0 and its edges are removed from G_0', the remaining graph is a simplex S_k.

The preceding discussion may be summarized as in Theorem 11.7.3.

Theorem 11.7.3. In order that a merger of two k-simplexes be e-critical it is necessary and sufficient that

$$1 \leqq \alpha \leqq k - 2 \qquad (11.7.8)$$

while no end point of $E_0 = (b_1, b_2)$ belongs to the merged set.

The number of vertices and edges in such a merger are seen to be

$$n_0' = 2k - \alpha, \qquad m_0' = k(k - 1) - 1 - \tfrac{1}{2}\alpha(\alpha - 1). \qquad (11.7.9)$$

The following observation is due to Dirac.

Theorem 11.7.4. There is no e-critical k-chromatic graph with $k + 1$ vertices.

Proof: A graph of this kind is a subgraph of a simplex S_{k+1}. This simplex becomes k-chromatic after the removal of a single edge. As in the proof of the lemma the removal of two edges without common end point produces a $(k - 2)$-colorable graph. When two or more edges with a common end point a_0 are removed, there still remains a simplex S_k and the graph is not e-critical.

This result brings up the following question which we shall now solve. *For given k and n when does there exist an e-critical k-chromatic graph with n vertices?*

For $k = 2$ the e-critical graphs are single edges; hence such a graph must have $n = 2$ vertices.

For $k = 3$ we recall that one can only have $\varkappa(G) \geq 3$ when G contains an odd circuit. Thus the e-critical 3-chromatic graphs are odd circuits so they can only exist for n odd.

The remaining cases are taken care of by the general result shown by Theorem 11.7.5.

Theorem 11.7.5. For each $n \geq k \geq 4$, $n \neq k + 1$ there exist k-chromatic e-critical graphs with n vertices.

The proof is based upon actual construction of such graphs. For each n let H_n denote an e-critical k-chromatic graph with n vertices, provided such a graph exists. In Theorem 11.7.3 we have constructed graphs H_n for

$$n = k + 2, \ldots, 2k - 1. \qquad (11.7.10)$$

When one forms a conjunction of a graph H_n with a simplex S_k, it follows from Theorem 11.5.3 that the resulting graph is a graph H_{n+k-1} with

$$m' = m + \tfrac{1}{2}k(k - 1) - 1$$

edges where m is the number of edges in H_n. By repeating this procedure t times one arrives at a graph

$$H_{n+t(k-1)}$$

whose number of edges is

$$m^{(t)} = m + \tfrac{1}{2}k(k - 1)t - t. \tag{11.7.11}$$

As a starting point for such a series of conjunctions we use the graphs

$$H_n = H_{2k-\alpha} \tag{11.7.12}$$

corresponding to the $(k - 2)$ values in (11.7.10). This produces graphs H_n for all n with

$$n \not\equiv 2(\mathrm{mod}\ k - 1). \tag{11.7.13}$$

For a given n let us divide $n - 2$ by $k - 1$ and write

$$n - 2 = t(k - 1) + r, \qquad r = 1, 2, \ldots, k - 2. \tag{11.7.14}$$

Since

$$(2k - \alpha) - 2 = (k - 1) + r$$

the values in (11.7.10) correspond to

$$r = k - 1 - \alpha, \qquad t = 1. \tag{11.7.15}$$

We apply the formula (11.7.11) to the graph (11.7.12) for $t - 1$ conjunctions with simplexes S_k. This yields a graph H_n with m edges where

$$m = \tfrac{1}{2}k(k - 1)t - t + (r + 1)(k - 1 - \tfrac{1}{2}r). \tag{11.7.16}$$

Our construction as we noted does not apply when

$$n \equiv 2(\mathrm{mod}\ k - 1). \tag{11.7.17}$$

Here it is necessary to construct an e-critical graph H_{2k}. For this purpose we take the graph H_{k+2} which we obtained as a merger of two simplexes S_k with $\alpha = k - 2$. We merge H_{k+2} with a simplex S_k such that the merged part consists of a single edge

$$E' = (a_0, a_0')$$

while none of the vertices b_1 and b_2 are merged. The resulting graph H_{2k} has $2k$ vertices as desired while the number of edges is

$$m = (k + 3)(k + 2) \tag{11.7.18}$$

as one readily verifies from (11.7.9).

It remains to show that this graph H_{2k} is e-critical and k-chromatic. We use the same notations as before, writing

$$G_1 = H_{k+2}, \qquad G_2 = S_k.$$

It is readily seen that their merger H_{2k} is k-colorable, hence k-chromatic. To show that H_{2k} is e-critical we must establish that $H_{2k} - E$ is $(k - 1)$-colorable for all choices of the edge E in H_{2k}.

1. $E = E_0$. Here

$$H_{2k} - E = (G_1 - E_1) + (G_2 - E_2), \qquad (G_1 - E_1) \cap (G_2 - E_2) = E'.$$

Since both graphs are $(k - 1)$-colorable, the same holds for $H_{2k} - E_0$.

2. $E = E'$. Here $G_1 - E'$ is $(k - 1)$-colorable with the same color at a_0 and a_0'. The graph

$$G_2 - E' - E_2$$

is $(k - 1)$-colorable with the same color at a_0 and a_0' and a different color at b_2 according to the lemma. If $k \geq 4$, the color at b_2 may be chosen such that it is different from the color at b_1 so the two colorations can be combined with E_0 added to give a $(k - 1)$-coloration of $H_{2k} - E$.

3. $E \subset G_2 - E_2, E \neq E'$. When E has no end point at a_2 or b_2, the graph

$$G_2 - E_2 - E \tag{11.7.19}$$

has a $(k - 2)$-coloration and this leads to a $(k - 1)$-coloration of $H_{2k} - E$. When E has an end point at a_0 or b_2, the graph (11.7.19) has a $(k - 1)$-coloration with different colors at a_0 and b_2. The graph $G_1 - E_1$ has a $(k - 1)$-coloration with the same color at a_0 and b_1. The two can be combined with E_0 added to give a $(k - 1)$-coloration of $H_{2k} - E$.

4. $E \subset G_1 - E_1, E \neq E'$. There exists a $(k - 1)$-coloration of $G_1 - E$ such that b_1 and a_0 have different colors and also a $(k - 1)$-coloration of $G_2 - E_2$ such that a_0 and b_2 have the same color. Again the colorations can be combined to a $(k - 1)$-coloration of $H_{2k} - E$.

From the existence of H_{2k} we obtain an e-critical graph H_n for every n satisfying (11.7.17) by taking $t - 2$ conjunctions with simplexes S_k where

$$n = t(k - 1) + 2.$$

According to (11.7.18) and (11.7.11) the number of edges in this graph is

$$m = \tfrac{1}{2}k(k - 1)t + 2k - 4.$$

One may conjecture that the e-critical graphs we have just constructed for n vertices are the k-chromatic graphs with a minimal number of edges.

CHAPTER 12

PLANAR 5-CHROMATIC GRAPHS

12.1. Separations

We shall apply the preceding discussion of critical graphs to the case where the graphs in question are planar. We begin with a few observations valid for arbitrary planar graphs.

Theorem 12.1.1. Let G be a planar graph with a minimal separating set T having at least three vertices. Then there are only two bridges with respect to T.

Proof: From any vertex in a bridge there are arcs to each attachment. If there were more than two bridges, this would lead to a subgraph conformal to the Kuratowski graph $K = (3, 3)$.

Theorem 12.1.2. When G is a planar graph with a minimal separating set T, the separating graph is a circuit or a sum of disjoint arcs. When G is maximal, it is a circuit.

Proof: When $G(T)$ includes a circuit C, the two bridges will have arcs to all corners of C. This is only possible when one bridge B_0 lies inside C and the other B_1 outside C. There can be no vertices of T outside C for there can be no arc from B_0 to such a vertex. For the same reason there are no vertices of T inside of C. When $G(T)$ has no circuits, each of its connected components is a tree. If such a tree were not an arc, there would be at least three terminal vertices t_1, t_2, t_3. Within each bridge B_0 and B_1 there are arcs to each t_i and this would lead to a subgraph conformal to a Kuratowski graph. When G is maximal, any two consecutive attachments of any one of the bridges must be connected by an edge since all faces in G are triangles. For the same reason a separating circuit is minimal only when it has no diagonals.

We shall bring the four-color problem into connection with the c-critical graphs by examining the properties which a 5-chromatic planar c-critical graph must possess. From Theorem 11.2.6 one sees that such a graph must have valences $\rho(v) \geqq 5$.

Theorem 12.1.3. A planar 5-chromatic c-critical graph has a Hamilton circuit and the same is true for every maximal section graph

$$G(V - a), \qquad a \in V.$$

Proof: Theorem 11.2.6 shows that such a graph cannot be separated by four vertices. Thus the theorem is a consequence of Tutte's result (Theorem 5.2.2).

According to Theorem 8.3.2 every planar graph with a Hamilton circuit is face colorable in four colors so we may state the following theorem.

Theorem 12.1.4. Every c-critical planar 5-chromatic graph is face colorable in four colors.

Next we shall deduce a separation theorem due to Birkhoff, which has played an important role in many investigations on the four-color problem.

Theorem 12.1.5. When G is a c-critical 5-chromatic planar graph, then G cannot be separated by a 5-circuit C_5 except when one of its bridges is a star graph.

Proof: Let T be a separating set with five vertices and the separating circuit

$$G(T) = C_5 = (t_1, t_2, t_3, t_4, t_5).$$

We contract the inner bridge B_0 for C_5 into a star graph S_0 with a central vertex s_0 and five edges.

$$E_i = (s_0, t_i), \qquad i = 1, 2, 3, 4, 5.$$

When the contraction of B_0 to S_0 is a proper one, the resulting graph G_1 is colorable in four colors since G is c-critical. Since all vertices on C must have colors different from the color δ at s_0, the outer bridge B_1 is colorable in four colors such that the vertices on C take only the three colors α, β, γ. These colorations on C must have one color which occurs singly while the two other colors appear twice, for instance,

$$\varkappa(t_1) = \gamma; \qquad \varkappa(t_2) = \varkappa(t_4) = \alpha; \qquad \varkappa(t_3) = \varkappa(t_5) = \beta.$$

The vertex with the single color we call the *marked vertex*.

The same procedure applies to the outer bridge B_1. We contract it to a star graph S_1 with edges

$$(s_1, t_i), \qquad i = 1, 2, 3, 4, 5$$

from a central vertex s_1. This leads to a contraction G_0 of G with a coloration of B_0 in four colors with three colors for C_5 (Fig. 12.1.1).

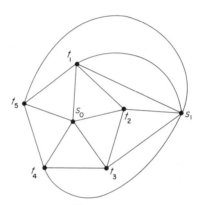

Fig. 12.1.1.

When the two 3-colorations on C have the same marked vertex, the two bridges have compatible colorations and may be combined into a coloration of G in four colors. We shall examine the other alternatives and show that their colorations can always be changed so that the marked vertices correspond; hence a 4-coloration of G results. Since G is 5-chromatic this is impossible. We conclude that the assumption that the contractions of B_0 or B_1 to S_0 or S_1 were both proper contractions cannot be correct; hence our theorem follows.

Suppose first that the two marked vertices on C_5 are not consecutive. We show that they can be changed so they become consecutive. The colorations may be, respectively,

$$I_0 = (\gamma, \alpha, \beta, \alpha, \beta), \qquad I_1 = (\alpha, \beta, \gamma, \alpha, \beta)$$

in G_0 and G_1 in the cyclic order on C. In I_1 we may assume that there exists an alternating β, γ-arc from t_2 and t_3 to t_5 in B_1, for otherwise the colors on t_2 and t_3 could be interchanged to make t_2 the marked vertex. When there is such a β, γ-arc from t_2 and t_3 to t_5, there can exist no α, δ-arc between t_1 and t_4 since G is planar. Thus the coloration of G_1 can be changed to

$$I_1' = (\alpha, \beta, \gamma, \delta, \beta).$$

Next we contract G_0 further by contracting the arc t_2, s_1, t_5 in S_1 to a single vertex t_{25}. The resulting graph G_0' can be colored in four colors. By reseparating t_{25} into t_2 and t_5 one obtains a coloration of B_0 with

$$I_0' = (x, \alpha, x, x, \alpha)$$

on C. If we call the two last unknown colors β and γ, we have the alternatives

$$I_0' = (\beta, \alpha, \beta, \gamma, \alpha), \qquad (\gamma, \alpha, \beta, \gamma, \alpha), \qquad (\delta, \alpha, \beta, \gamma, \alpha).$$

The first has t_4 as the marked vertex, adjacent to the marked vertex t_3 in I_1'. The second has the same marked vertex t_3 as I_1' and the third is the same as I_1'.

Suppose, secondly, that the two marked vertices are adjacent, for instance,

$$I_0 = (\gamma, \alpha, \beta, \alpha, \beta), \qquad I_1 = (\beta, \gamma, \alpha, \beta, \alpha)$$

for G_0 and G_1, respectively. Consider the β, γ-vertices in I_1. If there should be no β, γ-arc in B_1 connecting t_1, t_2 with t_4, we could interchange the colors on t_1 and t_2 to make t_1 the marked vertex also in B_1. Thus we may suppose that there exists such a β, γ-arc; hence there is no α, δ-arc between t_3 and t_5. The color at t_3 may be changed to δ, giving

$$I_1' = (\beta, \gamma, \delta, \beta, \alpha).$$

Next we contract G_0 such that t_1 and t_4 having the same color

$$I_0 = (\beta, x, x, \beta, x).$$

This leads to three different possible types of colorations of C in B_0,

$$(\beta, \gamma, \delta, \beta, \alpha), \qquad (\beta, \gamma, \delta, \beta, \gamma), \qquad (\beta, \gamma, \delta, \beta, \delta).$$

The first is the I_1' just defined on B_1. The last has t_2 as the marked vertex as in I_1. The remaining one has the marked vertex at t_3 so that from the marked vertices $t_1 \in B_0, t_2 \in B_1$ we have obtained the marked vertices $t_3 \in B_0, t_2 \in B_1$. By repeating the same operation one obtains a marked vertex for B_1 at t_4 and then at t_1 as desired.

We shall later encounter a number of other investigations of the color configurations on a separating circuit. On a circuit C_6 the possible equivalent schemes have been enumerated by Bernhart.

12.2. Irreducible Graphs

We continue our study of the properties of planar 5-chromatic graphs. We shall concentrate upon the *critical graphs* to be defined below.

We recall that if in a planar graph G one coalesces or identifies two vertices a and b not connected by an edge and both lying on the boundary of the same face F, one obtains a new planar graph G'. Any coloration of G' gives a coloration of G with the same color $\varkappa(a) = \varkappa(b)$ at a and b. By repeated applications of this process one arrives at a maximal planar graph G_0 such that any coloration of G_0 leads to a coloration of G in the same colors.

An *irreducible graph* G is characterized by the properties:

1. G is maximal planar.
2. G is 5-chromatic.
3. G is contraction critical.

It is clear that from any planar 5-chromatic graph one can construct an irreducible graph by vertex identifications and repeated formation of subcontractions. Any 5-chromatic graph with a minimal number of vertices or edges is irreducible. According to Theorem 12.1.2 any minimal separating graph $G(T)$ for an irreducible graph is a circuit.

An important direction in the study of the four-color problem has been the search for *reducible configurations*, that is, types of subgraphs which cannot occur in irreducible graphs. These investigations are based upon the examination of minimal separating circuits and the verification that certain types of bridges are excluded. Birkhoff's Theorem 12.1.5 is a typical result of this kind. The principal results on reducible configurations are due to Birkhoff, Franklin, Errera, and Winn.

The general procedure for these investigations may be described as follows. Let

$$C_n = (v_1, v_2, \ldots, v_n)$$

be some minimal separating circuit. Its outer and inner bridges shall be B_1 and B_0. We perform a contraction of B_0 which leaves the attachments on C unchanged. This is also a contraction G' of G; hence it yields a coloration of G' in four colors and so also a coloration of the augmented bridge

$$B_1{}^+ = B_1 + C_n.$$

The colors on C_n will depend on the contraction of B_0. Similarly by a contraction of B_1 one obtains a 4-coloration of

$$B_0^+ = B_0 + C_n.$$

If the colorations of B_0^+ and B_1^+ coincide on C_n, we can color G in four colors and so we have a reducible configuration. The same is true if the two colorations can be varied such that they coincide on C_n.

A common method is to divide the vertices on C into two alternating sets

$$A = v_1, v_3, \ldots, \qquad \bar{A} = v_2, v_4, \ldots.$$

When n is even, every second vertex belongs to A; when n is odd, there will be an instance of two successive vertices in $\bar{A}$. In B_0 we contract to a point the subgraph consisting of all edges except those with an end point in $\bar{A}$. This yields a coloration of B_1^+ in which all vertices in A have the same color α.

When such an *initial color type* on C has been fixed, there will be various colors for the vertices in $\bar{A}$ which are not determined. We examine all possible choices for the colors on $\bar{A}$. Some of them will have the property that the coloration itself or one derived from it by alternating color paths in B_1 can be extended to a coloration of B_0 so we have a 4-coloration of G. When this can be shown to be the case for all possible choices of colors in $\bar{A}$, the bridge B_0 is a reducible configuration.

It is convenient to introduce a special terminology. A vertex is an *n-vertex* when $\rho(v) = n$; for irreducible graphs $n \geq 5$. A vertex is *minor* when $n = 5$ or $n = 6$; it is *major* when $n \geq 7$.

The neighbor vertices a_i of an n-vertex v_0 lie on the (*first*) *neighbor circuit*

$$C_n = (a_1, a_2, \ldots, a_n) = D_1. \qquad (12.2.1)$$

The *first neighbor graph*

$$G_1(v_0) = G(v_0 + D_1) \qquad (12.2.2)$$

is a wheel graph with $n + 1$ vertices, $n + 1$ faces and $2n$ edges.

From each of the vertices a_i on D_1 in (12.2.1) there are $\rho(a_i) - 3$ edges to new vertices b_{ij} at a distance $d = 2$ from v_0. These second neighbors to v_0 will lie on the second neighbor circuit

$$D_2 = (\ldots, b_{ij}, \ldots). \qquad (12.2.3)$$

In constructing D_2 the last vertex $b_{i-1,k}$ for a_{i-1} will coincide with the first vertex $b_{i,1}$ for a_i (Fig. 12.2.1). We put

$$b_i = b_{i,1} = b_{i-1,k}.$$

No other vertices b_{ij} can coincide for it would lead to a separation of G by a circuit of length 4. Nor can there be any diagonal edges for D_2 in (12.2.3) according to Theorem 12.1.5. The length of D_2 is

$$l_2 = \sum (\rho(a_i) - 4) \tag{12.2.4}$$

as one readily verifies. The graph

$$G_2(v_0) = G(v_0 + D_1 + D_2) \tag{12.2.5}$$

is the *second neighbor graph*. Its vertex set consists of all vertices whose distance from v_0 is at most 2.

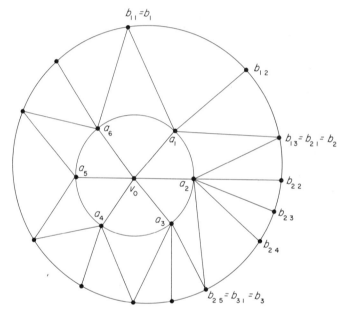

Fig. 12.2.1.

12.3. Reductions for Minor Vertices

In this section we shall deduce a variety of reducibility results for the neighbors of minor vertices. Our first theorem is due to Birkhoff.

Theorem 12.3.1. A 5-vertex is reducible when it has three consecutive 5-vertex neighbors.

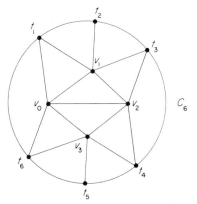

Fig. 12.3.1.

Proof: We draw the edges from the given 5-vertex v_0 to the consecutive 5-neighbors v_1, v_2, v_3 as in Fig. 12.3.1. Since G is maximal we can complete the adjoining triangular faces with corners at the v_i as shown in the figure. This leads to a circuit C_6 with corners t_i and an inner bridge B_0 with the four vertices v_i as inner vertices. To prove that no bridge of this kind can exist we shall establish that it leads to a coloration of G in four colors.

For this purpose we contract the six vertices t_4, t_6, and the v_i to a vertex along their connecting edges. This leads to an initial coloration of the outer augmented bridge

$$B_1^+ = B_1 + C_6$$

in four colors such that C_6 has the color type

$$(\beta, \gamma, x, \alpha, x, \alpha).$$

Correspondingly, we have six alternatives for the colors on C_6,

$$(\beta, \gamma, \beta, \alpha, \beta, \alpha)$$

$$(\beta, \gamma, \beta, \alpha, \gamma, \alpha) \qquad (\delta, \alpha, \gamma, \beta)$$

$$(\beta, \gamma, \beta, \alpha, \delta, \alpha) \qquad (\gamma, \alpha, \delta, \beta)$$

$$(\beta, \gamma, \delta, \alpha, \beta, \alpha) \qquad (\delta, \alpha, \beta, \gamma)$$

$$(\beta, \gamma, \delta, \alpha, \gamma, \alpha) \qquad (\delta, \alpha, \beta, \delta)$$

$$(\beta, \gamma, \delta, \alpha, \delta, \alpha) \qquad (\delta, \alpha, \beta, \gamma)$$

In each of these cases except the first one finds a corresponding coloration of the whole graph with the colors for the vertices v_i given in the second column. In the remaining first case each β-vertex is connected to another by a β, δ-arc since otherwise one could change one color β to δ and pass to one of the cases already colored. But then an interchange of colors α and γ is permitted at any α or γ-vertex. Thus we pass to

$$(\beta, \gamma, \beta, \gamma, \beta, \alpha) \qquad (\gamma, \delta, \alpha, \delta)$$

colorable as indicated.

An analogous result holds for 6-vertices.

Theorem 12.3.2 (Franklin). No 6-vertex v_0 can have three consecutive 5-vertices v_1, v_2, v_3 as neighbors.

Proof: (see Fig. 12.3.2): In this case the configuration is separated by a circuit C_7. We contract the arc t_1, v_0, t_6 to a single vertex and similarly the arc t_2, v_1, v_2, v_3, t_5. This leads to a coloration for C_7 of the type

$$(\alpha, \beta, x, x, \beta, \alpha, x).$$

From the symmetry in Fig. 12.3.2 one finds five essentially different colorations for C_7,

$$(\alpha, \beta, \alpha, \gamma, \beta, \alpha, \gamma)$$

$$(\alpha, \beta, \alpha, \delta, \beta, \alpha, \gamma) \qquad (\delta, \gamma, \beta, \gamma)$$

$$(\alpha, \beta, \gamma, \delta, \beta, \alpha, \gamma) \qquad (\beta, \delta, \alpha, \gamma)$$

$$(\alpha, \beta, \alpha, \gamma, \beta, \alpha, \beta) \qquad (\gamma, \delta, \beta, \delta)$$

$$(\alpha, \beta, \gamma, \delta, \beta, \alpha, \beta)$$

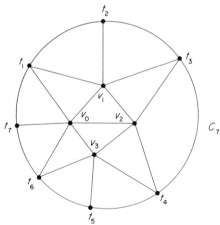

Fig. 12.3.2.

The three middle cases lead directly to colorations of $B_0{}^+$ with the colors of the vertices v_i given in the second column.

We shall examine the two remaining cases. For this kind of analysis it is advantageous to introduce a shorthand notation. When in a coloration two vertices a and b are connected, respectively, not connected by an arc colored alternatingly in the colors α and β, we write

$$[a, b; \alpha, \beta]; \qquad [a, b; \alpha, \beta]^*.$$

Case 1. $[t_1, t_6; \alpha, \delta]$.

We can change $t_7 = \gamma$ to $t_7 = \beta$ giving Case 4 $[t_3, t_6; \alpha, \delta]$. Make

$$t_4 = \beta, t_5 = \gamma$$

$$(\alpha, \beta, \alpha, \beta, \gamma, \alpha, \gamma)(\beta, \delta, \gamma, \delta)$$

$$[t_1, t_6; \alpha, \delta]^*, \qquad [t_3, t_6; \alpha, \delta]^*, \qquad t_6 = \delta$$

$$(\alpha, \beta, \alpha, \gamma, \beta, \delta, \gamma), \qquad (\beta, \gamma, \delta, \alpha).$$

Case 5. $[t_1, t_6; \alpha, \delta]$, $\qquad t_7 = \gamma$ $\qquad$ Case 3.

$$[t_4, t_6; \alpha, \delta], \qquad t_5 = \gamma$$

$$(\alpha, \beta, \gamma, \delta, \gamma, \alpha, \beta)(\gamma, \delta, \alpha, \beta)$$

$$[t_1, t_6; \alpha, \delta]^*, \qquad [t_4, t_6; \alpha, \delta]^*, \qquad t_6 = \delta$$

$$(\alpha, \beta, \gamma, \delta, \beta, \delta, \beta)(\gamma, \delta, \beta, \alpha).$$

Theorem 12.3.3 (Franklin). A 5-vertex is reducible when it has three 5-vertices and a 6-vertex as neighbors.

Proof: In any way such a configuration is drawn there is either a 5-vertex with three consecutive 5-neighbors or a 6-vertex with three consecutive 5-neighbors.

Theorem 12.3.4 (Franklin). A 5-vertex with two 5-neighbors and three 6-neighbors is reducible.

Proof: As before we denote the given 5-vertex by v_0 and its neighbors by v_i, $i = 1, \ldots, 5$. The two 5-neighbors must be consecutive since otherwise one would obtain a 6-vertex with three consecutive 5-neighbors. We draw the star graph at v_0 as in Fig. 12.3.3. This gives a configuration separated by a C_i with the vertices t_j, $j = 1, \ldots, 8$. We contract the vertices v_i and all even numbered vertices t_j to a single vertex; hence in $B_1{}^+$ all even numbered vertices on C_8 have the color α. Suppose first that not all odd-numbered vertices have the same color. Then there will

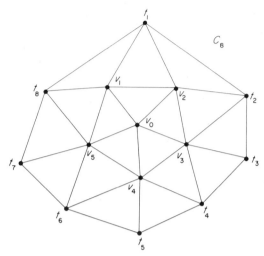

Fig. 12.3.3.

be a pair of consecutive odd vertices with different colors β and γ. Due to symmetry one need only consider the cases where these odd pairs are t_1, t_3 or t_3, t_5. In either case one assigns $v_0 = \alpha$. In the first case we put $v_2 = \gamma$, in the second $v_3 = \gamma$. This in both cases leads to a coloration of B_0 defined uniquely by a stepwise coloration. Secondly, let all odd-numbered vertices have the same color β. If one odd vertex is not connected to any other by a β, γ-arc, one can change its color to γ and return to the first case. On the other hand, when such β, γ-arcs exist for all β-vertices, one can change the color of t_2 to δ, and put $v_0 = \beta$ and give the v_i the colors

$$(\delta, \alpha, \gamma, \delta, \gamma).$$

We turn to the case where the 5-vertex v_0 has only one 5-neighbor v_1, the others being 6-vertices.

Theorem 12.3.5 (Winn). A 5-vertex with neighbor type (5, 6, 6, 6, 6) is reducible.

Proof: Here the separating circuit is a C_9 and one can assume that it is colored as indicated in Fig. 12.3.4,

$$(\beta, \gamma, \alpha, x, \alpha, x, \alpha, x, \alpha).$$

We separate the proof into three alternatives according to the color of t_4. $t_4 = \beta$. It suffices to make $v_0 = \alpha$. A coloration follows directly for all

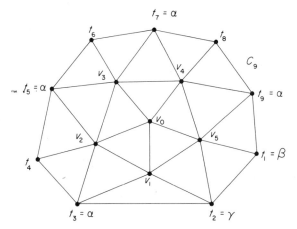

Fig. 12.3.4.

choices of colors for t_6 and t_8.

$t_4 = \delta.\ t_6 \neq \delta$ or $t_8 \neq \gamma$. Take $v_0 = \alpha$

$\quad t_6 = \delta, \qquad t_8 = \gamma$

$\quad (\beta, \gamma, \alpha, \delta, \alpha, \delta, \alpha, \gamma, \alpha)$

$[t_1, t_4; \beta, \delta],\quad t_2 = \alpha,\quad t_3 = \gamma,\quad v_0 = \alpha$

$[t_1, t_4; \beta, \delta]^*,\quad t_4 = \beta,\quad t_6 = \beta$ or δ; in either case $v_0 = \alpha$.

$t_4 = \gamma,\quad t_6 \neq t_8,\quad v_0 = \alpha$

$\quad t_6 = t_8 = \delta,\quad v_0 = \alpha$

$\quad t_6 = t_8 = \gamma$

$\quad (\beta, \gamma, \alpha, \gamma, \alpha, \gamma, \alpha, \gamma, \alpha)$

$[t_2, t_4; \beta, \gamma],\quad t_3 = \delta,\quad v_0 = \gamma$

$[t_2, t_4; \beta, \gamma]^*,\quad t_4 = \beta,\quad t_6 = t_8 = \beta, \gamma,\quad v_0 = \alpha$

$\quad t_6 = t_8 = \beta$

$\quad (\beta, \gamma, \alpha, \gamma, \alpha, \beta, \alpha, \beta, \alpha)$

$[t_1, t_6; \beta, \delta]^*,\quad t_1 = \delta,\quad t_8 = \beta$ or $\delta,\quad v_0 = \alpha$

$[t_1, t_6; \beta, \delta],\quad t_7 = t_9 = \gamma$

$$(\beta, \gamma, \alpha, \gamma, \alpha, \beta, \gamma, \beta, \gamma)$$

$$[t_2, t_4; \beta, \gamma], \quad t_3 = \delta, \quad v_0 = \gamma$$

$$[t_2, t_4; \beta, \gamma]^*, \quad (\beta, \gamma, \alpha, \beta, \alpha, \beta, \gamma, \beta, \gamma)$$

$$[t_4, t_6; \beta, \delta], \quad t_5 = \gamma, \quad v_0 = \gamma$$

$$[t_1, t_6; \beta, \delta], \quad t_7 = t_9 = v_0 = \alpha$$

$$[t_1, t_6; \beta, \delta]^*, \quad [t_4, t_6; \beta, \delta]^*, \quad t_6 = \delta, \quad t_8 = \beta \text{ or } \delta, \quad v_0 = \gamma$$

The proof of the next reduction is also quite complicated.

Theorem 12.3.6 (Choinacki–Winn). A 5-vertex whose neighbors are 6-vertices is reducible.

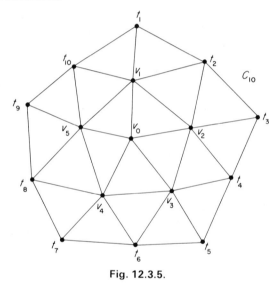

Fig. 12.3.5.

Proof:　Here the separating circuit is a C_{10} and we can assume the initial color type

$$(x, \alpha, x, \alpha, x, \alpha, x, \alpha \; x, \alpha).$$

It is readily seen that any coloration of the even-numbered vertices leads to a coloration of G, provided these vertices do not all have the same color β (see Fig. 12.3.5). In case all even vertices are β-vertices there can be no α, γ-arcs joining any of the α-vertices, for it would be possible to change some but not all β-vertices into δ-vertices, leading to the case just resolved. But when there are no α, γ-arcs, an arbitrary set of α-vertices can be changed to γ-vertices. Thus it is sufficient to show that

(1) $$(\beta, \gamma, \beta, \gamma, \beta, \alpha, \beta, \alpha, \beta, \alpha)$$

leads to a 4-coloration of G.

Case 1. $[t_1, t_9; \beta, \gamma], t_{10} = \delta.$

(2) $$(\beta, \gamma, \beta, \gamma, \beta, \alpha, \beta, \alpha, \beta, \delta)$$

$$[t_5, t_3; \beta, \delta], \quad t_4 = \alpha, \quad v_0 = \beta$$

$$[t_5, t_7; \beta, \delta], \quad t_6 = \gamma, \quad v_0 = \beta$$

$$[t_5, t_1; \beta, \delta], \quad t_2 = t_4 = \alpha, \quad t_3 = t_7 = \delta$$

$$(\beta, \alpha, \delta, \alpha, \beta, \alpha, \delta, \alpha, \beta, \delta)$$

$$[t_1, t_9; \beta, \gamma], \quad t_{10} = \alpha, \quad \text{initial case}$$

$$[t_1, t_9; \beta, \gamma]^*, \quad t_1 = \gamma, \quad t_9 = \beta, \quad t_5 = \beta \text{ or } \gamma, \quad v_0 = \alpha$$

Thus we have shown that there is no β, δ-arc from t_5. In (2) we can then make $t_5 = \delta$:

$$(\beta, \gamma, \beta, \gamma, \delta, \alpha, \beta, \alpha, \beta, \delta)$$

$$[t_{10}, t_2; \gamma, \delta], \quad t_1 = \alpha, \quad v_0 = \alpha$$

$$[t_{10}, t_4; \gamma, \delta], \quad t_1 = \alpha, \quad t_3 = \alpha \text{ or } \delta, \quad v_0 = \alpha$$

$$[t_{10}, t_2; \gamma, \delta]^*, \quad [t_{10}, t_4; \gamma, \delta]^*, \quad t_{10} = \gamma$$

$$(\beta, \gamma, \beta, \gamma, \delta, \alpha, \beta, \alpha, \beta, \gamma)$$

$$[t_9, t_7; \beta, \delta], \quad t_8 = \gamma, \quad v_0 = \gamma$$

$$[t_9, t_5; \beta, \delta], \quad t_6 = t_8 = \gamma, \quad \text{initial case}$$

$$[t_9, t_7; \beta, \delta]^*, \quad [t_9, t_5; \beta, \delta]^*, \quad t_9 = \delta, \quad t_1 = \beta \text{ or } \delta, \quad v_0 = \gamma$$

Case 2. $[t_1, t_9; \beta, \gamma]^*.$ For reasons of symmetry we can also suppose

$$[t_5, t_7; \beta, \gamma]^*, \quad t_7 = t_9 = \gamma$$

and the color type (1) is changed to

(3) $$(\beta, \gamma, \beta, \gamma, \beta, \alpha, \gamma, \alpha, \gamma, \alpha)$$

$$[t_5, t_1; \beta, \delta], \quad t_2 = t_4 = \alpha, \quad v_0 = \alpha$$

$$[t_5, t_3; \beta, \delta], \quad t_4 = \alpha$$

$$(\beta, \gamma, \beta, \alpha, \beta, \alpha, \gamma, \alpha, \gamma, \alpha)$$

$$[t_2, t_4; \alpha, \gamma], \quad t_3 = \delta, \quad v_0 = \alpha$$

$$[t_2, t_{10}; \alpha, \gamma], \quad t_1 = \delta, \quad v_0 = \alpha$$

$$[t_2, t_4; \alpha, \gamma]^*, \quad [t_2, t_{10}; \alpha, \gamma]^*, \quad t_2 = \alpha, \quad \text{initial case.}$$

$$[t_5, t_1; \beta, \delta]^*, \quad [t_5, t_3; \beta, \delta]^*. \quad \text{In (3) } t_5 = \delta, \quad v_0 = \gamma.$$

By combining the preceding reductions one obtains the result due to Winn.

Theorem 12.3.7. A 5-vertex is reducible when all its neighbors are minor vertices.

A similar analysis can be carried out for 6-vertices. A first step in this direction is Theorem 12.3.2. Another result is due to Bernhart.

Theorem 12.3.8. A 6-vertex cannot have three successive neighbors which are 5, 6, 5-vertices.

We shall not give the details of the proof. The remaining cases for 6-vertices have been resolved by Winn to establish the following theorem.

Theorem 12.3.9. A 6-vertex is reducible when all its neighbors are minor.

The special reducible configurations discovered by various writers are numerous and it would carry too far to reproduce them here. We shall only include some observations on consecutive 5-neighbors. In Theorems 12.3.1 and 12.3.2 we saw that no 5- and 6-vertices can have three consecutive 5-neighbors. From the theorems of Errera in the next section it follows that an n-vertex, n even, can have at most $n - 3$ consecutive 5-vertices while for n odd there can at most be $n - 2$ such neighbors. For $n = 7$ the latter result has been improved by Winn.

Theorem 12.3.10. No 7-vertex can have more than four consecutive 5-neighbors.

Proof: Let v_0 be the 7-vertex with the neighbors v_i, $i = 1, 2, \ldots, 7$ with valences

$$(n_1, n_2, n_3, 5, 5, 5, 5).$$

The second neighbors are t_i with the notations chosen as in Fig. 12.3.6.

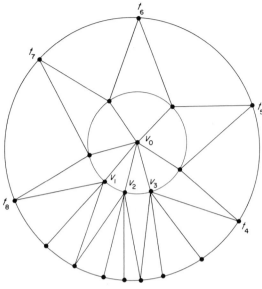

Fig. 12.3.6.

The separating circuit shall be

$$C_8 = (v_1, v_2, v_3, t_4, t_5, t_6, t_7, t_8).$$

To verify that this is a reducible configuration we contract the inner bridge B_0 so that we can assume that in B_1^+ the colors on C_8 are

$$t_4 = t_6 = t_8 = \alpha, \qquad v_1 = \beta, \qquad v_2 = \gamma.$$

This leaves the possibilities $v_3 = \delta$ or $v_3 = \beta$. In the first case one obtains a coloration for G with $v_0 = \alpha$ regardless of the colors at t_5 and y_7. Thus we may assume that the color scheme on C_8 is

$$(\beta, \gamma, \beta, \alpha, t_5, \alpha, t_7, \alpha).$$

When $t_5 = \beta$ or $t_7 = \beta$, one obtains a coloration with $v_0 = \alpha$. Due to symmetry this leaves us with three cases:

Case 1. $t_5 = \gamma, \quad t_7 = \delta$

$$[t_5, v_3; \beta, \gamma]^*, \quad t_5 = \beta, \quad v_0 = \alpha$$

$$[t_5, v_3; \beta, \gamma], \quad t_4 = \delta$$

$$(\beta, \gamma, \beta, \delta, \gamma, \alpha, \delta, \alpha)$$

$[t_6, t_8; \alpha, \gamma]^*, \quad t_8 = \gamma, \quad v_2 = \alpha \text{ or } \gamma, \quad v_0 = \delta$

$[t_6, t_8; \alpha, \gamma], \quad t_7 = \beta$

$[v_3, t_5; \beta, \gamma], \quad t_4 = v_0 = \alpha$

$[v_3, t_5; \beta, \gamma]^*, \quad t_5 = \beta, \quad t_7 = \beta, \gamma, \quad v_0 = \alpha.$

Case 2. $t_5 = t_7 = \delta$

$\qquad (\beta, \gamma, \beta, \alpha, \delta, \alpha, \delta, \alpha)$

$\qquad [t_7, v_1; \beta, \delta], \quad t_8 = \gamma, \quad v_0 = \delta$

$\qquad [t_7, v_1; \beta, \delta]^*, \quad [t_7, v_3; \beta, \delta], \quad t_8 = \gamma, \quad v_2 = \alpha, \gamma, \quad v_0 = \delta$

$\qquad [t_7, v_1; \beta, \delta]^*, \quad [t_7, v_3; \beta, \delta]^*, \quad t_7 = \beta, \quad t_5 = \beta, \delta, \quad v_0 = \alpha.$

Case 3. $t_5 = t_7 = \gamma$

$\qquad (\beta, \gamma, \beta, \alpha, \gamma, \alpha, \gamma, \alpha)$

$\qquad [t_5, t_7; \beta, \gamma]^*, \quad t_5 = \beta, \quad v_1, v_2, v_3 = \beta, \gamma, \beta \text{ or } \gamma, \beta, \gamma, \quad v_0 = \alpha$

$\qquad [t_5, t_7; \beta, \gamma], \quad t_6 = \delta$

$\qquad (\beta, \gamma, \beta, \alpha, \gamma, \delta, \gamma, \alpha)$

$\qquad [v_1, v_3; \beta, \delta], \quad v_2 = \alpha, \quad v_0 = \gamma$

$\qquad [v_1, t_6; \beta, \delta], \quad t_7 = \alpha, \quad t_8 = \gamma, \quad v_0 = \alpha$

$\qquad [v_1, v_3; \beta, \delta]^*, \quad [v_1, t_6; \beta, \delta]^*, \quad v_1 = \delta$

$\qquad (\delta, \gamma, \beta, \alpha, \gamma, \delta, \gamma, \alpha)$

$\qquad [t_4, t_6; \alpha, \delta]^*, \quad [t_6, t_8; \alpha, \delta]^*, \quad t_6 = v_0 = \alpha.$

a. $[t_4, t_6; \alpha, \delta], \quad t_5 = \beta$

$\qquad (\delta, \gamma, \beta, \alpha, \beta, \delta, \gamma, \alpha)$

$\qquad [t_8, v_3; \alpha, \beta], \quad v_1 = \gamma, \quad v_2 = \delta, \quad v_0 = \alpha$

$\qquad [t_8, v_3; \alpha, \beta]^*, \quad t_8 = \beta$

$\qquad [t_8, v_3; \beta, \delta], \quad v_2 = \alpha, \quad v_0 = \gamma$

$\qquad [t_8, t_6; \beta, \delta], \quad t_7 = v_0 = \alpha$

$\qquad [t_8, v_3; \beta, \delta]^*, \quad [t_8, t_6; \beta, \delta]^*, \quad v_1 = \beta, \quad t_8 = \delta, \quad v_0 = \delta.$

b. $[t_6, t_8 ; \alpha, \delta], \quad t_7 = \beta$

$\quad (\delta, \gamma, \beta, \alpha, \gamma, \delta, \beta, \alpha)$

$\quad [v_3, t_8 ; \alpha, \beta], \quad v_1 = \gamma, \quad v_2 = \delta, \quad v_0 = \alpha$

$\quad [v_3, t_8 ; \alpha, \beta]^*, \quad t_7 = \alpha, \quad t_8 = \beta$

$\quad (\delta, \gamma, \beta, \alpha, \gamma, \delta, \alpha, \beta)$

$\quad [v_1, t_7 ; \alpha, \delta], \quad t_8 = \gamma, \quad v_0 = \alpha$

$\quad [v_1, t_4 ; \alpha, \delta], \quad v_2 = \beta, \quad v_3 = \gamma, \quad v_0 = \alpha$

$\quad [v_1, t_4 ; \alpha, \delta]^*, \quad [v_1, t_7 ; \alpha, \beta]^*, \quad v_1 = \alpha$

$\quad (\alpha, \gamma, \beta, \alpha, \gamma, \delta, \alpha, \beta)$

$\quad [v_1, v_3 ; \alpha, \beta], \quad v_2 = \delta, \quad v_0 = \gamma$

$\quad [v_1, v_3 ; \alpha, \beta]^*, \quad v_1 = \beta, \quad t_7 = \beta, \quad t_8 = \alpha, \quad v_0 = \alpha.$

We mention without proof a few other reductions due to Winn.

R_1: A 5-vertex is reducible when it has a neighbor sequence

$$(5, \rho_2, \rho_3, 5), \qquad \rho_2, \rho_3 = 5, 6.$$

R_2: A 6-vertex is reducible when it has a neighbor sequence with valence types

$$(5, 5, 6, 5) \quad \text{or} \quad (5, 5, 6, 6, 5).$$

An immediate consequence is that a 6-vertex with four 5-neighbors must have neighbor type

$$(\rho_1, 5, 5, \rho_4, 5, 5), \qquad \rho_1, \rho_2 \geqq 7.$$

The following can also be shown.

R_3: In this neighbor type for a 6-vertex at most one of the pairs of 5-vertices can belong to a triangle of 5-vertices.

R_4: From R_2 it follows that a 6-vertex with three 5-neighbors must have at least two major neighbors.

R_5: A 7-vertex with five 5-neighbors must have the type

$$(5, 5, 5, \rho_4, 5, 5, \rho_7), \rho_4, \rho_7 \geqq 7.$$

R_6: A 7-vertex with four 5-neighbors and three 6-neighbors is reducible.

12.4. Errera Circuits and 5-Components

Some important reducible circuits consisting mainly of 5- and 6-vertices were discovered by Errera. His main result is as follows.

Theorem 12.4.1. A minimal separating circuit C is reducible when (1) C consists of an even sequence of 5-vertices and one arbitrary vertex or two arbitrary consecutive vertices, (2) C has an even number of 5- and 6-vertices, the 5-vertices occurring in consecutive pairs.

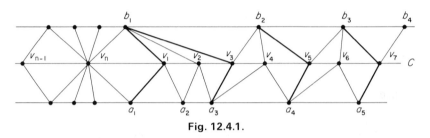

Fig. 12.4.1.

Proof: We consider Case 1. In Fig. 12.4.1 we have drawn the vertices v_i on C and their two classes of neighbors a_j and b_k; the arbitrary vertex on C is v_n and v_{n-1} if it exists. We contract G along the heavily drawn arcs of length 2 connecting a vertex a_j with a vertex b_k. One such arc passes through each odd-numbered 5-vertex $v_1, v_3, v_5, \ldots$, on C. This contraction leads to a coloration of that part G' of G which remains after all 5-vertices $v_1, v_2, \ldots$, and their edges have been removed, except for v_n and eventually v_{n-1}. In the coloration of G' the two end points of a contracted arc have the same color. We shall show that this coloration can be extended to the vertices of C to give a 4-coloration of G. Suppose $v_n = \alpha$ is the color at v_n. The vertex v_1 has the neighbors b_1, a_1 and v_n, a_2 disregarding for the moment the following vertex v_2 on C. We may suppose $a_1 = b_1 = \beta$. If $a_2 = \gamma$ one must put $v_1 = \delta$. If on the other hand $a_2 = \alpha$, we have two choices γ, δ at v_1. Next we color v_2. If there are two choices $v_1 = \gamma, \delta$, we have two choices $v_2 = \delta, \gamma$ compatible with the colors at b_1, v_1, a_2, a_3. If there is no choice at $v_1 = \delta$, we must put $v_2 = \alpha$.

From v_2 we continue the coloration process. If at any vertex v_i, there is a color choice there will be choices at each subsequent vertex. It is clear that when there is only one arbitrary vertex v_n one can make the color at v_{n-1} different from $v_n = \alpha$; similarly one can make the color at v_{n-2} different from the color at v_{n-1} when there are two arbitrary vertices v_{n-1} and v_n.

There remains the case where there are no color choices for the vertices v_i. Then all even numbered vertices $v_2, v_4, \ldots$, have the color α. This gives $v_{n-2} = \alpha$ when there are two arbitrary vertices v_{n-1} and $v_n = \alpha$, hence G is colorable. When there is only one arbitrary vertex $v_n = \alpha$, we obtain $v_{n-3} = \alpha$. In this case we do not contract the arc through v_{n-2} as for the other odd vertices v_i, but we contract the arc (v_n, v_{n-1}, a_r) as in Fig. 12.4.2. Then $a_r = \alpha$ and we can color v_{n-2} and v_{n-1} in two colors different from α.

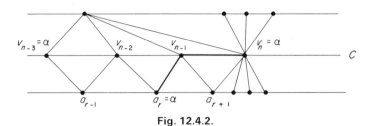

Fig. 12.4.2.

Case 2 in Theorem 12.4.2 can be proved by similar arguments. For the details we refer to the paper by Errera.

Theorem 12.4.1 applies immediately to the case where C is the neighbor circuit to a vertex. Then C is obviously a minimal separating circuit.

The set of all 5-vertices in an irreducible graph G define a section subgraph G_5, the *5-graph* of G. It consists of a family of connected components K_5, the 5-components of G. These may include isolated vertices. Theorem 12.3.1 shows that the valence $\rho_5(v)$ of a vertex v in a K_5 cannot exceed 3. As a consequence, at any separating vertex in K_5 one of the edges must be a separating edge.

We shall determine the lobe graphs of a component K_5. A set of three 5-vertices forming the corners of a triangle in G and G_5 we call a *triad*. Any two triads are disjoint since a common edge or corner would lead to a 5-vertex with three consecutive 5-neighbors. Suppose that a lobe graph L has a circuit C_n not a triad as the boundary of one of its faces. Then there will be vertices of G both inside and outside C_n since G is maximal. However, this contradicts Errera's theorem. We conclude that if L has circuits all face boundaries in L must be triads. Since no triads are adjacent it follows that L is either a single triad or a single edge or vertex.

Theorem 12.4.2. Each 5-components K_5 is a treelike graph consisting of triads and single arcs connecting them. If there are no triads, then K_5 is an arc or a single vertex.

In Fig. 12.4.3 we have drawn one of these components.

The vertices in K_5 are of various types. A vertex is a *triad vertex* when it belongs to a triad; it is a *triad terminal* when there are no edges in K_5 to vertices not in its triad (v_1 is a triad terminal). A vertex not in a triad is *simple*: A *simple terminal* is the end point of a terminal edge in K_5 (as for instance v_2 in Fig. 12.4.3).

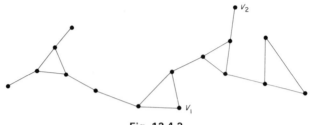

Fig. 12.4.3.

Each component K_5 has a *neighbor set* N_5 consisting of all vertices not in K_5, but connected to K_5 by at least one edge. According to the definition of K_5 each such neighbor n has valence ≥ 6. The edges from any $n \in N_5$ to K_5 must go to consecutive vertices on K_5; otherwise one would have a separating circuit in G consisting of 5-vertices and one arbitrary vertex, contradicting Theorem 12.4.1. We conclude that the set of all neighbors v_i will lie on a circuit, the *neighbor circuit* $C(K_5)$ of K_5. The graph $N(K_5)$ consisting of K_5 and $C(K_5)$ and all edges connecting these two graphs we call the *neighbor graph* of K_5. We observe that $N(K_5)$ need not be a section subgraph of G with respect to its vertex set

$$V(N(K_5)) = V(K_5) + V(C(K_5))$$

since there may be outer edges connecting two nonconsecutive vertices on $C(K_5)$. It is possible, we notice, that an edge in $C(K_5)$ may also belong to the neighbor circuit $C(K_5')$ of some other 5-component K_5'.

We shall examine the neighbor graphs in some further detail. Let $E = (a, b)$ be an arbitrary edge of K_5. It forms the basis for two triangles

$$(a, b, c_1), \qquad (a, b, c_2)$$

in $N(K_5)$. When E belongs to a triad, either c_1 or c_2, say c_2, is the third corner of the triad while $c_1 = n_1$ is a neighbor of K_5. In general, we call n_1 the summit of the triangle

$$T = (a, b, n_1).$$

When E is not a triad edge, we have two triangles

$$(a, b, n_1) \qquad (a, b, n_2)$$

with base E. We call n_1 and n_2 *opposite summits* (Fig. 12.4.4).

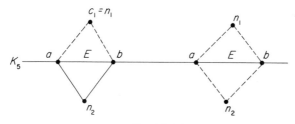

Fig. 12.4.4.

A neighbor n is the summit for an edge in K_5 if, and only if, there are at least two edges from n to K_5. The neighbors which are not summits shall be called *terminal neighbors*. They are connected to K_5 by a single edge to one of its terminal vertices. At each triad terminal there is just one such terminal neighbor. At each simple terminal there are two terminal neighbors (Fig. 12.4.5).

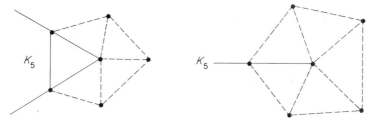

Fig. 12.4.5.

Let us examine when a summit can be a 6-vertex.

Lemma 12.4.1. A summit n of a triad edge $E = (a, b)$ can be a 6-vertex only when both a and b are triad terminals.

Proof: Suppose there is an edge (a, d) to a 5-vertex d not in the triad (a, b, c) (Fig. 12.4.6).

Since a cannot have three consecutive 5-neighbors there must be an edge (n, d), but then n would become a 6-vertex with three consecutive 5-neighbors.

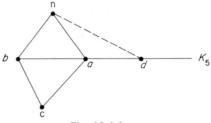

Fig. 12.4.6.

Lemma 12.4.2. When one of the end points of E is a triad vertex none of its summits can be a 6-vertex.

Proof: Suppose a is a triad vertex. One sees from Fig. 12.4.7 that both n and n' have three consecutive 5-neighbors.

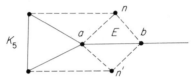

Fig. 12.4.7.

Lemma 12.4.3. When neither end point of $E = (a, b)$ is a triad vertex, at most one of its summits n and n' (say n) can be a 6-vertex provided K_5 does not consist only of E. When there exists an edge $E_1 = (a, a_1)$ in K_5, the neighbor summit n_1 to n defined by E_1 is not a 6-vertex.

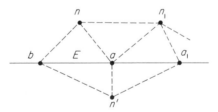

Fig. 12.4.8.

Proof: When n is a 6-vertex, there can be no edge (n, a_1) for n would have three consecutive 5-neighbors (Fig. 12.4.8). Thus there is an edge (n', a_1) and n' is not a 6-vertex. Furthermore, there must be an edge (n_1, a_1). Then n_1 cannot be a 6-vertex for it would contradict a reduction obtained by Winn:

A 5-vertex is reducible when it has a neighbor sequence

$$5, \rho_2, \rho_3, 5, \rho_2, \rho_3 = 5, 6.$$

12.5. Lower Bounds for Irreducible Graphs

Franklin made the first estimate of the minimal number of vertices in an irreducible graph. He showed that such a planar graph must have at least 26 vertices. This number was raised to 28 by Reynolds and then again to 32 by Franklin. In 1938 it was shown by Winn that there must be at least 36 vertices.

Theorem 12.5.1. The four-color conjecture is true for all graphs with 35 or fewer faces.

To date this is the best result obtained. We shall reproduce Winn's proof here, considering as usual, vertex coloration.

In the irreducible graph G we denote by a_i the number of vertices v_i with $\rho(v_i) = i$. The number of vertices $v_i^{(r)}$ with r 5-neighbors shall be $a_i^{(r)}$ so that

$$a_i = \sum_{r=0}^{i-2} a_i^{(r)}. \tag{12.5.1}$$

The number of edges E_{ij} connecting an i-vertex with a j-vertex we denote by

$$v_i(j) = v_j(i). \tag{12.5.2}$$

From these definitions we obtain

$$v_5(j) = \sum_{r=1}^{j-2} r \cdot a_j^{(r)}, \qquad j \geq 6. \tag{12.5.3}$$

Next we introduce the auxiliary quantity

$$L = v_5(6) + 2 \sum_{j \geq 7} v_5(j). \tag{12.5.4}$$

Each 5-vertex contributes a certain amount to L. The contribution cannot exceed 10 and this occurs when all its neighbors are major. It cannot be less than 4 and this value occurs only for triad vertices, as one sees from the Lemmas in the preceding section. We write

$$L = L_0 + 4a_5 \tag{12.5.5}$$

and conclude from our remarks that

$$0 \leq L_0 \leq 6a_5. \tag{12.5.6}$$

When (12.5.3) is substituted into (12.5.4), one obtains

$$L = \sum_{r=1}^{4} r \cdot a_6^{(r)} + 2 \cdot \sum_{j \geq 7} \sum_{r=1}^{j-2} r \cdot a_j^{(r)}. \tag{12.5.7}$$

According to (12.5.1) we have

$$a_i \geq \sum_{r=1}^{i-2} a_i^{(r)}$$

where equality holds if, and only if, $a_i^{(0)} = 0$, that is, there are no vertices v_i without 5-neighbors. This gives

$$\sum_{j \geq 7} (6j - 34)a_j \geq \sum_{j \geq 7} \sum_{r=1}^{j-2} a_j^{(r)}(6j - 34).$$

This in turn may be written

$$\sum_{j \geq 7} (6j - 34)a_j - \sum_{j \geq 7} \sum_{r=1}^{j-2} (6j - 34 - 2r)a_j^{(r)} \geq 2 \sum_{j \geq 7} \sum_{r=1}^{j-2} r \cdot a_j^{(r)}.$$

It yields when substituted in (12.5.7)

$$L \leq \sum_{r=1}^{4} ra_6^{(r)} + \sum_{j \geq 7} (6j - 34)a_j - \sum_{j \geq 7} \sum_{r=1}^{j-2} (6j - 34 - 2r)a_j^{(r)}.$$

This we rewrite as

$$L + \sum_{j \geq 7} \sum_{r=1}^{j-2} (6j - 34 - 2r)a_j^{(r)} \leq \sum_{j \geq 6} (6j - 34)a_j - a_6^{(1)} + a_6^{(3)} + 2a_6^{(4)}$$

where equality holds only if $a_j^{(0)} = 0$ for $j \geq 6$, that is, all vertices in G belong to a neighbor graph $N(K_5)$.

The only negative term in the double sum on the left is $-2a_7^{(5)}$. When one denotes by an asterisk that this term has been omitted in the sum, it follows that

$$L + \sum_{j \geq 7}^{*} \sum_{r=1}^{j-2} a_j^{(r)}(6j - 34 - 2r) \leq a_6^{(3)} + 2a_6^{(4)} + 2a_7^{(5)} + \sum_{j \geq 6} (6j - 34)a_j$$

$$\tag{12.5.8}$$

where equality holds when

$$a_6^{(1)} = 0, \qquad a_j^{(0)} = 0, \qquad j = 6, 7, \ldots.$$

Suppose now that it can be shown that

$$D_0 = L_0 + \sum_{j \geq 7}^{*} \sum_{r=1}^{j-2} a_j^{(r)}(6j - 34 - 2r) - a_6^{(3)} - 2a_6^{(4)} - 2a_7^{(5)} \geq 0. \tag{12.5.9}$$

From (12.5.8) and (12.5.5) one then obtains

$$\sum_{j \geq 6} (6j - 34)a_j \geq 4a_5.$$

According to Euler's relation one has

$$a_5 = 12 + \sum_{j \geq 7} (j - 6)a_j \qquad \text{(Relation (4.1.8) for } \rho_0{}^* = 3)$$

or

$$\sum_{j \geq 6} (6j - 36)a_j = 6a_5 - 72.$$

From our last inequality we conclude

$$6a_5 - 72 + 2a_6 + 2a_7 + \cdots \geq 4a_5$$

so the number of vertices in G satisfies

$$v_v(G) = a_5 + a_6 + a_7 + \cdots \geq 36$$

as required by Theorem 12.5.1.

To prove Theorem 12.5.1, that is, the inequality (12.5.9) we shall have to investigate the three types of 6- and 7-vertices contributing to the last three terms. To each of them we associate one or two adjacent vertices contributing to L_0 or to the sum Σ^*. To define these we make use of the following short-hand notation for the various classes of vertices:

> N-vertex: A vertex v with $\rho(v) \geq 7$.
> n-vertex: $\rho(v) \geq 6$.
> m-vertex: No valence restriction.

$a_6^{(3)}$.

From Reduction R_4 (Section 12.3) one sees that a 6-vertex $v_6^{(3)}$ must belong to one of the following three neighbor types, taken in one or the other directions:

$$\alpha: (5, n, 5, N, 5, N)$$

$$\beta: (5, 5, N, 5, N, n)$$

$$\gamma: (5, 5, N, 5, n, N).$$

α (Fig. 12.5.1): Here we associate the vertex $v_6^{(3)}$ with the last 5-vertex u in the neighbor symbol. The corresponding symbol for u is then of the type:

$$\text{I} \qquad u(6, N, m, m, N)$$

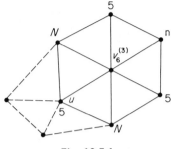

Fig. 12.5.1.

where the first 6 corresponds to the source $v_6^{(3)}$. If all neighbors of $v_6^{(3)}$ which are not 5-vertices should be major, any one of the 5-neighbors may be taken to be u.

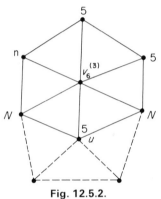

Fig. 12.5.2.

β (Fig. 12.5.2): In this case the u corresponding to $v_6^{(3)}$ is the single 5-vertex and its type is

$$\text{I}' \qquad u(6, N, m, m, N)$$

as in I. Both in I and I' the vertex u is a terminal vertex, either a simple or triad terminal or an isolated 5-vertex.

γ (Fig. 12.5.3): We denote the neighbors of $v_6^{(3)}$ by $u_1, \ldots, u_6$. The edge (u_6, u_5) defines a summit s different from $v_6^{(3)}$. There are several alternatives depending on the valences of the vertices u_4 and s.

When $\rho(u_4) \geqq 7$, we associate with $v_6^{(3)}$ the vertex u_3 with the neighbor type

$$\text{I}'' \qquad u_3(6, N, m, m, N).$$

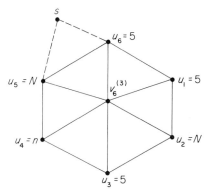

Fig. 12.5.3.

When $\rho(u_4) = 6$, we have three cases depending on the valence of s: $\rho(s) = 5$. We associate $v_6^{(3)}$ with u_6,

$$\text{II} \qquad u_6(6, 5, N, 5, N).$$

$\rho(s) \geqq 7$. We associate $v_6^{(3)}$ with u_6,

$$\text{III} \qquad u_6(6, 5, m, N, N).$$

$\rho(s) = 6$. We associate $v_6^{(3)}$ with u_5,

$$\text{IV} \qquad u_5(6, 6, m, \cdots m, 6, 5).$$

In the latter case if $\rho(u_5) = 7$ there can be at most three 5-neighbors. This is a consequence of reduction R_6.

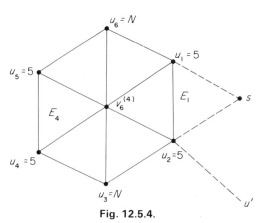

Fig. 12.5.4.

$a_6^{(4)}$.

(See Fig. 12.5.4.) From reduction R_2 it follows that the neighbor valences of a vertex $v_6^{(4)}$ must be of the type $(5, 5, N, 5, 5, N)$. From R_3 one sees that one of the edges $E_1 = (u_1, u_2)$ $E_4 = (u_3, u_5)$ is not a triad edge. Suppose that E_1 is not in a triad.

By our assumption the summit $s \neq v_6^{(4)}$ of E_1 is not a 5-vertex. Nor can it be a 6-vertex if there is some other 5-neighbor u' of u_1 or u_2. In this case we associate $v_6^{(4)}$ with the two 5-vertices u_1 and u_2. Their neighbor types are

$$V \qquad u_1, u_2(6, 5, N, m, N)$$

when $\rho(s) \geq 7$ and

$$VI \qquad u_1, u_2(6, 5, 6, n, N)$$

when $\rho(s) = 6$; hence there is no vertex u'.

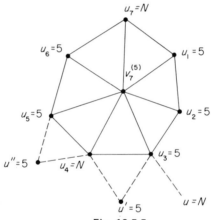

Fig. 12.5.5.

$a_7^{(5)}$.

According to reduction R_5 the neighbor type of a vertex $v_7^{(5)}$ is

$$(5, 5, 5, N, 5, 5, N).$$

Here we have two alternatives (see Fig. 12.5.5). Under the first either u_4 or u_7 or both are $v_7^{(5)}$-vertices. Suppose v_4 is such a vertex. We associate $v_7^{(5)}$ with both 5-vertices u_3 and u_5. Their neighbor types are

$$VII \qquad u_3, u_5(7, 5, N, 5, 7)$$

since $u = 6$ would give a 6-vertex with three consecutive 5-neighbors.

Under the second alternative neither u_4 nor u_7 is a vertex $v_7^{(5)}$. The vertex u_2 must have at least one major neighbor different from $v_7^{(5)}$ as seen from a previous reduction. Such a vertex will also be a major neighbor for u_1 or u_3. Let us suppose that u_3 has such a common major neighbor with u_2. We then associate $v_7^{(5)}$ with u_3. The neighbor type is then

$$\text{VIII} \qquad u_3(7, 5, N, m, N')$$

where N' does not correspond to a vertex $v_7^{(5)}$.

By the preceding method each of the vertices $v_6^{(3)}$ has been associated with a single 5-vertex, except in case IV where the associated vertex is major. Each vertex $v_6^{(4)}$ has been associated with two 5-vertices. Each vertex $v_7^{(5)}$ has been associated with two 5-vertices except in case VIII. If we count this last vertex with multiplicity 2, it follows that the number of associated vertices, each counted with its multiplicity is

$$a_6^{(3)} + 2a_6^{(4)} + 2a_7^{(5)}.$$

To prove the inequality (12.5.9) we shall have to establish that the number of associated vertices does not exceed

$$L_0 + \sum_{j \geq 7}^{*} \sum_{r=1}^{j-2} a_j^{(r)}(6j - 34 - 2r). \qquad (12.5.10)$$

By checking all alternatives in the preceding one sees that an associated 5-vertex always contributes at least 5 to the number L in (12.5.4); hence it has a positive contribution to L_0 in (12.5.5).

We shall now investigate how many times a 5-vertex can appear as an associated vertex. In general, let us denote such a vertex by $t_5(k)$ where k is the amount of its contribution to L; hence $k - 4$ its contribution to L_0. We consider separately the various values of k from 5 to 10. If one can show that the contribution $k - 4$ of a vertex $t_5(k)$ to L_0 is not less than the number of times it may appear as an associated vertex, it follows that the number of associated 5-vertices does not exceed L_0.

$t_5(5)$. Such a vertex must have a neighbor type of one of the kinds:

> one 5-vertex, three 6-vertices, one major
> two 5-vertices, one 6-vertex, two majors.

When one checks the previously derived neighbor types, one finds that a vertex $t_5(5)$ can only occur in the following cases:

$$\text{I, I}', \text{I}'' \qquad (6, N, 5, 5, N)$$

$$\text{II, V} \qquad (6, 5, N, 5, N)$$

III	$(6, 5, 5, N, N)$
VI	$(6, 5, 6, 6, N)$.

In each case $t_5(5)$ is the image of the first vertex in its neighbor type. It is clear that $t_5(5)$ can be the image of at most one 6-vertex.

$t_5(6)$. Each such vertex contributes two units to L_0. Its neighbor type must belong to one of the three categories:

    no 5-vertices, four 6-vertices, one major
    one 5-vertex, two 6-vertices, two majors
    two 5-vertices, no 6-vertices, three majors.

One checks that the first type cannot occur as the neighbor type of any associated 5-vertex. The other two possibilities can occur in the following cases.

I, I', I'', V	$(6, N, 5, 6, N)$
III, VI	$(6, 5, 6, N, N)$
VII	$(7, 5, N, 5, 7)$
VIII	$(7, 5, N, 5, N')$

The first two types are distinct from the last two. In the first two cases $t_5(6)$ can at most be the image of two 6-vertices. The last two types are also distinct due to the fact that in VII the last 7-vertex is a vertex $v_7^{(5)}$ while in VIII it is not. Thus in the third case $t_5(6)$ can be the image of two vertices $v_7^{(5)}$. In the fourth it is associated with a unique $v_7^{(5)}$; hence in this case $t_5(6)$ has the multiplicity 2 as required by the agreement for VIII.

$t_5(7)$. The neighbor valences must be:

    no 5-vertices, three 6-vertices, two majors
    one 5-vertex, one 6-vertex, three majors.

The corresponding neighborhoods for associated 5-vertices are:

I, I', I''	$(6, N, 6, 6, N)$
I, I', I''	$(6, N, 5, N, N)$
III, V	$(6, 5, N, N, N)$
VIII	$(7, 5, N, 6, N')$.

If $t_5(7)$ has a neighbor type of the first kind including three 6-vertices, it can only be associated with a single vertex $v_6^{(3)}$. The same is true in the second case. In the third $t_5(7)$ is associated with a single vertex $v_6^{(3)}$ or $v_6^{(4)}$. In the fourth case $t_5(7)$ is associated with a single $a_7^{(5)}$ since N' does not correspond to such a vertex by assumption while the middle major vertex has a 6-neighbor and this is impossible for $a_7^{(5)}$. By agreement $t_5(7)$ shall be counted double in this case. But $t_5(7)$ could also have been associated with a single vertex $a_6^{(3)}$ since its neighbor type is also included in the second type. Thus the multiplicity of $t_5(7)$ is at most 3, the same as the contribution of $t_5(7)$ to L_0.

$t_5(8)$. Here there are two kinds of neighbor valences:

> two 6-vertices, three majors
> one 5-vertex, four majors.

These are the only possible cases

$$\text{I, I}', \text{I}'' \qquad (6, N, 6, N, N)$$

$$\text{VIII} \qquad (7, 5, N, N, N').$$

A vertex $t_5(8)$ associated with a vertex $a_6^{(3)}$ as in the first case can be so in at most two ways. When it is associated with a vertex $a_7^{(5)}$ as in the second case, it could also be associated with the third vertex since this has a 5-neighbor. Corresponding to the double count of $t_5(7)$ in this case it gives a maximal multiplicity of 4.

$t_5(9)$. The only neighbor type is one 6-vertex, four majors. This occurs only as

$$\text{I, I}', \text{I}'' \qquad (6, N, N, N, N)$$

hence $t_5(9)$ is associated with at most a single vertex $a_6^{(3)}$.

$t_5(10)$. All neighbors are major and no associated 5-vertex has this type.

This concludes the proof that the number of associated 5-vertices counted with their multiplicities cannot exceed L_0.

It remains to show that the number of associated major vertices cannot exceed the double sum in (12.5.10). Only in case IV is a major vertex associated and this occurs only for vertices $v_6^{(3)}$. Let us investigate when the multiplicity of $v_j^{(r)}$ can be greater or equal to the coefficient of $a_j^{(r)}$ in (12.5.10). The multiplicity of $v_j^{(r)}$ cannot exceed $j - r$ so our condition requires

$$j - r \geq 6j - 34 - 2r \quad \text{or} \quad 5j \leq 34 + r.$$

The form of $v_j^{(r)}$ in IV shows that $r \leq j - 3$ so we conclude that $j = 7$ with $r = 1, 2, 3, 4$. In the case $r = 1$ equality holds. Let us check the others.

$r = 2$. The coefficient of $a_7^{(2)}$ in (12.5.10) is 4. The possibilities in IV are

$$(6, 6, 5, n_1, n_2, 6, 5) \ (6, 6, n_1, 5, n_2, 6, 5) \ (6, 6, n_1, n_2, 5, 6, 5).$$

Only when $n_1 = n_2 = 6$ is it possible that $v_7^{(2)}$ can be associated with several $a_6^{(3)}$. We examine the resulting types.

$$(6, 6, 5, 6, 6, 6, 5) \ (6, 6, 6, 5, 6, 6, 5) \ (6, 6, 6, 6, 5, 6, 5)$$

In the last $v_7^{(2)}$ can be associated with at most two $v_6^{(3)}$. The first two types are the same and here $v_7^{(2)}$ might be associated with four $a_6^{(3)}$.

$r = 3$. The coefficient of $a_7^{(3)}$ is 2. The neighborhoods IV have the forms

$$(6, 6, 5, 5, n, 6, 5) \ (6, 6, 5, n, 5, 6, 5) \ (6, 6, n, 5, 5, 6, 5).$$

Only for $n = 6$ can $v_7^{(3)}$ be associated with several vertices $v_6^{(3)}$. We have the alternatives

$$(6, 6, 5, 5, 6, 6, 5) \ (6, 6, 5, 6, 5, 6, 5) \ (6, 6, 6, 5, 5, 6, 5).$$

In the last case $v_7^{(3)}$ is associated with at most one $a_6^{(3)}$, in the first two cases with at most two.

$r = 4$. Here IV becomes reducible

$$(6, 6, 5, 5, 5, 6, 5).$$

This concludes the proof of Theorem 12.5.1.

Let us make some additional remarks about known facts concerning the four-color problem.

Winn has shown that an irreducible planar graph must have at least six major vertices.

He also obtained an arbitrary maximal planar graph with at most one major vertex can be vertex colored in four colors.

By means of this result a further four-color case has been obtained by Dirac.

A *skeleton R* of a graph G is a subgraph such that each vertex in G is edge connected with at least one vertex in R. It can be shown that G is 4-colorable if it has a connected skeleton R such that for any vertex $r \in R$ the G-valence satisfies

$$\rho_G(r) \leqq 4$$

with at most five exceptions.

CHAPTER 13

THREE COLORS

13.1. Formulations of the Three-Color Problem

We shall investigate briefly the problem when a planar graph can be face-colored in three colors. Not all graphs can be so colored. The graph with the smallest number of edges not colorable in three colors is the self-dual tetrahedron graph (Fig. 13.1.1).

Fig. 13.1.1.

The three colors to be used shall be denoted by α, β, γ. We begin by establishing a few special results.

Theorem 13.1.1. A necessary and sufficient condition that in a planar graph G all but a single face be colorable in two colors is that the boundary of this exceptional face include all odd vertices.

Proof: When G is face colorable in this special way, there are only two colors represented at each vertex not on the boundary of the special face F_0. Hence the boundary of F_0 includes all odd vertices. Suppose, on the other hand, that F_0 has this property. We select a point v_0 inside F_0 and construct a new graph G_1 by adding an edge from v_0 to each of the odd vertices. Since there is an even number of odd vertices in G, all vertices in G_1 become even. As a consequence G_1 can be colored in two colors.

When v_0 and its edges are removed, one obtains the desired coloration for G by giving F_0 a third color.

A family of faces in a planar graph G shall be called *isolated* when no two of its faces have a corner in common. A coloring of G in $m \geq 3$ colors is *isolated in the color* α when the faces with this color form an isolated face family. We then have the extension of Theorem 13.1.1.

Theorem 13.1.2. A necessary and sufficient condition that a planar graph have a face coloring in three colors which is isolated in one of them is that there exists an isolated face family whose boundaries include all odd vertices in such a way that each boundary passes through an even number of odd vertices.

Proof: Let $\{F_i\}$ be an isolated family of faces with the given properties. In each F_i we select a point v_i and as before we enlarge G to a new planar graph G_1 by drawing an edge from v_i to each odd vertex on the boundary B_i of F_i. Under the given conditions G_1 becomes an even graph and so its faces can be colored in two colors β and γ. The desired three-coloring of G is obtained by assigning the color α to all faces F_i and leaving the colors of the other faces in G as in G_1.

Suppose, on the other hand, that G is face colored in three colors such that those with the color α form an isolated family $\{F_i\}$. At an odd vertex in G all three colors must be represented among the adjoining faces so that the boundaries B_i of the faces F_i must pass through all odd vertices. That the number of such odd vertices on B_i is even is simple to see when B_i is a single minimal circuit. The other faces on B_i must have alternating colors β and γ around B_i (Fig. 13.1.2).

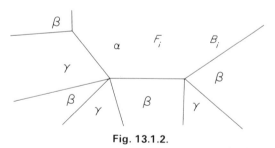

Fig. 13.1.2.

As a consequence the valences of the vertices B_i satisfy the condition

$$\sum_v \rho(v) \equiv 0 \ (\text{mod } 2), \qquad v \in B_i \tag{13.1.1}$$

When the boundary of F_i consists of several circuits (there are no acyclic edges), the condition (13.1.1) is satisfied for the vertices lying on each of these circuits with respect to the subgraphs they surround (Fig. 13.1.3). When all these conditions are added, one obtains the congruences (13.1.1) taken with respect to the valences on B_i.

Fig. 13.1.3.

In a regular graph of valence three all three colors must be represented at each vertex so the coloration is isolated in each of the three colors. We conclude that the graph is face colorable in three colors if, and only if, all faces have even valence; this is the dual of Theorem 7.4.3.

We have mentioned the isolated colorings of a graph especially to point out another type of color problem which can be formulated for planar graphs. Here one is supposed to find colorations in which faces with the same color not only have no common boundary edges, but more strictly, that they shall not even have corners in common.

We turn to the general problem: When is a family of faces $\{F_i\}$ with edge disjoint boundaries the family of faces with color γ in some 3-coloration of G? We say that two faces F_1 and F_2 are *corner neighbors* when they have a corner but no edge in common. Two faces F_0 and F_n are *corner connected* in $\{F_i\}$ when there exists a sequence of faces

$$F_0, F_1, \ldots, F_n$$

where each face is a corner neighbor of the preceding. By this definition the faces in $\{F_i\}$ fall into *corner connected components* Ψ.

Theorem 13.1.3. Let $\{F_i\}$ be a family of faces in G with edge disjoint boundaries. A necessary and sufficient condition that $\{F_i\}$ represent the family of γ-colored faces in some face coloration of G in three colors is that each corner connected component Ψ of $\{F_i\}$ have an even number of odd vertices of G on its boundary and that each odd vertex lie on such a boundary.

Proof: We saw in Theorem 13.1.2 that the theorem is true when each component consists of a single face. The general case may be reduced to this. In a component Ψ let F_0 and F_1 be corner neighbors with a corner v_0 in common. We separate the vertex v_0 with respect to the two faces F_0 and F_1. This yields a new graph G_1 in which the two faces are joined into a single face $F_0 + F_1$. There may possibly be several angles of F_0 and F_1 at v_0; in that case we separate with regard to a particular set of angles. By the separation the number of edges in G and G_1 remain the same. If v_0 separates into two vertices v_0' and v_0'', their valences satisfy

$$\rho(v_0) = \rho_1(v_0') + \rho_1(v_0''). \tag{13.1.2}$$

Suppose that $\{F_i\}$ is the family of all γ-colored faces in a three coloration of G. Then $\{F_i\}$ with F_0 and F_1 replaced by $F_0 + F_1$ is also such a family for G_1 and vice versa. In G_1 the component Ψ in G changes into a component Ψ_1. If we suppose that the theorem holds for G_1, there will be an even number of odd vertices of G_1 on the boundary of Ψ_1; hence according to (13.1.2) an even number of odd vertices of G on the boundary of Ψ. On the other hand when all Ψ have this property it also holds for the Ψ_1 and so $\{F_i\}$ in G_1 is a color family of faces in this graph; by coalescing v_0 the corresponding family $\{F_i\}$ has this property in G.

Let us consider the corresponding results also for the vertex coloration. Suppose the graph G is vertex colored in three colors α, β, γ. This corresponds to a disjoint decomposition

$$V = V_\alpha + V_\beta + V_\gamma \tag{13.1.3}$$

of the vertex set into independent subsets. Consider the section graph defined by two of the sets (13.1.3),

$$G_{\alpha+\beta} = G(V_\alpha + V_\beta). \tag{13.1.4}$$

This graph is vertex colored in two colors; in other words, it is a bipartite graph. On the other hand, if V has two disjoint subsets V_1 and V_2 such that $G(V_1 + V_2)$ is bipartite, while the remaining set

$$V_3 = V - V_1 - V_2$$

is independent then G is vertex colorable in three colors.

For planar graphs this criterion may be restated in the form that there shall exist an independent subset V_3 such that each face with odd valence has a vertex from V_3 on its boundary. The dual of Theorem 13.1.1 states that in order that all but one vertex be colorable in two colors it is necessary and sufficient that all faces with an odd number of boundary edges have a common corner.

1. What is the dual of an isolated face coloring?
2. State the dual of Theorem 13.1.2.

13.2. The Theorem of Grötzsch

The following interesting theorem concerning the coloration in three colors is due to Grötzsch.

A planar graph without triangular circuits is vertex colorable in three colors.

Instead of deriving this theorem directly we shall prefer to prove the following somewhat more general theorem due to Grünbaum.

Theorem 13.2.1. A planar graph with no more than three 3-circuits is vertex colorable in three colors.

In a certain sense this is a best possible result since as we mentioned in the preceding section the tetrahedron graph with four triangles is not 3-colorable for G. A fixed planar representation is given. We may suppose as usual that G is connected without separating vertices, lobes, or multiple edges. A more incisive reduction is the following.

One may suppose that the graph G has no faces with more than five boundary edges.

Proof: Suppose a face F has more than five boundary edges. One can always find a pair of nonadjacent vertices a_i and a_j on the boundary such that they are not connected by an edge (a_i, a_j). We add a new vertex v_0 in the interior of F and connect v_0 by edges to a_i and a_j. The new graph G_1 contains G and has no more triangles than G. If G_1 is 3-colorable so is G.

The proof of the theorem shall be given by induction with respect to the number of vertices; it is evident for the smallest values of v_v. In order to conduct the induction suitably we shall widen the form of the theorem slightly.

Suppose that a graph G is vertex colored in three colors. Let us investigate how the colors can be distributed on the boundary C_4 or C_5 of one of the quadrangular or pentagonal faces

$$C_4 = (a_1, a_2, a_3, a_4).$$

When there is an outside diagonal edge, the coloration is unique except for the names of the colors. This cannot occur when G has at most one triangle. When there is no diagonal, the colorations of C_4 are of two essentially different kinds.

Two colors: Opposite vertices a_1 and a_3 as well as a_2 and a_4 have the same colors

$$\varkappa(a_1) = \varkappa(a_3) = \alpha, \qquad \varkappa(a_2) = \varkappa(a_4) = \beta.$$

Three colors: One pair of opposite vertices a_1 and a_2 have the same color while the two remaining ones have different colors

$$\varkappa(a_1) = \varkappa(a_3) = \alpha, \qquad \varkappa(a_2) = \beta, \qquad \varkappa(a_4) = \gamma.$$

We say the type of the coloration of a quadrangle is given when one specifies whether the coloration is in two or three colors, and in the latter case, which pair of opposite vertices have the same color

$$C_5 = (a_1, a_2, a_3, a_4, a_5).$$

If C_5 has two outside diagonals, they must have a common end point (and the coloration is unique).

If there is one diagonal edge (a_1, a_3), the vertices a_1, a_2, a_3 have different colors

$$\varkappa(a_1) = \alpha, \qquad \varkappa(a_2) = \beta, \qquad \varkappa(a_3) = \gamma.$$

For the coloration of the two remaining vertices one has the alternatives.

$$\varkappa(a_4) = \alpha, \qquad \varkappa(a_5) = \gamma,$$
$$\varkappa(a_4) = \alpha, \qquad \varkappa(a_5) = \beta,$$
$$\varkappa(a_4) = \beta, \qquad \varkappa(a_5) = \gamma.$$

When there are no diagonals in C_5, the type is determined by the *singular vertex*, that is, the vertex in C_5 whose color occurs only once.

We are now ready to announce the theorem of Grötzsch in the form in which it is going to be proved.

Theorem 13.2.2. Let G be a planar graph whose faces have valences $\rho^*(F) = 3, 4, 5$ with at most three circuits C_3. Then G is vertex colorable in three colors. Furthermore, the colors on an arbitrarily given face may be given an arbitrary color type in case G includes not more than one 3-circuit.

The face F_0 whose color type is prescribed shall be called the marked face.

As we stated the theorem shall be proved by induction with respect to the number of vertices. We pass through a fairly long series of reductions.

1. *Each C_3 is a face boundary.*

If G has a separation by a triangle $S_3 = C_3$, we color each of the two components and these colorations can be combined to a coloration of G. In the following we denote the number of triangular faces by $t = 0, 1, 2, 3$.

2. *Each C_4 is a face boundary.*

We separate two cases.

$t = 2$ or $t = 3$. Let C_4 separate G into two components K_1 and K_2. One of them, say K_2, includes at most one triangle. We color K_1 and then K_2 such that C_4 has the color already determined in K_1. This is possible by taking C_4 as the marked face boundary in K_2.

$t = 0$ or $t = 1$. The marked face is contained in one of the components, say K_1. We first 3-color K_1 as desired and then combine this coloration with a coloration of K_2 by taking C_4 as the marked boundary in K_2.

3. *Each C_5 is a face boundary.*

$t = 0$. The marked face lies in one of the two components K_1 and K_2 defined by a C_5-separation. If it lies in K_1, we color this graph first and combine it with a 3-coloration of K_2 by using C_5 as the marked face.

$t = 1$. The same method can be used except when C_5 has a diagonal edge. Then the two parts A and B are faces since there are no separations by circuits C_3 or C_4 (Fig. 13.2.1). If a_2 and a_4 or a_3 and a_5 should be

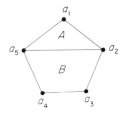

Fig. 13.2.1.

joined by an outside arc of length at most 3, we would have a separation of G by a circuit C_5 without diagonals so a reduction could be performed. Thus we may suppose that any outside arcs $Q_1(a_2, a_4)$ and $Q_2(a_3, a_5)$ have lengths of at least 4 if they exist. We can then coalesce one of these pairs, say (a_2, a_4) without producing more triangles. The resulting graph G_1 may be 3-colored such that the marked face, lying outside C_5 will have the prescribed colors. By separating a_2 and a_4 again one obtains the desired coloration for G.

$t = 2$. If both triangles belong to the same component determined by C_5, we color this part first and then the second, using C_5 as the marked boundary. If C_5 separates the two triangles, we use C_5 as marked boundary for both components. Since each component has a single triangle, the 3-colorations can be chosen such that they correspond on C_5.

$t = 3$. We may suppose that one component K_1 contains one triangle and the other K_2 two triangles. We first color K_2 and then K_1 using C_5 as the marked boundary. This reduction applies in all cases except when K_2 is not a graph with fewer vertices, that is, K_1 has the form given in Fig. 13.2.1. Here as before we try to obtain a reduction by coalescing a_2 and a_4 or a_3 and a_5. This is possible unless both operations should produce new triangles. For this to be the case there must exist arcs $Q_1(a_2, a_4)$ and $Q_2(a_3, a_5)$ of length 3 having no edges in common with Fig. 13.2.1. By considering the various alternatives one obtains the three alternatives depicted in Fig. 13.2.2. The two first possibilities are ruled out since they produce C_3 or C_4 separations. The third configuration would produce a separation of G by C_5 which were not of the exceptional type in Fig. 13.2.1.

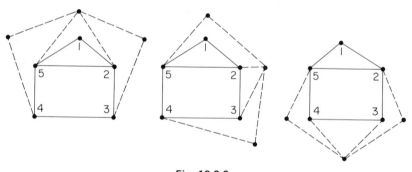

Fig. 13.2.2.

We notice also that the preceding reductions rule out the possibility that a triangle have an edge in common with another C_3 or with a C_4.

4. $\rho(v) \geqq 3$ *for all vertices.*

Suppose $\rho(v_0) = 2$ for some vertex. Its neighbors shall be v_1 and v_2. The two faces incident to v_0 must be pentagons since otherwise one would have a separation by a C_4 or C_5.

Assume first that v_0 does not lie on the marked face boundary. We eliminate v_0 and replace its edges by a single edge (v_1, v_2) provided this edge does not already occur. No new triangles can be produced since in that case G would have a separation by a C_4 or C_5. The reduced graph G_1 can be colored with the assigned coloration to the marked face; in turn we obtain a coloration of G by giving v_0 the color different from those at v_1 and v_2.

Assume secondly that v_0 lies on the marked pentagonal face boundary. This C_5 can have no diagonal according to our previous reductions. If v_0 should be the singular vertex or a neighbor to the singular vertex, the same method as before can be used. When v_0 is one of the two other vertices, we coalesce v_1 and v_2. Since G cannot be separated by a C_4 and C_5 this process introduces at most two new triangles; hence the reduced graph can be colored. This gives a coloration of G with the same color at v_1 and v_2. The color at v_0 can be chosen such that the correct vertex becomes the singular one.

5. *No quadrilateral faces.*

Suppose F_4 is such a face with the boundary C_4. When F_4 is not the marked face, one of the corners v_1 on C_4 is not on the boundary of the marked face. We coalesce v_1 with its opposite vertex on C_4. No new triangles can appear due to our separation reductions. The reduced graph can be colored as desired and so one obtains a coloration for G.

After all such reductions are performed we are left with a graph with a single face F_4 and this is the marked face. Since there is a marked face $t \leqq 1$, consequently one of the boundary edges (v_3, v_4) of F_4 is incident to a pentagon (Fig. 13.2.3).

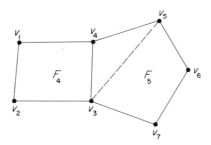

Fig. 13.2.3.

We eliminate the edge (v_3, v_4) and draw instead the edge (v_3, v_5). In the resulting graph G_1 we take

$$C_5 = (v_5, v_3, v_2, v_1, v_4)$$

as the marked face boundary. Since G_1 has a 4-circuit which is not marked it can be reduced as before so G_1 is 3-colorable with a prescribed coloration on C_5. But this can be taken such that it coincides with the coloration of $C_4 = (c_1, c_2, c_3, c_4)$ prescribed in G; hence G is colored as desired.

6. $\rho(v) \geq 4$ *for all triangle corners.*

Let v_0 be a triangle corner of $C_3 = (v_0, v_1, v_2)$ with $\rho(v_0) = 3$. The two other faces at v_0 must be pentagons F_5 and F_5' and we can assume that F_5 is not the marked face (Fig. 13.2.4).

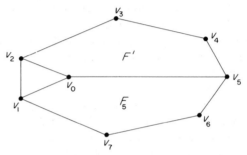

Fig. 13.2.4.

We eliminate the edges at v_0 and coalesce v_1 and v_5 to obtain the graph G_1. The number of triangles in G_1 is the same as in G. A coloration of G_1 yields a coloration of G as desired except possibly when F_5' is the marked face. In this case we use

$$C_4' = (v_1 = v_5, v_2, v_3, v_4)$$

as the marked face boundary in G_1. By a suitable coloration of G_1 one can obtain that the boundary C_5' of F_5' has any one of the vertices v_2, v_0, v_5 as singular vertex. To make one of the vertices v_3 or v_4 the singular vertex we proceed as follows. As before the edges at v_0 are eliminated but now we connect v_1 and v_5 by an edge to obtain the graph G_2. In G_2 there are no triangles so it may be 3-colored with

$$C_5'' = (v_1, v_2, v_3, v_4, v_5)$$

as the marked face. By the selection of v_3 or v_4 as the singular vertex one obtains a coloration of G and C_5' such that v_4 or v_3 will be the singular vertex.

7. *Final reduction.* Through the preceding reductions we have arrived at a graph with the properties:

a. G is not separated by any circuit C_i, $i \leq 5$.

b. Each face is a triangle or pentagon.

c. $\rho(v) \geq 3$ for all vertices and $\rho(v) \geq 4$ for the triangle corners. The final step in our proof is to show that such a graph is reducible.

We begin by showing G must contain a pentagon F_0 whose corner valences are $\rho(v) = 3$ for four corners and $\rho(v) \leq 5$ for the fifth. We may assume further that neither F_0 nor any of its neighbors are the marked face.

To establish this fact we return to Euler's relation (4.3.3) extended over all faces F in G,

$$\sum_F \phi(F) = 2 \qquad (13.2.1)$$

where

$$\phi(F) = 1 - \tfrac{1}{2}\rho^* + \sum_i \frac{1}{\rho_i} \qquad (13.2.2)$$

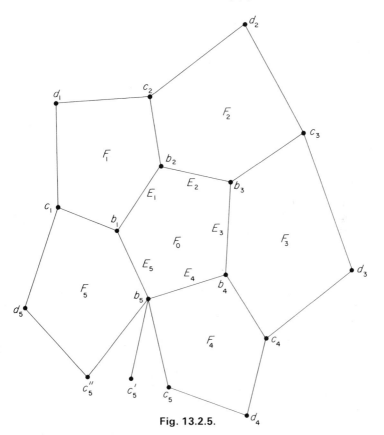

Fig. 13.2.5.

is the face contribution of F with $\rho^* = \rho^*(F)$ and the ρ_i its corner valences. According to (13.2.1) there must exist positive face contributions which add up to at least 2. For a triangle one has $\rho_i \geq 4$ for all corners so its maximal contribution is $\frac{1}{4}$. Since there are at most three triangles there must be pentagons with positive contributions adding up to at least $\frac{5}{4}$. The maximal pentagon contribution occurs for $\rho_i = 3$ and equals $\frac{1}{6}$ so there must be at least eight such pentagons. A positive contribution can only occur when $\rho_i = 3$, $i = 1, 2, 3, 4$ and $\rho_5 \leq 5$ as desired.

We conclude from this observation that in G there exists a subgraph H as drawn in Fig. 13.2.5 consisting of a pentagon F_0 surrounded by five pentagons F_i. The valence at b_5 may be 3, 4, 5; hence there may be 1, 2, 3 vertices c_5, c_5', c_5''. The complement of H in G we denote by $\bar{H}$. The distance in H between any two of its vertices is at most 5 so no two of them can coincide.

From G and H we derive the reduced graph G_1 as follows. We eliminate the vertices b_1, b_2, b_3 and the seven edges incident to them. This creates a new face

$$F' = F_0 + F_1 + F_2 + F_3 + F_5.$$

From G_1 we construct a new planar graph G_1' by coalescing the vertices c_2 and c_3 and also the pair c_1 and b_4. By this operation the face F' in G_1 is divided into three new faces in G_1', namely:

1. A face with two corners

$$d_2, c_2 = c_3.$$

2. A pentagon with the corners

$$c_2 = c_3, d_1, c_1 = b_4, c_4, d_3.$$

3. A quadrangle with the corners

$$c_1 = b_4, d_5, c_5'', b_5.$$

By the induction G_1'' can be vertex colored with prescribed colors for the marked face. We separate the coalesced vertices to obtain a coloration of the same kind for G_1 with

$$\varkappa(c_2) = \varkappa(c_3), \qquad \varkappa(c_1) = \varkappa(b_4).$$

We return to G by reintroducing the vertices b_1, b_2, b_3 and their seven edges. The coloration of G_1 can be extended to G by defining the colors on the three vertices in the following manner.

1. When

$$\varkappa(c_2) = \varkappa(c_3) = \alpha, \qquad \varkappa(c_1) = \varkappa(b_4) = \beta,$$

we put

$$\varkappa(b_3) = \gamma, \qquad \varkappa(b_2) = \beta,$$

and b_1 is assigned the third color different from β and $\varkappa(b_5) \neq \beta$.

2. When

$$\varkappa(c_2) = \varkappa(c_3) = \varkappa(c_1) = \varkappa(c_4) = \alpha, \qquad \varkappa(b_5) = \gamma,$$

we put

$$\varkappa(b_3) = \beta, \qquad \varkappa(b_2) = \gamma, \qquad \varkappa(b_1) = \beta.$$

This reduction is predicated upon the coalescence operations not producing any new triangles. The coalescence of c_2 and c_3 cannot produce a new triangle for it would imply the existence of a separating pentagon in G. If the coalescence of c_1 and b_4 should produce a triangle, there would have to exist an arc $A_3(c_1, b_4)$ of length 3 in G_1. Such an arc would have to begin in one of the edges (b_4, c_4) or (b_4, b_5). But in the last case A_3 would have to continue in an edge to one of the vertices c_5, c_5', c_5'' and then in an edge in $\bar{H}$ to c_1. However, such an edge cannot exist since it would create a separating C_5 in G.

We conclude that the arc $A_3(b_4, c_1)$ would have to begin in the edge (b_4, c_4) and then continue in an arc in $\bar{H}$,

$$A_2(c_4, c_1)$$

of length 2. There can only be one such arc since two of them would produce a C_4. Also, A_2 cannot include the edge (c_4, d_4) since it would create a separating C_5. However, A_2 may include (c_4, d_3) provided there exists an edge (c_1, d_3) in $\bar{H}$. When this is not the case,

$$A_2 = (c_1, v) + (v, c_4) \tag{13.2.3}$$

when v is a vertex outside of H.

Suppose that such an arc A_2 exists. We then use another reduction of G_1 obtained by coalescing c_1 and c_2 as well as c_3 and b_5. Again the coalesced vertices are not connected by edges. In the resulting graph G_1'' the face F' is decomposed into three parts.

1. A face with two corners

$$d_1, c_1 = c_2.$$

2. A pentagon with the corners

$$c_1 = c_2, d_2, c_3 = b_5, c_5'', d_5.$$

3. A quadrangle with the corners

$$c_3 = b_5, d_3, c_4, b_4.$$

If no new triangles are produced by coalescing these vertices, we obtain a coloration of G_1 of the desired kind with

$$\varkappa(c_1) = \varkappa(c_2), \qquad \varkappa(c_3) = \varkappa(b_5).$$

This we extend to a coloration of G as follows.

1. When

$$\varkappa(c_1) = \varkappa(c_2) = \alpha, \qquad \varkappa(c_3) = \varkappa(b_5) = \beta,$$

we put

$$\varkappa(b_1) = \gamma, \qquad \varkappa(b_2) = \beta$$

while b_1 takes the color different from β and $\varkappa(b_4) \neq \beta$.

2. When

$$\varkappa(c_1) = \varkappa(c_2) = \varkappa(c_3) = \varkappa(b_5) = \alpha, \qquad \varkappa(b_4) = \beta,$$

we put

$$\varkappa(b_3) = \gamma, \qquad \varkappa(b_2) = \beta, \qquad \varkappa(b_3) = \gamma.$$

This second reduction requires that no new triangles are created by the coalescences. As before one sees that this is not the case by the coalescence of c_1 and c_2. If the coalescence of c_3 and b_5 should produce a triangle, there must exist an arc $B_3(c_3, b_5)$ of length 3 in G_1, hence some arc B_2 of length 2 between c_3 and one of the vertices c_5, c_5', c_5''. This is not possible when there exists an edge (c_1, d_3) in $\bar{H}$ so we may suppose that the arc A_2 has the form (13.2.3). But then one must have edges (v, c_3) and (v, c_4) in G, creating a C_4.

This concludes the proof of Theorem 13.2.1. It can be considerably simplified if one restricts oneself to Grötzsch's original theorem when there are no triangles.

CHAPTER 14 | *EDGE COLORATION*

14.1. General Observations

In Section 6.1 we defined an *edge coloration* of a graph G to be a decomposition of its edges into classes

$$G = H_1 + H_2 + \cdots + H_l \qquad (14.1.1)$$

such that no edges in the same class have a common vertex; in other words, the valence of each of the subgraphs H_i does not exceed 1. The smallest $l_0 = \varepsilon(G)$ for which such a decomposition (14.1.1) is possible is the *edge coloration number* or the *edge chromatic number* for G. This definition shows that the edge coloration number must be at least equal to the maximal valence

$$l_0 \geqq \rho_1 = \max \rho(v), \qquad v \in V. \qquad (14.1.2)$$

When $l_0 = \rho_1$, we say that G *decomposes completely*.

We suppose, generally, that G is a graph without loops, but it may have multiple edges. We denote by $\rho(a, b)$ the number of edges connecting vertices $a \neq b$. When G has only two vertices, then

$$l_0 = \rho(a, b).$$

When there are three vertices a, b, c,

$$l_0 = \rho(a, b) + \rho(b, c) + \rho(c, a).$$

The reduced graph G' of G is a graph with the same vertices and edges except that all multiple edges are replaced by single ones. The *reduced valence* $\rho'(a)$ of a vertex a is the valence of a in the reduced graph.

In a disconnected graph the edge coloration number l_0 is the maximal coloration number for the components. Thus in determining the coloration number one can assume G connected. Next let s be a separating vertex for G corresponding to a decomposition

$$G = G_1 + G_2, \qquad G_1 \cap G_2 = \{s\}. \tag{14.1.3}$$

The edge coloration numbers of the two components we denote by l_1 and l_2, respectively.

Lemma 14.1.1. For a graph with a separation (14.1.3) the edge coloration number is determined by

$$l_0 = \max(l_1, l_2, \rho(s)). \tag{14.1.4}$$

Proof: At s let there be σ_1 edges in G_1 and σ_2 edges in G_2 so that

$$\rho(s) = \sigma_1 + \sigma_2.$$

We suppose $l_1 \geq l_2$ and color the edges at s in $\rho(s)$ colors. To color the remaining part of G_1 one needs $l_1 - \sigma_1$ colors. When

$$l_1 - \sigma_1 \leq \sigma_2,$$

we can take these colors among the σ_2 used at s in G_2. The same applies to G_2 so we obtain a coloration of G in $\rho(s)$ colors. When

$$l_1 - \sigma_1 > \sigma_2,$$

we need an additional

$$l_1 - \sigma_1 - \sigma_2 = l_1 - \rho(s)$$

colors so the total number of colors is l_1. By repeated applications of (14.1.4) one finds Theorem 14.1.1.

Theorem 14.1.1. When G is a graph composed of lobe graphs $\{L_i\}$, $i = 1, \ldots, r$, each with the coloration number l_i then the coloration number of G is

$$l_0 = \max(\rho_1, l_i), i = 1, \ldots, r.$$

Another general result on edge coloration is the following theorem.

Theorem 14.1.2. Any bipartite graph decomposes completely.

This theorem may be considered to be a reformulation of Theorem 7.5.6 in Ore [1]. It is also a special case of our subsequent Theorem 14.2.1.

Let us consider the edge coloration of a few special graphs. A *chain* is a graph whose reduced graph is an arc. As an application of Theorem

14.1.1 one sees that a chain decomposes completely. The same is true for any graph whose reduced graph is a tree.

A *ring R* is a graph whose reduced graph is a circuit

$$C = (a_1, \ldots, a_n).$$

It is even or odd according to the parity of n. From Theorem 14.1.2 we conclude the following theorem.

Theorem 14.1.3. A ring of even length is completely decomposable.

The case of an odd ring is more complicated, as one has already seen for the case $n = 3$. The number is as shown by Theorem 14.1.4.

Theorem 14.1.4. A ring R of odd length n has edge coloration number

$$l_0 = \max\left(\rho_1, \left\{\frac{2v_e}{n-1}\right\}\right).$$

Here v_e is the number of edges in R while $\{x\}$ denotes the smallest integer $\geq x$.

This result was first deduced by two of my students: B. Rothschild and J. Stemple. The proof is a little involved and shall be left to the reader.

14.2. Coloration of an Augmented Graph

Let G be a graph which is edge colored in l colors. These colors we denote by $\alpha, \beta, \gamma, \ldots$. When E_0 is an α-edge, let E_1 be a β-edge at one of the end points of E_0. At the other end of E_1 there may be an α-edge E_2, and so on. In the same manner one may continue from the other end point of E_0. In this manner we obtain an *alternating* (α, β)-*arc A*. When this process is continued as far as possible, two cases may occur. Either A returns in itself to produce an *alternating* (α, β)-*circuit* with an even number of edges, or $A = (a_0, \ldots, a_n)$ is a *maximal* (α, β)-*arc* connecting two vertices a_0 and a_n at which there is either no α-edge or no β-edge. By interchanging the colors along an alternating circuit or a maximal (α, β)-arc one obtains another edge coloration of G in l colors. Two edges or vertices lying on the same alternating arc may be called (α, β)-*connected*.

To the graph G_0 we shall now add a new edge $E = (a, b)$; it is possible that the two vertices a and b are already previously connected by other edges. We wish to examine conditions under which the *augmented graph*

$$G_1 = G_0 + E, \qquad E = (a, b) \tag{14.2.1}$$

is also edge colorable in l colors. For this purpose we assume that G_1 cannot be edge colored in l colors and draw various conclusions from this supposition.

Under this condition the edge colors at a and b will fall into three classes.

1. $M(a, b) = M(b, a)$ consists of the

$$\mu_{a, b} = \mu_{b, a}$$

colors which occur both at a and b. All edges (a, b) in G_0 have colors in this class.

2. $N(a, b)$ consists of the $v_{a, b}$ colors occurring at a but not at b.

3. $N(b, a)$ consists of the $v_{b, a}$ colors occurring at b but not at a.

The set of $\rho_0(v)$ colors in G_0 at a vertex v we denote by $R(v)$. There can be no colors which are missing both at a and b for such a color could be used to color E. Thus we have

$$R(a) = M(a, b) + N(a, b), \qquad R(b) = M(a, b) + N(b, a). \quad (14.2.2)$$

This gives the numerical relations

$$\rho(a) = \mu_{a, b} + v_{a, b}, \qquad \rho(b) = \mu_{a, b} + v_{b, a}, \qquad (14.2.3)$$

and

$$l = \mu_{a, b} + v_{a, b} + v_{b, a}. \qquad (14.2.4)$$

By elimination follows

$$v_{a, b} = l - \rho(b), \qquad v_{b, a} = l - \rho(a), \qquad (14.2.5)$$

and

$$\mu_{a, b} = \rho(a) + \rho(b) - l. \qquad (14.2.6)$$

Suppose now that α and β are colors for which

$$\alpha \in N(a, b), \qquad \beta \in N(b, a). \qquad (14.2.7)$$

The corresponding α and β-edges at a and b we denote, respectively, by

$$E_1 = (a, a_1), \qquad E_1' = (b, b_1). \qquad (14.2.8)$$

Lemma 14.2.1. A pair of edges (14.2.8) with colors (14.2.7) are the terminal edges of a maximal (α, β)-arc A_0 in G_0.

Proof: We construct the maximal (α, β)-arc A_0 which begins in E_1. If its last edge were not E_1', one could interchange the colors along A_0 and obtain a coloration of G_0 in which the color α is missing both at a and b.

Since each color pair α, β in (14.2.7) gives rise to an even alternating arc $A_0(a, b)$ we see that when G_0 is not l-colorable, there must be at least

$$\tau_0(E) = \min (l - \rho_0(a), l - \rho_0(b))$$
$$= l - \max (\rho_0(a), \rho_0(b)) \tag{14.2.9}$$

edge disjoint arcs between a and b. This remark can be used to give an upper bound for the edge coloration number.

Let E be some edge (a, b) in a graph G. In general, there will be odd circuits O_E passing through E. A family $\{O_E\}$ of such circuits is called *edge disjoint* when each pair of them has only the edge E in common. The *odd circuit index* $\tau(E)$ of E is the maximal number of circuits in such an edge disjoint family $\{O_E\}$. Then we have the following theorem.

Theorem 14.2.1.   Let $E = (a, b)$ run through the edges of the graph G. Then G can be edge colored in

$$l = \max_E (\tau(E)) + \max (\rho(a), \rho(b)) \tag{14.2.10}$$

colors.

Proof: We apply induction with respect to the number v_e of edges in G; for small values of v_e one verifies the theorem directly. An edge $E = (a, b)$ is removed from G. This does not increase the number on the right in (14.2.10) so by induction $G_0 = G - E$ is l-colorable. In G_0 the maximal number of edge disjoint even arcs from a to b is $\tau(E)$. We conclude from (14.2.9) that when

$$\tau(E) < l - \max (\rho_0(a), \rho_0(b)),$$

then also the graph G is l-colorable. Since

$$\rho_0(a) = \rho(a) - 1, \qquad \rho_0(b) = \rho(b) - 1, \tag{14.2.11}$$

this last inequality can also be written

$$l > \tau(E) - 1 + \max (\rho(a), \rho(b))$$

and it is satisfied when l has the value (14.2.10).

In the case of a bipartite graph, $\tau(E) = 0$ so Theorem 14.1.2 follows.

14.3. The Theorem of Shannon

We return to the graphs G_1 and G_0 in (14.2.1) where G_0 is l-colorable and G_1 is not. Using the same notations as before we shall show Lemma 14.3.1.

Lemma 14.3.1. Let $a_1 \neq b$ be a neighbor of the endpoint a of the edge $E = (a, b)$. When the edge $E_2 = (a, a_1)$ has a color $\alpha \in N(a, b)$, then

$$R(a_1) = N(a, b) + N(b, a) + M_1(a, b),$$

$$M_1(a, b) \subseteqq M(a, b). \tag{14.3.1}$$

Proof: According to Lemma 14.2.1 there exists an alternating (α, β)-arc $A_0(a, b)$ for any $\beta \in N(b, a)$, hence

$$R(a_1) \supseteqq N(b, a). \tag{14.3.2}$$

When there is only one such neighbor a_1 to a, it is clear that also

$$R(a_1) \supseteqq N(a, b). \tag{14.3.3}$$

Suppose, therefore, that there is some edge $E_2 = (a, a_2)$ with $a_2 \neq a_1$ and color $\gamma \in N(a, b)$. At a_2 also the color α must be represented. If this were not the case, one could construct a maximal (β, α)-arc B_0 from a_2. This arc cannot end at a or b since these vertices are already connected by a maximal (α, β)-arc $A_0(a, b)$ beginning in E_1. Thus by interchanging the colors along B_0 we obtain a coloration of G_0 in which there is no β-edge at a and a_2. Then E_2 can be given the color β and the color γ can be assigned to E.

We conclude that

$$R(a_2) \supseteqq N(a, b).$$

By interchanging the roles of a_1 and a_2 it follows that (14.3.3) must also hold, and by combining (14.3.2) and (14.3.3) the desired relation (14.3.1) is obtained.

When the values (14.2.5) and (14.2.6) are used in (14.3.1), one finds

$$2l = \rho_0(a_1) + \rho_0(a) + \rho_0(b) - \mu_1; \qquad \mu_1 \leqq \mu_{a,b}. \tag{14.3.4}$$

Let us apply this result in case

$$l > \rho_0(a), \qquad l > \rho_0(b), \tag{14.3.5}$$

so there exist colors α and β satisfying (14.2.7). Since (14.3.4) was derived under the assumption that the graph G_0 is l-colorable, but $G_0 + E$ is not, this yields the following lemma.

Lemma 14.3.2. Let G_0 have an edge coloration in l colors where l satisfies (14.3.5) and assume

$$l > \tfrac{1}{2}(\rho_0(a_1) + \rho_0(a) + \rho_0(b)) \qquad \cdot \tag{14.3.6}$$

for all neighbors a_1 of a. Then the graph $G_0 + (a, b)$ also has an l-coloration.

We use this result to derive an upper bound for the edge coloration number of a graph. We define

$$\sigma_a = \max \left(\rho(a) + \rho(a_1) + \rho(a_2) \right) \tag{14.3.7}$$

where $a_1 \neq a_2$ run through all neighbors of the vertex a; furthermore put

$$\sigma = \max \sigma_a, \qquad a \in V. \tag{14.3.8}$$

We shall show the following theorem.

Theorem 14.3.1. In a graph G let ρ_1 be the maximal valence and σ the quantity defined in (14.3.7) and (14.3.8). Then G is edge colorable in l colors when

$$l \geqq \max \left(\rho_1, \left[\tfrac{1}{2}\sigma \right] \right) \tag{14.3.9}$$

where the bracket indicates greatest integer.

Proof: We assume a fixed vertex set V and apply induction with respect to the number v_e of edges in G. For the smallest values $v_e = 1, 2, 3$ the result is immediate. The removal of an edge $E = (a, b)$ from G does not increase ρ_1 or σ so by the induction assumption the graph $G_0 = G - E$ is l-colorable. In G_0 the condition (14.3.5) is satisfied since the relations (14.2.11) hold. From (14.3.9) follows

$$l \geqq \left[\tfrac{1}{2}\sigma \right] \geqq \left[\tfrac{1}{2}(\rho(a) + \rho(b) + \rho(a_1)) \right]$$

and so according to (14.2.11)

$$l \geqq \left[\tfrac{1}{2}(\rho_0(a) + \rho_0(b) + \rho_0(a_1)) \right] + 1.$$

This shows that the condition (14.3.6) is satisfied. From Lemma 14.3.2 we conclude that $G = G_0 + E$ is l-colorable as desired.

An immediate consequence of Theorem 14.3.1 is the theorem of *Shannon* which follows.

Theorem 14.3.2. Any graph can be edge colored in l colors where

$$l = \left[\tfrac{3}{2}\rho_1 \right]$$

and ρ_1 is the maximal valence.

14.4 The Theorem of Vizing

In a graph G we denote by $\rho(a, b)$ the number of edges connecting any pair of vertices a and b. For a given a let

$$\pi(a) = \max_b \rho(a, b) \tag{14.4.1}$$

be the greatest of these numbers where b runs through the neighbors of a. We then define the *enlarged valence* of a to be the number

$$\rho^+(a) = \rho(a) + \pi(a). \qquad (14.4.2)$$

We shall then deduce the following result.

Theorem 14.4.1.   Any graph is edge colorable in $l \geq \rho_1{}^+$ colors where

$$\rho_1{}^+ = \max_a \rho^+(a) \leq l \qquad (14.4.3)$$

is the maximal enlarged valence.

Proof: If the theorem were not true, we could color edges in G successively until one reaches a maximal l-colorable subgraph G_0. Then the addition of any new edge

$$E = (a, b) \subset G$$

would result in a new graph

$$G_1 = G_0 + E$$

which is not l-colorable. For the coloration of the graphs G_0 and G_1 we use the notations and facts of Section 14.2.

We obtain our theorem by showing that G has no proper subgraph G_0. The edges at the vertex a we denote by

$$E_i = (a, a_i), \quad a_0 = b, \quad i = 0, \ldots, \rho(a) - 1. \qquad (14.4.4)$$

For each i the number of edges (a, a_i) is $\rho_0(a, a_i)$. In the l-coloration of G_0 the edges (14.4.4) at a all have different colors α_i. Furthermore, according to (14.4.2) there are at least $\pi(a_i)$ of the l colors missing at each a_i. Thus to each E_i we can define an *associated color* $\gamma_i \neq \alpha_i$ among the missing colors at a_i. This shall be done in such a manner that all edges E_i at a given a_i have different associated colors. For different vertices a_i and a_j the colors associated with edges E_i and E_j may possibly be the same. At the vertex $a_0 = b$ the edge E of G is missing in G_0, so here there will be at least one missing color γ_0 not associated with any of the edges (a, b).

We now construct a family of distinct edges

$$E^{(1)}, E^{(2)}, \ldots, E^{(k)} \qquad (14.4.5)$$

chosen from the edges (14.4.4) in the following way. The color γ_0 must occur at a and we select $E^{(1)}$ as the edge with this color. To $E^{(1)}$ there is an associated color γ_1. If γ_1 occurs at a, we select $E^{(2)}$ as the edge with this color; its associated colors shall be γ_2. Next $E^{(3)}$ is the edge at a with the color γ_2 and associated color γ_3, and so on.

This construction cannot come to a halt by the color γ_k being absent at a, so no further edge $E^{(k+1)}$ could be selected. In this case one could recolor the edges in (14.4.5), giving each its associated color. Since the associated colors of the $E^{(i)}$ are all different, this represents a coloration of G_0 in which $E^{(1)}$ has the color γ_1 and the color γ_0 is missing both at a and at b. Thus E could be added to the coloration with color γ_0. This argument yields Lemma 14.4.1.

Lemma 14.4.1. At no endpoint $a^{(i)}$ of an edge $E^{(i)} = (a, a^{(i)})$ in (14.4.5) can any color

$$\beta \in N(b, a) \qquad (14.4.6)$$

be missing.

Proof: Assume that $E^{(i)}$ is the first edge in (14.4.5) with the endpoint $a^{(i)}$. If at $a^{(i)}$ there were a color β missing which is present at b but not at a, one could associate $E^{(i)}$ with the color β. This produces a sequence to $E^{(i)}$ of the type just discussed and it would lead to an l-coloration of $G_0 + E$.

We conclude that in a sequence (14.4.5) all associated colors must be colors at a. Thus the sequence can only come to an end when the last associated color γ_k is the same as the color of one of the previous edges. We shall show that also this leads to a contradiction.

Case 1. $\gamma_k = \gamma_0$

From the condition (14.4.3) on l we see that there is some color β missing at a, hence present at b. According to Lemma 14.2.1 there exists a maximal (γ_0, β)-path $P(a, b)$ from a to b. The color $\gamma_0 = \gamma_k$ is missing also at $a^{(k)}$ so this vertex is the endpoint of another maximal (β, γ_0)-path $Q(a^{(k)}, t)$. The other endpoint t cannot coincide with a or b or the vertex $a^{(1)}$ lying on $P(a, b)$. When t is different from all previous vertices $a^{(i)}$, we can interchange the colors γ_0 and β along Q without interfering with the choice of the associated colors. Then there will be no color β at $a^{(k)}$ contradicting Lemma 14.4.1. In case $t = a^{(i)}$ for some i the arc Q must end in a β-edge at $a^{(i)}$ since such an edge is present. The color interchange will again yield a coloration of G_0 having a sequence (14.4.5) in which the color β is missing at $a^{(i)}$.

Case 2. $\gamma_k = \gamma_{k-1}$

This is impossible since the color of E_k would coincide with its associated color.

Case 3. $\gamma_k = \gamma_i$
for some $i = 1, 2, \ldots, k - 2$.

The two vertices $a^{(k)}$ and $a^{(i)}$ are different since otherwise two edges (14.4.4) to the same vertex a_i would be associated with the same color. We select some color β as in (14.4.6). Then as we have seen β occurs at the vertices b, $a^{(i)}$, $a^{(k)}$, but not at a. The color γ_k is missing at $a^{(i)}$ and $a^{(k)}$, but occurs at a.

We now construct maximal alternating (β, γ_k)-paths P_k and P_i from $a^{(k)}$ and $a^{(i)}$. A path P_k cannot end in a vertex different from a, b, $a^{(k)}$, $a^{(i)}$ for the colors could be interchanged along P_k. This would not interfere with the associated colors except that β would be missing at $a^{(k)}$; however, this is impossible according to the lemma. The same argument applies to an arc P_i. Next we notice that the maximal arc cannot have $a^{(i)}$ and $a^{(k)}$ as endpoints. Here the interchange of colors would leave unchanged the choices for the associated colors except that β would be missing at both $a^{(k)}$ and $a^{(i)}$; again this is impossible.

Next we observe that none of the arcs P_i and P_k can end at b. This is evident when there is both a β-edge and a γ_k-edge at b. If there is no γ_k-edge, we conclude from Lemma 14.2.1 that there is a maximal (β, γ_k)-arc $Q(b, a)$; this excludes b as an endpoint for the arcs P_i and P_k. This leaves us with the impossible alternative that both P_i and P_k have a as an endpoint.

An immediate consequence of Theorem 14.4.1 is the theorem of *Vizing* which follows.

Theorem 14.4.2.   A graph is edge colorable in l colors when

$$l \geq \rho_1 + \pi_1$$

where ρ_1 is the maximal valence and

$$\pi_1 = \max \rho(a, b), \qquad a, b \in V.$$

BIBLIOGRAPHY

The general graph theoretical results referred to in the text are from Ore (1) below, and the reader may also consult Ore (2).

(1) Ore, O., "Theory of Graphs." (Am. Math. Soc. Colloquium Publ., Vol. 38). Am. Math. Soc., Providence, 1962.

(2) Ore, O., "Graphs and Their Uses." (New Mathematical Library, Vol. 10). Random House, New York (1963).

The following papers contain presentations of the history of the four-color problem.

Brahana, H. R., "The Four Color Problem." *Am. Math. Monthly.* **30**, 234–243 (1923).

Errera, A., Exposé historique du problème des Quatres Couleurs. *Periodica di Mat.* **7**, 20–41 (1927).

Winn, C. E., Sur l'historique du problème des Quatres Couleurs. *Bull. Inst. Egypte.* **20**, 191–192 (1939).

Franklin, P., "The Four Color Problem." Galois Lectures. *Scripta Mathematica Library No. 5.* (1941).

May, K. O., "The Origin of the Four-Color Conjecture. *Isis.* **56**, 346–348 (1965).

An excellent presentation of the coloration problems for graphs both in the plane and on surfaces can be found in the back.

Ringel, G., "Färbungsprobleme auf Flächen und Graphen." Berlin (1959).

A more elementary work is:

Dynkin, E. B., and Uspensky, W. A., "Mathematische Unterhaltungen: Mehrfarbenprobleme." Berlin (1955).

The subsequent bibliography includes titles more or less directly connected with the questions treated in the text. For a general biography of papers on graph theory, including coloration problems, we must refer to the nearly complete list compiled by J. W. Moon, L. Moser, and A. A. Zykov, Theory of Graphs and its Applications. *Proceedings of the Symposium held in Smolenice in June 1963.*

249

Bibliography

Chapter 1
1.3. Fáry, I., On straight line representation of planar graphs. *Acta Sci. Math. Szeged* **11**, 229–233 (1948).
Tutte, W. T., Convex representations of graphs. *Proc. London Math. Soc.* **10**, 304–320 (1960).
Wagner, K., Bemerkungen zum Vierfarbenproblem. *J. ber. Deut. Math. Ver.* **46**, Abt. 1, 26–32 (1936).
Wagner, K., Ein Satz über Komplexe. *J. ber. Deut. Math. Ver.* **46**(2), 21–22 (1936).

Chapter 2
2.6. Kuratowski, G., Sur le problème des courbes gauches en topologie. *Fund. Math.* **15**, 271–283 (1930).
Dirac, G. A., and Schuster, S., A theorem of Kuratowski. *Indag. Math.* **16**, 343–348 (1954).
Halin, R., Bemerkungen über eben Graphen. *Math. Ann.* **153**, 38–46 (1964).
Wagner, K., Über eine Erweiterung eines Satzes von Kuratowski. *Deut. Math.* **2**, 280–285 (1937).
2.7. Wagner, K., Zwei Bemerkungen über Komplexe. *Math. Ann.* **112**, 316–321 (1936).

Chapter 3
3.2. Whitney, H., Congruent graphs and the connectivity of graphs. *Am. J. Math.* **54**, 150–168 (1932).
3.4. Whitney, H., Non-separable and planar graphs. *Trans. Am. Math. Soc.* **34**, 339–362 (1932).
Whitney, H., Planar graphs. *Fund. Math.* **21**, 73–84 (1933).
MacLane, S., A structural characterization of planar combinatorial graphs. *Duke Math. J.* **3**, 460–472 (1937).
MacLane, S., A combinatorial condition for planar graphs. *Fund. Math.* **28**, 22–32 (1937).
3.5. Smith, C. A. B., and Tutte, W. T., A class of self-dual maps. *Can. J. Math.* **2**, 179–196 (1950).

Chapter 4
4.3. Lebesgue, H., Quelques conséquences simples de la formule d'Euler. *J. de Math.* **9**. Sér. 19, 27–43 (1940).

Chapter 5
5.2. Whitney, H., A theorem on graphs. *Ann. Math.* **32**, 378–390 (1931).
Tutte, W. T., A theorem on planar graphs. *Trans. Am. Math. Soc.* **82**, 99–116 (1956).
Tutte, W. T., On Hamiltonian circuits. *J. London Math. Soc.* **21**, 98–101 (1946).
Tutte, W. T., A non-Hamiltonian graph. *Can. Math. Bull.* **3**, 1–5 (1960).

Chapter 6
6.4. Heawood, P. J., Map-colour theorems. *Quart. J. Math. Oxford Ser.* **24**, 322–338 (1890).
Dirac, G. A., Percy John Heawood. *J. London Math. Soc.* **38**, 263–277 (1963).
6.5. Brooks, R. L., On colouring the nodes of a network. *Proc. Cambridge Phil. Soc.* **37**, 194–197 (1941).

Chapter 7
7.3. Minty, G. J., A theorem on n-coloring the points of a linear graph. *Am. Math. Monthly.* **69**, 623–624 (1962).

Chapter 8

8.4. Aarts, J. M., and de Groot, J., A case of colouration in the four colour problem. *Nieuw Arch. Wis.* **11**(3), 10–18 (1963).

Chapter 9

9.2. Wernickle, P., Über den kartographischen Vierfarbensatz. *Math. Ann.* **58**, 413–426 (1904).

Franklin, P., The four color problem. *Am. J. Math.* **44**, 225–236 (1922).

Lebesgue, H., *loc. cit.* 4.3.

9.3. Heawood, P. J., On the four-colour map theorem. *Quart. J. Math.* **29**, 270–285 (1897).

Heawood, P. J., On extended congruences connected with the four-colour map theorem. *Proc. London Math. Soc.* **33**(2), 253–286 (1932).

Heawood, P. J., Failures in congruences connected with the four-colour map theorem. *Proc. London Math. Soc.* **40**(2), 189–202, (1936).

Heawood, P. J., Note on a correction in a paper on map-congruences. *J. London Math. Soc.* **18**, 160–167 (1943); **19**, 18–22 (1944).

Veblen, O., An application of modular equations in Analysis Situs. *Ann. Math.* **14**(2), 163–178 (1913).

Franklin, P., Note on the four color theorem. *J. Math. Phys.* **16**, 172–184 (1938).

9.5. Sedláček, J., Some properties of interchange graphs. Theory of graphs and its applications. *Symposium Smolenice 1963*, 145–150.

9.6. Johnson, E. L., A proof of the four-coloring of the edges of a regular three-degree graph. *O.R.C. 63–28 (R.R.)* Mimeographed report 1963. Operations Research Center, Univ. of Calif.

Chapter 10

10.1. Halin, R., Bemerkungen über ebene Graphen. *Math. Annalen* **53**, 38–46 (1964).

Harary, F., and Tutte, W. T., A dual form of Kuratowski's theorem. Mimeographed report.

10.4. Hadwiger, H., Über eine Klassifikation der Streckenkomplexe. *Vierteljahrschr. naturf. Ges. Zürich* **88**, 133–142 (1943).

Hadwiger, H., Ungelöste Probleme. *Element. Math.* **13**, 127–128 (1958).

Wagner, K., Über eine Eigenschaft der ebenen Komplexe. *Math. Ann.* **114**, 570–590 (1937).

Wagner, K., Bemerkungen zu Hadwigers Vermutung. *Math. Ann.* **141**, 433–451 (1960).

Wagner, K., Beweis einer Abschwächung der Hadwiger-Vermutung. *Math. Ann.* **153**, 139–141 (1964).

Dirac, G. G. A., A property of 4-chromatic graphs and some remarks on critical graphs. *J. London Math. Soc.* **27**, 85–92 (1952).

10.5. Halin, R., Über einen Satz von K. Wagner zum Vierfarbenproblem. *Math. Ann.* **153**, 47–62 (1964).

10.6. Dirac, G. A., A theorem of R. L. Brooks and a conjecture of H. Hadwiger. *Proc. London Math. Soc.* **7**(3), 161–195 (1957).

Dirac, G. A., In abstracten Graphen vorhandene vollständige 4-graphen und ihre Unterteilungen. *Math. Nachr.* **22**, 61–85 (1960).

Dirac, G. A., 4-chrome Graphen und vollständige 4-graphen. *Math. Nachr.* **22**, 51–60 (1960).

Dirac, G. A., Connectedness and structure in graphs. *Rend. Palermo* **9**(2), 114–124 (1960).

Dirac, G. A., Some results concerning the structure of graphs. *Can. Math. Bull.* **6**, 183–210 (1963).

Dirac, G. A., Homomorphism theorems for graphs. *Math. Ann.* **153**, 69–80 (1964).

Chapter 11

11.1. Dirac, G. A., Note on the colouring of graphs. *Math. Zeitschr.* **54**, 347–353 (1951).

Dirac, G. A., Some theorems on abstract graphs. *Proc. London Math. Soc.* **2**(3), 69–81 (1952).

Dirac, G. A., A property of 4-chromatic graphs and some remarks on critical graphs. *J. London Math. Soc.* **27**, 85–92 (1952).

Dirac, G. A., Map-colour theorems. *Can. J. Math.* **4**, 480–490 (1952).

Dirac, G. A., The structure of *k*-chromatic graphs. *Fund. Math.* **40**, 42–55 (1953).

Dirac, G. A., Theorems related to the four colour conjecture. *J. London Math. Soc.* **29**, 143–149 (1954).

Dirac, G. A., Circuits in critical graphs. *Monatsh. Math.* **59**, 178–187 (1955).

Dirac, G. A., Map colour theorems related to the Heawood colour formula. *J. London Math. Soc.* **31**, 460–471 (1956).

Dirac, G. A., A contraction theorem for abstract graphs. *Math. Ann.* **144**, 93–96 (1961).

Dirac, G. A., On the structure of 5- and 6-chromatic abstract graphs. *J. für. Math.* **214**, 43–52 (1964).

Dirac, G. A., Homomorphism theorems for graphs. *Math. Ann.* **153**, 69–80, (1964).

Zeidl, B., Über 4- und 5-chrome Graphen. *J. London Math. Soc.* **27**, 85–92 (1952).

11.2. Dirac, G. A., Trennende Knotenpunktmengen und Reduzibilität abstrakter Graphen mit Anwendung auf das Vierfarbenproblem. *J. für Math.* **204**, 116–131 (1960).

11.3. Gallai, T., Kritische Graphen, I and II. *Publ. Math. Inst. Hungarian Acad. Sci. A.* **8**, 165–192 (1963); **9**, 373–395 (1964).

11.4. Hajós, Über eine Konstruktion nicht n-färbarer Graphen. *Wiss. Zeitschr.* Martin Luther Univ. Halle-Wittenberg A10, 116–117 (1961).

Chapter 12

12.1. Birkhoff, G. D., The reducibility of maps. *Am. J. Math.* **35**, 115–128 (1913).

Bernhart, A., Six-rings in minimal five-color maps. *Am. J. Math.* **69**, 391–412 (1947).

12.3. Franklin, P., The four color problem. *Am. J. Math.* **44**, 225–236 (1922).

Franklin, P., Note on the four color problem. *J. Math. Phys.* **16**, 172–184 (1938).

Winn, C. E., A case of coloration in the four color problem. *Am. J. Math.* **49**, 515–528 (1937).

Winn, C. E., On certain reductions in the four color problem. *J. Math. Phys.* **16**, 159–171 (1938).

Winn, C. E., Sur quelques réductibilités dans la théorie des cartes. *C. R. Acad. Paris* **205**, 352–354 (1937).

Choinacki, C., A contribution to the four color problem. *Am. J. Math.* **64**, 36–54 (1942).

Ratib, I., Sur le problème des quatres couleurs. *Proc. Math. Phys. Soc. Egypt* **2**, 49–59 (1944).

Bernhart, A., Another reducible edge configuration. *Am. J. Math.* **70**, 144–146 (1948).

12.4. Errera, A., Une contribution au problème des quatres couleurs. *Bull. Soc. Math. France* **53**, 42–55 (1925).

12.5. Reynolds, C. N., On the problem of coloring maps in four colors. *Ann. Math.* **28**(2), 1–15 (1926).

Franklin, P., Note on the four color problem. *J. Math. Phys.* **16**, 172–184 (1938).

Winn, C. E., On the minimum number of polygons in an irreducible map. *Am. J. Math.* **62**, 406–416 (1940).

Dirac, G. A., On the four-colour conjecture. *Proc. London Math. Soc.* **13**(3), 193–218 (1963).

Chapter 13

13.2. Grötzsch, H., Ein Dreifarbensatz für dreikreisfreie Netze auf der Kugel. *Wiss. Z. Martin Luther Univ., Halle-Wittenberg. Math. Naturwiss Reihe* **8**, 109–119 (1958).

Grünbaum, B., Grötzsche's theorem on 3-colorings. *Michigan Math. J.* **10**, 303–310 (1963).

Chapter 14

14.2. Shannon, C. E., A theorem on coloring the lines of a network. *J. Math. Phys.* **28**, 148–151 (1949).

Johnson, E. I., A proof of four-coloring the edges of a regular three-degree graph. Operations Research Center, University of California, Berkeley, 1963.

Vizing, V. G., On an estimate of the chromatic class of a *p*-graph. *Diskret. Analiz. No.* **3**, 25–30 (1964).

AUTHOR INDEX

255

SUBJECT INDEX